STATISTICS FOR BEGINNERS

The Ultimate Step by Step Guide to Acing Statistics

By

Reza Nazari

ISBN: 978-1-63719-789-9

Published by: **Effortless Math Education**

for Online Math Practice Visit www.EffortlessMath.com

Introduction

"Statistics for Beginners" is meticulously crafted to serve as a foundational guide for those embarking on their journey into the realm of statistics. This textbook is tailored to encompass all the essential topics that a beginner in statistics would encounter, ensuring a thorough grounding in this critical subject. The book is structured to provide lucid explanations and illustrative examples of fundamental statistical concepts, making it an invaluable resource for understanding this often-intimidating field.

To bolster the learning experience, "Statistics for Beginners" includes a variety of practice problems and quizzes. These are designed to test and reinforce your comprehension of the material, allowing you to gauge your progress and identify areas needing further attention. What sets this textbook apart is its commitment to clarity and accessibility. Recognizing that statistics can be challenging for many, it adopts a user-friendly approach. This makes the content approachable and comprehensible, especially for those who may have previously found mathematics and statistics daunting.

An integral feature of this textbook is its inclusion of detailed, step-by-step solutions to problems. This aspect is particularly beneficial as it enables learners to verify their answers and, more importantly, understand the methodologies for solving similar statistical problems independently. Such guidance is crucial for developing a robust statistical acumen and confidence in applying these skills in various contexts.

Understanding that different learners have varied preferences and needs, "Statistics for Beginners" is equipped with an array of visual aids. These include diagrams, graphs, and charts, all of which are strategically used to clarify and reinforce statistical concepts. These visual elements play a pivotal role in making abstract ideas more tangible, thereby enhancing comprehension and retention.

The versatility of "Statistics for Beginners" is another of its strengths. It is designed to be adaptable, making it a perfect companion for different learning environments. Whether you are supplementing your learning in a traditional classroom setting or using it as a primary resource for self-study, this textbook is equipped to support your learning journey.

How to Use This Book Effectively

Look no further when you need a study guide to improve your math skills to succeed on the Statistics test. Each chapter of this comprehensive guide to Statistics will provide you with the knowledge, tools, and understanding needed for every topic covered on the course.

It's imperative that you understand each topic before moving onto another one, as that's the way to guarantee your success. Each chapter provides you with examples and a step-by-step guide of every concept to better understand the content that will be on the course. To get the best possible results from this book:

➢ **Begin studying long before your test date**. This provides you ample time to learn the different math concepts. The earlier you begin studying for the test, the sharper your skills will be. Do not procrastinate! Provide yourself with plenty of time to learn the concepts and feel comfortable that you understand them when your test date arrives.

➢ **Practice consistently**. Study Statistics concepts at least 45 to 60 minutes a day. Remember, slow and steady wins the race, which can be applied to preparing for the Statistics test. Instead of cramming to tackle everything at once, be patient and learn the math topics in short bursts.

➢ Whenever you get a math problem wrong, **mark it off, and review it later** to make sure you understand the concept.

➢ Start each session by **looking over the previous material.**

➢ Once you've reviewed the book's lessons, **take a practice test at the back of the book** to gauge your level of readiness. Then, review your results. Read detailed answers and solutions for each question you missed.

➢ **Take another practice test** to get an idea of how ready you are to take the actual exam. Taking the practice tests will give you the confidence you need on test day. Simulate the Statistics testing environment by sitting in a quiet room free from distraction. Make sure to clock yourself with a timer.

Contents

CHAPTER

1 Introduction to Statistics

Topics that you'll learn in this chapter:

- ☑ Role of Statistics in Decision-Making
- ☑ Definitions of Statistics, Probability, and Key Terms
- ☑ Organizing Data
- ☑ Types and Characteristics of Data
- ☑ Data Collection Methods
- ☑ Sampling Techniques
- ☑ Variation in Data and Sampling
- ☑ Frequency and Frequency Tables
- ☑ Levels of Measurement
- ☑ Data Collection Experiments
- ☑ Sampling Experiments
- ☑ Experimental Design and Ethical Considerations

1

Role of Statistics in Decision-Making

- The role of statistics in decision-making encompasses gathering, analyzing, and interpreting data to resolve uncertainties and make evidence-based choices.

- Statistical analysis provides a quantitative foundation for decision-making, offering insights that might not be apparent from raw data alone.

Step-by-Step Guide:

- **Problem Definition:** Clearly define what decision needs to be made and what information is required.

- **Data Collection:** Gather the relevant data through surveys, experiments, or historical data analysis.

- **Data Analysis:** Use statistical methods to summarize and analyze the data, applying both descriptive and inferential statistics.

- **Interpretation:** Draw conclusions from the analysis, translating statistical findings into actionable insights.

- **Decision Implementation:** Make informed decisions based on the interpreted data and monitor the outcome to inform future decisions.

Example:

A company is considering expanding its market presence to a new region. write a statistical analysis to make a decision about the market.

Solution: The decision to expand into the new market is based on a thorough statistical analysis, which predicts a favorable outcome for the company's growth. The statistical analysis is as follows:

Data Collection: The company collects data on regional demographics, consumer behavior, and competitor presence.

Data Analysis: Statistical models are used to forecast market potential and consumer demand.

Interpretation: The analysis predicts a high demand in the new region with a competitive advantage due to low competitor presence.

Decision: The company decides to proceed with the market expansion.

Definitions: Statistics, Probability, and Key Terms

- Statistics is a branch of mathematics dealing with the collection, analysis, interpretation, and presentation of masses of numerical data.
- Probability is a way of quantifying the likelihood of an event occurring. It is a numerical value between 0 and 1, where 0 indicates impossibility and 1 indicates certainty.
  - **Population:** The entire group that you want to draw conclusions about.
  - **Sample:** A subset of the population that is used to represent the population.
  - **Parameter:** A numerical value that summarizes a characteristic of the population.
  - **Statistic:** A numerical value that summarizes a characteristic of a sample.
  - **Variable:** Any characteristic, number, or quantity that can be measured or counted.
  - **Random Variable:** A variable whose value is subject to variations due to randomness.
  - **Data:** Information collected from observations.

Examples:

Example 1. A researcher is studying the average height of adult men in a city. They measure the heights of 100 randomly selected adult men from this city. Define the population and the sample in this study.

Solution: Population: All adult men in the city.

Sample: The 100 randomly selected adult men.

Example 2. In a survey, 200 people are asked about their favorite fruit and the amount of fruit they consume weekly. What are the variables and the type of data in this survey?

Solution: Variables: Favorite fruit (categorical variable). Amount of fruit consumed weekly (numerical variable)

Data: The responses collected from the 200 people.

Organizing Data

- Data organization is a kind of categorization and classification of information to make it more utilizable. Organizing and presenting data is necessary for statistics. After data is gathered, the data may not be meaningful and reasonable when you look at it. That's why it's necessary to arrange and demonstrate the data using tables and charts. You should organize your data in the most reasonable way, so you can find the data you are looking for simply.

- There are two types of data: Categorical or Qualitative data and Quantitative data.

- Categorical or Qualitative data is a kind of data that after being recorded you can't easily recognize with the real numbers. Examples of Categorical data include the colors of something, the size of something as small, medium, large, and gender (male, female). To demonstrate this type of information you can use a bar graph or pie graph.

- Quantitative data is a kind of data that after being recorded can be easily recognized with real numbers. Examples of Quantitative data are age, height, and weight. The fact that you can identify Quantitative data with real numbers makes it easy to organize, compare, and communicate this data. you are also able to combine this data using algebraic operations.

Examples:

Example 1. In research, various types of blood groups (*A*, *B*, *AB*, and *O*) are studied. If we want to organize the data in this research, in which group of data organization are they placed?

Solution: The types of blood groups are qualitative data because you can't easily recognize them with real numbers.

Example 2. If you want to measure the amount of air pollutants during a month in parts per million (*ppm*), the data from this measurement will be classified in which category of data organization?

Solution: The amounts of air pollutants during a month in parts per million (*ppm*) are placed in the category of quantitative data because in this data set, you are dealing with real numbers.

Types and Characteristics of Data

In statistics, there are different types of data, each with its characteristics, and understanding these is vital for selecting the appropriate statistical methods for analysis.

- **Quantitative Data:** This type of data represents amounts or quantities and can be divided into two sub-categories:

  - **Discrete Data:** Consist of whole numbers and are countable. They often represent the number of occurrences of an event.
  - **Continuous Data:** Can take any value within a range and are measurable. They often represent measurements or scales.

- **Qualitative Data (Categorical Data):** This type of data represents characteristics or attributes and can be divided into two sub-categories:

  - **Nominal Data:** Categories without a natural order or rank.
  - **Ordinal Data:** Categories with a natural order but not precisely measured.

- **Characteristics of Data:**

  - **Level of Measurement:** The precision with which the data are expressed (nominal, ordinal, interval, ratio).
  - **Variability:** The extent to which the data points differ from each other.
  - **Distribution:** The way in which the data points are spread out or clustered together.

Examples:

Example 1. A survey collects the following data: age, gender, income level, and satisfaction rating with service (happy, neutral, unhappy). Classify each data type.

Solution: Age: Quantitative, discrete or continuous (depending on how it's measured). Gender: Qualitative, nominal. Income level: Quantitative, continuous. Satisfaction rating: Qualitative, ordinal.

Example 2. A researcher is investigating whether a new fertilizer increases plant growth more than the current market leader. Describe the data collection process.

Solution: Method: Experiment. Process: The researcher would use two groups of plants: one treated with the new fertilizer (experimental group) and one with the current market leader (control group). Growth rates would be measured over a set time period. The experiment should be randomized to reduce selection bias.

Data Collection Methods

The approach to data collection depends on the type of data and the intended analysis.

- **Surveys and Questionnaires:** Consist of a series of questions asked to individuals. Can be conducted in person, by phone, via mail, or online. Should be designed to minimize bias.

- **Observation:** Data collected by directly watching and recording behavior or phenomena as it occurs. Can be structured or unstructured.

- **Experiments:** Involve manipulation of variables to study effects on other variables. Randomized controlled trials are a form of experimental data collection.

- **Interviews:** Data collected through direct interaction and asking questions, either structured or unstructured.

- **Records and Documents:** Gathering data from existing records like medical records, financial reports, or educational records.

- **Sampling:** Selecting a subset of individuals from a population, which can be random, stratified, or systematic.

- **Characteristics of Good Data Collection:**
  - **Reliability:** Consistency of the measurement over time.
  - **Validity:** Accuracy of the measurement and whether it measures what it is supposed to measure.
  - **Precision:** Exactness of the measurement.
  - **Relevance:** The degree to which the data helps in answering the research question.

Example:

A university wants to assess the satisfaction of its students with the campus dining services. What data collection method should be used and what are key considerations?

Solution:

Method: Survey via questionnaires.

Considerations: The survey should be anonymous to encourage honesty, questions should be clear and unbiased, and the sample should represent the student population.

Sampling Techniques

Sampling is a statistical process whereby a subset of individuals is selected from a larger group to make inferences about that population.

- **Simple Random Sampling:** Each member of the population has an equal chance of being selected.

- **Stratified Sampling:** The population is divided into subgroups (strata) based on shared characteristics, and random samples are taken from each stratum.

- **Cluster Sampling:** The population is divided into clusters, some of which are randomly selected, and all members of the chosen clusters are sampled.

- **Systematic Sampling:** Every nth member of the population is selected after a random starting point.

- **Convenience Sampling:** Samples are chosen based on ease of access.

- **Snowball Sampling:** Existing study subjects recruit future subjects among their acquaintances.

- **Characteristics of Good Sampling:**

  - Representativeness: The sample should accurately reflect the population.
  - Randomness: The selection process should be random to prevent bias.
  - Size: Larger samples tend to be more representative of the population.
  - Variability: The sample should capture the diversity of the population.

Examples:

Example 1. A researcher wants to understand the shopping preferences of a town's population, divided equally among four age groups. What sampling technique should be used?
Solution: Technique: Stratified Sampling. Process: Divide the population into the four age groups (strata) and then perform simple random sampling within each stratum to ensure each age group is fairly represented.

Example 2. An agricultural study aims to measure the yield of a particular crop across different regions of a country. How should the researchers proceed?
Solution: Technique: Cluster Sampling. Process: Divide the country into regions (clusters), randomly select a number of these regions, and then measure the yield of all agricultural plots within these selected clusters.

Variation in Data and Sampling

- Sampling variation, also known as sampling error, is the difference between the statistic derived from a sample and the actual parameter of the population from which the sample is drawn. This type of variation is due to the fact that different samples from the same population will naturally produce different estimates.

- **Understanding Sampling Variation:**
  - It occurs because a sample is only a part of the whole population.
  - The size of the sampling variation typically decreases as the sample size increases.
  - It is a natural and expected part of the sampling process.

- **Reducing Sampling Variation:**
  - Increase the sample size.
  - Ensure the sample is as representative of the population as possible.
  - Use random sampling techniques to minimize bias.

Examples:

Let's say you have a large bowl of colored beads with equal numbers of red, blue, and green beads, and you want to estimate the proportion of red beads without counting them all.

Example 1. You take a simple random sample of 10 beads, and 6 out of 10 are red. What does this tell you about sampling variation?

Solution: The proportion of red beads in the sample is 60%, but since the actual proportion is 33.3%, the sampling variation in this case is (60% − 33.3% = 26.7%). If you take another sample of 10 beads, you might find a different proportion of red beads, illustrating the concept of sampling variation.

Example 2. If you increase the sample size to 100 beads and 35 are red, how does this affect sampling variation?

Solution: Now, the proportion of red beads in the sample is 35%, which is closer to the actual proportion of 33.3%. This shows that increasing the sample size tends to reduce sampling variation, making the sample estimate closer to the true population parameter.

Frequency and Frequency Tables

- Frequency in statistics refers to the number of times a particular value or a range of values occurs within a dataset. A frequency table is a simple way to display the frequency of various outcomes in a sample. Each entry in the table contains the frequency or count of the occurrences of values within a particular group or interval.

- Creating Frequency Tables

  ▪ **Data Organization:** Collect the raw data. And determine the range of the data (from the smallest to the largest value).

  ▪ **Creating Classes:** Divide the range into classes or intervals. And determine the width of each class, trying to keep them equal in size.

  ▪ **Tallying Frequencies:** For each data point, add a tally to the appropriate class. And count the tallies to find the total frequency for each class.

  ▪ **Completing the Frequency Table:** List the classes in one column. List the corresponding frequencies in the adjacent column.

Example:

Create a frequency table for the following set of exam scores:

$$55, 60, 65, 60, 70, 75, 65, 80, 85, 70, 55, 60$$

Solution: Range: 55 (minimum) to 85 (maximum).

Class Width: Let's use a width of 10, resulting in intervals of $55 - 64$, $65 - 74$, $75 - 84$, $85 - 94$.

Tallying Frequencies: $55 - 64$: | | | | |, $65 - 74$: | | | |, $75 - 84$: | |, $85 - 94$: |

(since 85 is the only score and it falls in this interval)

Frequency Table	
Score Interval	Frequency
$55 - 64$	5
$65 - 74$	4
$75 - 84$	2
$85 - 94$	1

Levels of Measurement

- In statistics, the Levels of Measurement refer to the different ways that variables can be quantified and categorized.

- There are four main levels of measurement in statistics:

  - **Nominal Level:** This is the simplest form of measurement. It involves categorizing or labeling variables without any inherent numerical value. For example, gender (male, female), or blood types (A, B, AB, O).

  - **Ordinal Level:** This level allows for the ranking or ordering of data, but the intervals between the data points are not necessarily equal. An example could be class grades (A, B, C, D, F).

  - **Interval Level:** Data at this level can be ordered, and the intervals between values are equal. However, there is no true zero point. An example is temperature measured in Celsius or Fahrenheit.

  - **Ratio Level:** This is the highest level of measurement. It has all the properties of interval measurement, but also includes a true zero point, which allows for the comparison of absolute magnitudes. Examples include weight in kilograms and distance in meters.

Example:

Identify the level of measurement for the following data sets:

a) Types of cars (Sedan, SUV, Hatchback)

b) IQ (Intelligence Quotient) Scores

c) Income levels (Low, Medium, High)

Solution:

a) Types of cars are nominal data as they are just labels.

b) The difference between scores indicates equal intervals of intellectual ability. An IQ score of zero does not mean a total absence of intelligence.

c) Income levels are ordinal as they can be ranked but the difference between levels is not quantifiable.

Data Collection Experiments

- Data collection is a critical process in any scientific experiment. It involves gathering information to answer research questions, test hypotheses, or support or refute a theory. The accuracy and integrity of data collection significantly impact the validity of an experiment's results.

- Conducting Data Collection Experiments Step-by-Step:

  - **Define Objectives:** Clearly define what you want to achieve with your experiment.

  - **Choose the Method:** Select the data collection method that best suits your objectives.

  - **Design the Experiment:** Plan how you will conduct the experiment, including the selection of subjects, tools for data collection, and procedures.

  - **Collect Data:** Gather the data systematically, ensuring accuracy and reliability.

  - **Analyze Data:** Process and analyze the data to interpret the results.

  - **Report Findings:** Present the findings in an honest and clear manner.

Examples:

Example 1. How does weather affect the feeding behavior of birds in a park?

Solution: Method: Observational study.

Data Collection: Record the number and behavior of birds feeding under different weather conditions over a set period.

Analysis: Compare bird behavior across different weather patterns.

Example 2. Does the color of light affect plant growth?

Solution: Method: Controlled experiment.

Data Collection: Grow plants under different colored lights and measure their growth over time.

Analysis: Analyze growth patterns to determine the effect of light color on plant growth.

Sampling Experiments

- Sampling experiments are a fundamental aspect of statistical studies, particularly when it's impractical or impossible to study an entire population.

- In these experiments, a subset (sample) of a population is selected and analyzed to make inferences about the entire population.

- Conducting Sampling Experiments Step-by-Step:

  ▪ **Define the Population:** Clearly identify the population from which you want to draw conclusions.

  ▪ **Choose a Sampling Method:** Random sampling, stratified sampling, cluster sampling.

  ▪ **Determine Sample Size:** Decide how many observations are needed for reliable and valid results.

  ▪ **Collect Data:** Gather data from your sample using well-defined procedures to maintain accuracy and reduce bias.

  ▪ **Analyze Results:** Analyze the sample data to make inferences about the overall population.

  ▪ **Report Findings:** Present your findings, noting any limitations due to sampling methods or sample size.

Example:

How can a university accurately assess the health habits of its student body?

Solution: Sampling Method: Stratified Sampling. Divide the student body into different strata (e.g., year of study, faculty) and randomly select a certain number of students from each stratum.

Data Collection: Conduct a survey on health habits among the selected students.

Analysis: Analyze the survey data to infer the health habits of the entire student body.

Experimental Design and Ethical Considerations

- Experimental design is a fundamental aspect of conducting research in various fields. The key elements of the experimental design are:

  - **Hypothesis:** A clear, testable statement predicting the outcome of the experiment.
  - **Variables:** Identification of independent (cause) and dependent (effect) variables.
  - **Control Group:** A group that does not receive the experimental treatment, used as a baseline.
  - **Random Assignment:** Assigning participants to groups randomly to eliminate bias.
  - **Replicability:** Designing the experiment so it can be replicated for reliability.

- **Ethical research** involves obtaining informed consent from participants, maintaining their confidentiality, ensuring their safety, and reporting results honestly without manipulating data.

Example:

You are a high school student conducting a research project to determine if regular exercise affects stress levels in teenagers. Design an experiment considering the key elements of experimental design and ethical considerations.

Solution: Hypothesis: Regular exercise reduces stress levels in teenagers.
Independent Variable: Regular exercise (e.g., 30 minutes a day). Dependent Variable: Stress levels, measured by a standardized stress assessment tool.
Control Group: A group of teenagers who do not participate in any additional exercise routine. Experimental Group: A group of teenagers who follow a 30-minute daily exercise routine. Randomly assign a sample of teenagers into either the control or the experimental group to avoid selection bias.
Ethical Considerations: Obtain informed consent from all participants and their guardians. Ensure confidentiality by anonymizing participant data. Clearly communicate to participants that they can withdraw from the study at any time. Ensure the exercise routine is designed to avoid any harm or excessive strain.
Monitor and record the stress levels of both groups over a defined period, say 8 weeks, using the stress assessment tool. Compare the average stress levels between the control and experimental groups. Use statistical methods to determine if any observed differences are significant. Finally, the results will be reported honestly, including any anomalies and discussing limitations like sample size or stress measurement methods.

Chapter 1: Practices

✎ Answer the questions.

1) In a small weather survey, you record the temperature (in degrees Celsius) at five different times during the day. The readings are as follows: two times it was 20 degrees, one time it was 22 degrees, one time it was 18 degrees, and one time it was 15 degrees. The temperatures $(20, 20, 22, 18,$ and 15 degrees) represent what type of data?

2) You are tracking the number of goals scored by a soccer team in five different matches. In two matches, they score 2 goals, in one match they score 3 goals, in another match they score 1 goal, and in the last match, they score 0 goals. What kind of data are these goal counts $(2, 3, 1, 0)$?

3) In a survey, you count the number of passengers in five different cars. Two cars have four passengers, one car has three passengers, one car has two passengers, and one car has five passengers. What type of data are the passenger counts (four, three, two, five)?

4) A bakery keeps track of the number of different types of pastries sold in a day. They sell three types of croissants, two types of muffins, four types of donuts, and one type of bagel. What kind of data are these pastry counts (three, two, four, one)?

✎ **Fill in the letter of the phrase that best describes each of the items below.**

A study was conducted at a local hospital to analyze the average recovery time of patients who were treated for a specific surgery last year.

5) _____ Population.

6) _____ Statistic

7) _____ Parameter

8) _____ Sample

9) _____ Variable

10) _____ Data

a) all patients who were treated at the hospital last year

b) the recovery time of one patient who underwent the surgery last year

c) 30 days, 45 days, 60 days, 25 days

d) a group of patients who underwent the surgery at the hospital last year, randomly selected

e) the average recovery time of patients who underwent the surgery at the hospital last year

f) all patients who underwent the surgery at the hospital last year

g) the average recovery time of patients in the study who underwent the surgery at the hospital last year.

✎ Try to identify a major flaw with each interpretation before we describe it.

11) Interpretation in a Fitness Context: After the launch of a new fitness app in January, there was a 40% increase in gym memberships in the first quarter of the year. Thus, the fitness app was effective in boosting gym memberships.

12) Interpretation in a Traffic Study: A study shows that the more coffee shops there are in a city, the higher the rate of traffic accidents. Therefore, coffee shops lead to more traffic accidents.

13) Interpretation in an Online Education Trend: There has been a 50% increase in the enrollment of online courses compared to 10 years ago. Thus, people prefer online education over traditional classroom learning.

✎ Determine: What is the sample? What is the population? Can you identify any problems with choosing the sample.

A manager wants to assess the overall job satisfaction of employees in the department. The manager randomly selects five employees who were recently promoted and asks about their job satisfaction. Based on their positive responses, the manager concludes that the department's job satisfaction is high.

14) Population: 15) Sample: 16) Problem with Sample:

A university club president is interested in the most popular music genre among students at the university. Eight students, who are club members, volunteer to share their favorite music genres. After hearing their preferences, the president concludes that rock music is the most popular genre among all university students.

17) Population: 18) Sample: 19) Problem with Sample:

Determine what the key terms refer to in the following study.

In a study conducted to test the effectiveness of bicycle helmets, a safety research group collected and reviewed data on the impact of head injuries on test dummies in bicycle accidents. Here is the criterion they used:

Speed at which Bicycles Crashed	Position of Dummy
15 miles/hour	Riding with Helmet

Bicycles with dummies wearing helmets were crashed at a speed of 15 miles per hour. The objective is to determine the proportion of dummies wearing helmets that would have sustained head injuries if they were real cyclists. The study began with a simple random sample of 50 bicycles.

20) Population:

21) Sample:

22) Parameter:

23) Statistic:

24) Variable:

25) Data:

 Classify each item as quantitative (continuous or discrete) or qualitative data:

26) The number of books in your library.

27) The genre of your favorite movie.

28) Your preferred holiday destination.

29) The time it takes to commute to your office.

30) The number of courses you are enrolled in at college.

31) The cost of your monthly internet subscription.

32) The brand of your smartphone.

33) Ratings of restaurants you visit.

34) Your favorite music genre.

35) Heights of basketball players.

🖎 Determine the data types:

36) You measure the temperature of five different rooms. The temperatures are $22.5°C, 20.8°C, 23.1°C, 21.4°C$, and $19.9°C$. What type of data is this?

37) You record the volume of water (in liters) in five different tanks. The volumes are 100 liters, 150 liters, 120 liters, 200 liters, and 180 liters. What type of data is this?

38) You count the number of books in five different bookcases. The counts are $30, 45, 50, 55$, and 60 books. What type of data is this?

39) You observe the colors of five cars in a parking lot. The colors are red, blue, green, black, and white. What type of data is this?

40) You list the types of fruits in five different fruit baskets. The types are apples, oranges, bananas, grapes, and cherries. What type of data is this?

41) You check the star ratings of five hotels. The ratings are three stars, four stars, five stars, two stars, and three stars. What type of data is this?

42) You measure the height of five different trees. The heights are 10.2 meters, 12.5 meters, 9.8 meters, 11.4 meters, and 10.6 meters. What type of data is this?

43) You count the number of students in five different classrooms. The numbers are $20, 25, 30, 28$, and 22 students. What type of data is this?

44) You sample five T-shirts from a store. Their colors are blue, green, blue, red, and blue. What type of data is this?

45) You observe five trees in a park. The types of trees are oak, pine, oak, maple, and oak. What type of data is this?

46) You survey five libraries. One library has 2000 books, another has 1500, the third has 2500, the fourth has 1800, and the fifth has 2200 books. What type of data is this?

✍ Determine the type of data collection methods used.

47) What method involves collecting data through conducting interviews or distributing questionnaires to gather opinions, behaviors, or factual information from respondents?

48) What method involves systematically watching and recording behaviors or occurrences in their natural settings without interference?

49) What data collection method uses manipulation and controlled testing to understand causal relationships?

50) What is called when data is not collected directly by the researcher but obtained from existing sources?

51) What method involves a detailed and in-depth study of one individual or a small group, often over a prolonged period?

52) What method involves selecting a subset of individuals from a population to estimate characteristics of the whole population?

53) What method involves gathering a group of people to discuss a topic in depth, guided by a moderator to gain detailed qualitative insights?

✍ Determine the type of sampling used (simple random, stratified, systematic, cluster, or convenience).

54) An organization conducts an employee satisfaction survey in three of its departments, surveying every employee in those departments.

55) A librarian uses a computer to randomly select 200 library members from the library's database to survey their reading preferences.

56) A school researcher selects a few classes and interviews all students in those classes about their participation in extracurricular activities.

57) A student surveys his dormitory roommates to find out how many hours per day they spend on their smartphones.

58) A hospital administrator surveys 30 patients from each department (emergency, orthopedics, pediatrics, etc.) to assess satisfaction with care.

59) A company surveys every 10th employee on an alphabetical list to gather opinions on workplace environment.

✎ **Answer: Is this sample representative of all subscribers?**

60) A grocery store with a customer base of 10,000 wants to know if customers prefer organic or non-organic products. They survey 150 customers on a busy Saturday. 120 prefer organic, while 30 prefer non-organic. Is this sample representative of all 10,000 customers?

61) An online streaming service with 100,000 subscribers wants to know if viewers prefer documentaries or action movies. To find out, they survey a group of subscribers.
The service emails a survey to 500 randomly selected subscribers, of which 250 respond. 150 prefer documentaries, and 100 prefer action movies.

62) A fitness club with 3,000 members wants to know if members prefer yoga or aerobics classes. They survey 200 members attending a yoga class. 150 prefer yoga, 50 prefer aerobics.

63) A library serving 5,000 members wants to find out if members would prefer more digital books or physical books. They conduct a survey to determine preferences. During a general members' meeting, the library surveys 150 attendees randomly. 90 prefer digital books, and 60 prefer physical books.

✎ **Solve.**

A local library conducted a survey to find out the favorite book genres among its members. The survey included 50

Book Genre	Frequency
Mystery	20
Science Fiction	15
Fantasy	10
Historical Fiction	5

members, and the results are compiled in the following frequency table:

64) What is the total number of members who participated in the survey?

65) What fraction of the members chose Science Fiction as their favorite genre?

66) Which genre is the most popular among the library members?

67) If the library decides to purchase new books based on this survey, how many books should they purchase for each genre to proportionately represent the members' preferences?

Solve.

Fruit	Frequency
Apple	15
Banana	10
Orange	8
Strawberry	7

A teacher surveyed a group of 40 students to find out their favorite fruit. The results are summarized in the following frequency table:

68) How many students were surveyed in total?

69) What percentage of students chose Apple as their favorite fruit?

70) Which fruit was the least popular among the students?

71) If the teacher wanted to buy fruit for the class based on these preferences, ensuring each student gets their favorite, how many of each fruit should she buy?

Calculate the sampling error.

72) In a population where the average score is 70, a sample of 30 yields an average score of 65.

73) If the true proportion of a population characteristic is 40% and a sample proportion is 35%.

74) A researcher estimates the average height of a population to be 160 cm, but a sample shows an average height of 158 cm.

75) In a town where 60% of the population supports a policy, a sample shows 55% support.

76) If a sample of students has an average test score of 75 points and the true average is 78 points.

77) A political poll shows 45% support for a candidate, but the actual support in the population *is* 48%.

78) You have a large bowl containing an equal number of red, blue, green, yellow, and purple beads. To estimate the proportion of green beads, you take a simple random sample of 10 beads and find that 4 out of 10 are green.

79) In a garden with an equal number of red, blue, yellow, and white flowers, you randomly pick 10 flowers to estimate the proportion of white flowers. If 4 out of the 10 picked flowers are white.

Create a simple frequency table.

80) In a class of 30 students, 10 got *A* grade, 13 got *B*, 5 got *C*, and 2 got *D*. Create a simple frequency table for this data.

81) In a company's employee satisfaction survey, 50 employees rated their satisfaction as 'High', 30 as 'Medium', and 20 as 'Low'. Create a simple frequency table for this data.

Identify the level of measurement (nominal, ordinal, interval, or ratio) for the following data:

82) Different brands of smartphones (e.g., Apple, Samsung, Huawei).

83) Temperature readings in Celsius (e.g., $20°C, 30°C, 40°C$).

84) Ranking of students in a class based on their academic performance ($1st, 2nd, 3rd$, etc.).

85) The heights of students in a class measured in centimeters (e.g., $150\ cm, 160\ cm, 170\ cm$).

86) The ages of participants in a study (e.g., 21 years, 35 years, = years).

87) T-shirt sizes labeled as Small, Medium, Large, and Extra Large.

88) Colors of cars in a parking lot (e.g., red, blue, green).

89) Scores on a standardized test like the SAT, ranging from 400 to 1600.

Why is a randomized experiment not possible for the following contexts?

90) A researcher wants to study the effects of cultural background on language acquisition skills in children.

91) A study aims to explore the relationship between age and memory retention.

92) An investigation looks into how genetic predisposition affects the likelihood of developing certain diseases.

93) A study examines the impact of historical events on national identity.

✍ Answer the questions.

In a high school statistics class, students are conducting a "Data Collection Experiment" focusing on movie-watching habits. The purpose of this experiment is to understand how frequently students go to the movie theater.

Initial Data Collection: Each student in the statistics class asks five students from a different class about the number of movies they watched at the theater last month. The data is recorded. For example:

- Classmate A: 2 movies
- Classmate B: 5 movies
- Classmate C: 1 movie
- Classmate D: 0 movies (did not go to the theater)
- Classmate E: 3 movies

Random Sampling in Own Class: Back in their own class, each student randomly picks one person from the class list, then skips four names to mark the next person. This is repeated until 12 names are marked, looping back to the start of the list if necessary. For each of these 12 students, the five data values from the different class are recorded. This gives a total of 60 data values per statistics student. The recorded data might look like this for one student:

- Student 1: $2, 5, 1, 0, 3$
- Student 2: $1, 0, 3, 2, 5$
- Student 3: $3, 2, 5, 1, 0$
- ... (continues until 12 students)

94) How does the method of randomly selecting names from a class list contribute to the reliability of the data collected in this experiment?

95) Analyze the data collected and calculate the average number of movies watched by students last month. What does this average tell us about the movie-watching habits of the student population?

96) Identify any potential biases or limitations in the data collection method used in this experiment.

97) If you were to redesign this experiment to include a wider range of data on movie-watching habits (including streaming services), how would you modify the data collection process?

Use key terms from this module to describe the design of this experiment.

98) How does hydration affect cognitive performance? A study tested 20 students. Each student was tested in two conditions: one after normal hydration and one after deliberately not drinking water for 12 hours. The conditions were assigned randomly, and cognitive tests were administered in each session.

99) How does noise level impact concentration? A group of 25 office workers were tested under two scenarios: a quiet environment and a noisy environment. The order of the environments was randomized for each participant, and their concentration was measured through specific tasks.

100) Does exercise intensity affect memory recall? A group of 30 individuals were subjected to two exercise sessions: one light and one intense. Following each session, their memory recall was tested. The sequence of exercise intensity was randomized for each participant.

101) Can ambient temperature influence mood? A study involved 15 participants experiencing two different room temperatures: warm ($25°C$) and cool ($15°C$). The order of exposure was randomly assigned, and mood assessments were conducted in each setting.

Answers the questions.

A research group studied whether background music influences problem-solving skills. Participants solved puzzles in two settings: one with classical music playing and one in silence. They were randomly assigned to start with either the music or silent condition. Researchers measured the time to solve each puzzle and participants' opinions about the music: enjoyable, distracting, or neutral.

102) Describe the explanatory and response variables in this study.

103) Identify any lurking variables that could interfere with this study.

104) What are the treatments?

105) Is it possible to use blinding in this study?

✎ **Answer the questions.**

A marketing team at a financial firm decides to compare the performance of their investment fund (Acme Investments) with a competitor's fund (Other Guy's Investments). They create two graphs for an advertisement, showing the funds' performance over the last five years. The first graph has a lower slope but a steady upward trend, representing Acme. The second graph has a higher slope with more fluctuations, representing Other Guy's Investments. The ad claims, "Acme consistently outperforms the Other Guys.

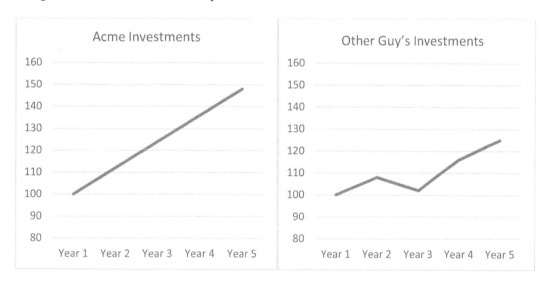

106) How might the graphical representation in the advertisement be potentially misleading?

107) What ethical considerations are involved in the way these investment performances are presented?

108) How can the representation of these investment funds be corrected to provide a fair comparison?

109) In what ways could biased or misleading data presentation in advertisements affect consumer decisions?

✍ Answer the question.

110) Imagine a graph showing the number of software issues reported to a tech support center for six different computer manufacturers in a single month. Let's say the graph indicates that HP, Dell, and Lenovo have a higher number of reports compared to Toshiba, Sony, and Asus.

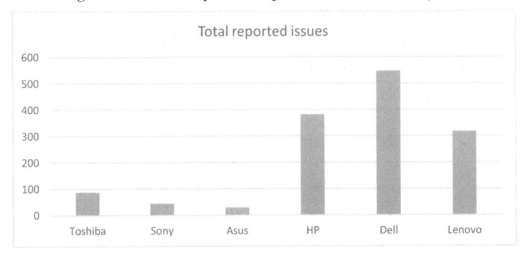

Can we conclude that HP, Dell, and Lenovo produce lower quality computers simply because they have more reported issues?

Chapter 1: Answers

1) The temperatures represent quantitative discrete data, as they are countable and express a distinct value.

2) The goal counts represent quantitative discrete data, as they can be counted, and each value is distinct and separate.

3) The passenger counts are examples of quantitative discrete data, as each value is countable and distinct.

4) These pastry counts are quantitative discrete data since each count is distinct and countable.

5) f	7) e	9) b
6) g	8) d	10) c

11) Major Flaw: The observed increase in gym memberships may not be due to the fitness app, but rather a common New Year's resolution trend to exercise more.

12) Major Flaw: The correlation between more coffee shops and higher traffic accidents likely reflects larger city populations, not a direct cause-effect relationship between coffee shops and accidents.

13) Major Flaw: The 50% increase in online course enrollments over 10 years doesn't necessarily indicate a preference for online education, as it could be influenced by other factors like technological advancements or societal changes.

14) All employees in the department.

15) The five recently promoted employees.

16) The sample might not be representative of the entire department. Recently promoted employees are likely to have higher job satisfaction, which may not reflect the views of all employees.

17) All students at the university.

18) The eight club member volunteers.

19) The sample is not representative of the entire student body. Club members may have similar music preferences, which are not necessarily reflective of the diverse tastes of all students. Additionally, the sample lacks diversity in terms of the broader student demographics, such as year of study or faculty, which might influence music preferences.

20) All helmeted bicycle riders in similar crash conditions.

21) 50 randomly chosen bicycle crashes with helmeted dummies.

22) Proportion of helmeted riders who would get head injuries in similar crashes.

23) Proportion of head injuries in the 50 helmeted dummies.

24) Incidence of head injuries in helmeted crash participants.

25) Yes/no records of head injuries in each crash test.

26) Quantitative discrete data.

27) Qualitative.

28) Qualitative.

29) Quantitative continuous data.

30) Quantitative discrete data.

31) Quantitative discrete data.

32) Qualitative.

33) Qualitative.

34) Qualitative.

35) Quantitative continuous data.

36) Quantitative continuous data.

37) Quantitative continuous data.

38) Quantitative discrete data.

39) Qualitative data.

40) Qualitative nominal data.

41) Qualitative ordinal data.

42) Quantitative continuous data.

43) Quantitative discrete data.

44) Qualitative data.

45) Qualitative data.

46) Quantitative discrete data.

47) Survey.

48) Observation.

49) Experiment.

50) Secondary Data.

51) Case Study

52) Sampling.

53) Focus Group.

54) Cluster sampling.

55) Simple random sampling.

56) Cluster sampling.

57) Convenience sampling.

58) Stratified sampling.

59) Systematic sampling.

60) Probably not, as the sample may be biased towards those who shop on weekends and might have a preference for organic products.

61) Yes, as the sample is randomly selected, it is more likely to be representative of all subscribers.

62) Likely not, as the sample is taken from a yoga class, thus may be biased towards those who prefer yoga.

63) Yes, if attendees are a random mix of all members, the sample can be considered more representative.

64) 50 members participated in the survey.

65) $\frac{15}{50}$ or 30% of the members chose Science Fiction.

66) Mystery is the most popular genre, with 20 members choosing it.

67) To proportionately represent preferences, the library should consider buying books in the ratio of the frequencies. For example, if they decide to purchase 100 new books in total, they could buy 40 Mystery, 30 Science Fiction, 20 Fantasy, and 10 Historical Fiction books, maintaining the same proportion as the survey results.

68) 40 students were surveyed in total.

69) $\frac{15}{40} \times 100 = 37.5\%$ of the students chose Apple.

70) Strawberry was the least popular, with 7 students choosing it.

71) She should buy 15 apples, 10 bananas, 8 oranges, and 7 strawberries.

72) 5 (70 − 65)

73) 5% (40% − 35%)

74) 2 cm (160 cm − 158 cm)

75) 5% (60% − 55%)

76) 3 points (78 − 75)

78) 20% (40% − 20%)

77) 3% (48% − 45%)

79) 15% (40% − 25%)

80)

Grade	Frequency
A	10
B	13
C	5
D	2

81)

Satisfaction Level	Frequency
High	50
Medium	30
Low	20

82) Nominal

86) Ratio

83) Interval

87) Ordinal

84) Ordinal

88) Nominal

85) Ratio

89) Interval

90) Cultural background cannot be randomly assigned to individuals. Without random assignment, other factors (like family environment or education) may influence the results, making it hard to isolate the impact of culture alone.

91) Age is a fixed characteristic and cannot be assigned or altered randomly for individuals. Non-randomized studies risk confounding variables impacting the observed relationship.

92) Genetic traits are inherent and cannot be randomly assigned. As a result, other uncontrolled variables might influence the study, complicating the interpretation of the genetic effects.

93) Historical events and their impact on individuals or societies cannot be assigned or manipulated in a randomized manner. The study could be confounded by various other social, economic, or political factors.

94) Random selection minimizes bias and ensures a representative sample, enhancing data reliability.

95) By calculating the average number of movies watched (the average number of movies watched by students last month would be 3.5), this statistic provides a snapshot of general movie-going frequency, suggesting how integral cinema is to students' leisure activities.

96) Potential biases include non-representative selection of classmates and exclusion of non-theater movie watching.

97) Include questions on streaming services, broaden the range of classes or grades surveyed, and possibly increase sample size for a more comprehensive understanding.

98) Design: This is a randomized crossover design. The independent variable is hydration status (normal hydration vs. dehydration), and the dependent variable is cognitive performance. Each participant experiences both conditions, and the order of the conditions is randomized to control for order effects.

99) Design: This experiment uses a randomized, within-subjects design. The independent variable is the noise level (quiet vs. noisy environment), and the dependent variable is the concentration level, as assessed by task performance. Randomizing the order in which participants experience the environments helps control for potential biases.

100) Design: This is a randomized crossover study. The independent variable is exercise intensity (light vs. intense exercise), and the dependent variable is memory recall. Participants engage in both types of exercise sessions, with the sequence randomized to minimize systematic bias.

101) Design: This study follows a randomized, within-subjects design. The independent variable is ambient temperature (warm vs. cool), and the dependent variable is mood, assessed through standardized mood assessments. Randomizing the order of temperature exposure ensures that each participant's response is not influenced by the sequence of the conditions.

102) The explanatory variable is the background condition (music vs. silence), and the response variable is the time taken to solve puzzles.

103) Participants' prior experience with puzzles, their preference for classical music, or the puzzle's difficulty level could be lurking variables. Random assignment helps minimize these effects.

104) The two treatments are solving puzzles with classical music and solving puzzles in silence.

105) Participants will know the background condition, so they can't be blinded. However, researchers analyzing the puzzle-solving time can be blinded to whether music was playing or not.

106) The graphs may exaggerate the performance of Acme by using different scales or omitting context, giving an illusion of consistent superiority.

107) Ethically, presenting data in a misleading way can be seen as deceptive, which violates principles of honesty and transparency in advertising.

108) Use the same scale and include all relevant context, like market conditions, to give a more accurate and fair comparison.

109) Misleading data can lead to uninformed or misguided consumer decisions, potentially resulting in financial loss or a breach of trust.

110) It would be premature to conclude that HP, Dell, and Lenovo produce lower quality computers simply because they have more reported issues. The higher number of complaints could be due to a larger customer base, more complex product lines, or even more proactive reporting mechanisms. To assess the quality accurately, we would need to consider additional factors like the severity of the issues, customer satisfaction scores, and the total number of products sold by each manufacturer.

CHAPTER

2 Descriptive Statistics

Topics that you'll learn in this chapter:

- ☑ Organizing and Summarizing Data
- ☑ Frequency Distributions
- ☑ Cumulative Frequency
- ☑ Cumulative Distribution Functions (CDF)
- ☑ Cumulative Distribution Graph
- ☑ Relative Frequency
- ☑ Stem-and-Leaf Plots
- ☑ Histograms
- ☑ Frequency Polygons
- ☑ Mean, Median, Mode, and Range of the Given Data
- ☑ Quartiles and Percentiles of the Given Data
- ☑ Three Standard Deviations
- ☑ Measures of Data Location
- ☑ Mean deviation
- ☑ Two Types of Variance
- ☑ Measures of Dispersion
- ☑ Box-and-Whisker Plots
- ☑ Skewness
- ☑ Kurtosis

Organizing and Summarizing Data

- Organizing and summarizing data involve transforming raw data into a format that is easily understandable and interpretable. Effective organization and summarization allow for a clearer understanding of what the data is conveying, leading to more accurate conclusions.

- The key steps in organizing data are: Data sorting, categorizing data, creating tables and charts.

- Key techniques in summarizing data include: Measures of central tendency, measures of spread, frequency distribution.

- Organizing and Summarizing Data Step-by-Step:

  - **Gather Your Data:** Collect the raw data you intend to analyze.
  - **Clean the Data:** Remove any errors or irrelevant data points.
  - **Sort and Categorize**: Arrange the data logically, and group similar data points.
  - **Choose Appropriate Summarization Techniques:** Decide whether to use measures of central tendency, measures of spread, or both, based on your data type.
  - **Create Visual Representations:** Use tables, charts, and graphs to visually represent your organized and summarized data.
  - **Interpret the Results:** Analyze the summarized data to draw meaningful conclusions.

Examples:

Example 1. A store owner needs to understand monthly sales trends.

Solution: Data Organization: Categorize sales data by month.
Data Summarization: Calculate the total sales for each month. Use a line graph to represent monthly sales trends.
Interpretation: Determine peak sales months and observe sales trends over the year.

Example 2. A teacher wants to summarize the final grades of a class.

Solution: Data Organization: List all student grades in ascending order.

Data Summarization: Calculate the mean, median, and mode of the grades. Plot a histogram to show the frequency distribution of the grades.
Interpretation: Identify the average performance, the spread of grades, and the most common grade.

Frequency Distributions

- A frequency distribution is a statistical tool used to organize and summarize data. It shows the number of occurrences (frequency) of each different value in a set of data.

- Components of Frequency Distributions:
  - **Classes:** Categories or intervals into which data is grouped or divided.
  - **Frequency:** The number of occurrences of each category or interval in a dataset.
  - **Relative Frequency:** The proportion of occurrences of each category or interval relative to the total number of data points.
  - **Cumulative Frequency:** The running total of frequencies up to a certain point in a dataset.

- Creating a Frequency Distribution Step-by-Step:
  - **Collect Data:** Gather the data you wish to analyze.
  - **Determine Classes:** Divide the data range into intervals (classes). Ensure they are mutually exclusive and collectively exhaustive.
  - **Tally Frequencies:** Count the number of data points in each class.
  - **Calculate Relative and Cumulative Frequencies:** Find the proportion of each class relative to the total and the cumulative total up to each class.
  - **Visualize the Distribution:** Often, frequency distributions are represented using histograms or frequency polygons for easier interpretation.

Example:

Create components of frequency distribution for the following test scores. Then, visualize it: $55, 58, 59, 60, 70, 75, 81, 87, 90, 95$

Solution: Classes: $50 - 59, 60 - 69, 70 - 79, 80 - 89, 90 - 99$.

Frequency: 4, 1, 2, 2, 1.

Relative Frequency: 0.4, 0.1, 0.2, 0.2, 0.1

$\frac{4}{10} = 0.4, \frac{1}{10} = 0.1, \frac{2}{10} = 0.2, \frac{2}{10} = 0.2, \frac{1}{10} = 0.1$.

Cumulative Frequency: 4, 5, 7, 9, 10

$4, 4 + 1 = 5, 5 + 2 = 7, 7 + 2 = 9, 9 + 1 = 10$.

Now, create a histogram with these values.

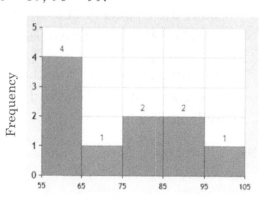

Cumulative Frequency

- In statistics, understanding the frequency of data points in a dataset is crucial. Two important concepts in this realm are cumulative frequency and relative frequency.

- Cumulative Frequency is the sum of frequencies of all values that are less than or equal to the current value. It gives us an idea of the number of observations that fall below a certain value in the dataset.

- **Step-by-Step Guide**

  - Calculate Individual Frequencies: First, determine the frequency of each distinct value in the dataset.

  - Arrange in Ascending Order: Arrange the values in ascending order.

  - Compute Cumulative Frequency: Add the frequency of the current value to the cumulative total of the previous values.

- The formula for cumulative frequency for a value x is given by:

$$CF(x) = f(x) + CF(previous\ value)$$

Where $CF(x)$ is the cumulative frequency for value x, and $f(x)$ is the frequency of x.

Example:

Consider a small survey conducted on a group of 10 students to find out the number of books they read in a month. The results are as follows:

$$0, 1, 1, 2, 2, 3, 3, 3, 4, 5$$

Create a table showing the cumulative frequency for this data set.

Solution: First, arrange the data in ascending order (which is already done).
Count the frequency of each number of books.
Calculate the cumulative frequency for each number.

The table shows the cumulative frequency of books read by students in a month.

Number of Books Read (x)	Frequency ($f(x)$)	Cumulative Frequency (CF)
0	1	1
1	2	$1 + 2 = 3$
2	2	$3 + 2 = 5$
3	3	$5 + 3 = 8$
4	1	$8 + 1 = 9$
5	1	$9 + 1 = 10$

Cumulative Distribution Functions (CDF)

- The CDF of a random variable X is a function, typically denoted by $F(x)$, that measures the probability that X will take a value less than or equal to x.

- Mathematical Expression: $F(x) = P(X \leq x)$

- **Characteristics of CDF:**

  - Range: The CDF ranges from 0 to 1.

  - Non-Decreasing: The function is always non-decreasing, meaning as x increases, $F(x)$ does not decrease.

  - Asymptotic Behavior: As x approaches negative infinity, $F(x)$ approaches 0; as x approaches positive infinity, $F(x)$ approaches 1.

- **Types of CDF:**

  - Continuous CDF: For continuous random variables, the CDF is a smooth curve.

  - Discrete CDF: For discrete random variables, the CDF is a step function.

Example:

Consider a fair six-sided dice to plot the CDF and calculate the probability that the outcome of a dice roll is less than or equal to 4.

Solution: Since each face of the dice is equally likely, the probability of each outcome $(1, 2, 3, 4, 5,$ or $6)$ is $\frac{1}{6}$.

CDF for Dice Roll: The CDF at any point x is the sum of probabilities of all outcomes less than or equal to x.

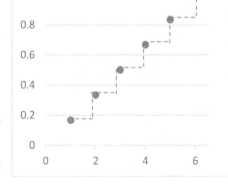

$P(X \leq 1) = \frac{1}{6} = 0.167$, $P(X \leq 2) = \frac{1}{6} + \frac{1}{6} = \frac{2}{6} = 0.333$

$P(X \leq 3) = \frac{3}{6} = 0.5$, $P(X \leq 4) = \frac{4}{6} \approx 0.667$

$P(X \leq 5) = \frac{5}{6} = 0.83$, $P(X \leq 6) = \frac{6}{6} = 1$

We will plot the CDF as a step function, as this is a discrete distribution.

As calculated and shown on the graph, the probability that the outcome is less than or equal to 4 $(P(X \leq 4))$ is approximately $\frac{2}{3}$ or 0.667. This means there's a 66.7% chance that a roll of the dice will result in a number 4 or lower.

Cumulative Distribution Graph

- A Cumulative Distribution Graph plots the CDF $F(x)$ of a random variable X against its possible values. This graph shows the probability that the random variable X is less than or equal to a particular value x.

- **Key Features of Cumulative Distribution Graphs**
  - **Shape:** The graph is non-decreasing, as the probability cannot decrease.
  - **Range:** The graph ranges from 0 to 1, representing the total probability.
  - **Asymptotes:** The graph approaches 0 as x approaches negative infinity and 1 as x approaches positive infinity.

- **Plotting a CDF Graph**
  - Calculate or obtain the CDF $F(x)$ of the random variable.
  - Select a range of x values.
  - Compute $F(x)$ for each selected x value.
  - Plot each x against its corresponding $F(x)$ value.
  - Connect the points to form a continuous line for continuous random variables or a step graph for discrete random variables.

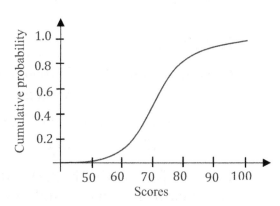

Example:

Given the CDF graph representing national exam scores, determine the probability that a student, chosen at random, scored below 75 on the exam.

Solution: The x−axis displays the exam scores, and the y−axis shows the cumulative probability for each score.

From the score of 75 on the x−axis, trace a vertical line upwards until it intersects the CDF curve. From the intersection point, trace a horizontal line towards the y−axis to find the corresponding cumulative probability.

Suppose the y−axis value at this intersection is approximately 0.70.

This indicates that there is a 70% chance that a randomly selected student scored less than 75 on the exam.

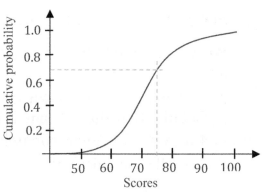

Relative Frequency

- Relative Frequency refers to the fraction or percentage of the time a value occurs in the dataset. It is calculated by dividing the frequency of a particular value by the total number of data points.

- **Step-by-Step Guide**
    - Count Total Observations: Determine the total number of data points in the dataset.
    - Calculate Individual Frequencies: Count how many times each value appears.
    - Compute Relative Frequency: Divide the frequency of each value by the total number of observations.

- The formula for relative frequency for a value x is given by:

$$RF(x) = \frac{f(x)}{N}$$

Where $RF(x)$ is the relative frequency of x, $f(x)$ is the frequency of x, and N is the total number of observations.

Example:

A teacher recorded the scores of a class of 20 students in a mathematics test. The scores are as follows:

$$95, 88, 73, 88, 95, 100, 88, 73, 95, 88, 100, 73, 88, 95, 100, 88, 73, 95, 88, 100$$

Determine the relative frequency of students scoring 88.

Solution: Count the total number of students, which is 20.

Count the number of students who scored 88.

Calculate the relative frequency.

Total number of students ($N = 20$)

Frequency of students scoring 88, $f(88) = 7$ (as 88 appears 6 times in the dataset)

The relative frequency for a score of 88 is calculated as:

$$RF(88) = \frac{f(88)}{N} = \frac{7}{20} = 0.35$$

So, the relative frequency of students scoring 88 is 0.35, meaning 35% of the students scored 88 in the test.

Stem-and-Leaf Plots

- A stem-and-leaf plot helps in understanding the shape of a data distribution and is particularly useful for small to moderate-sized datasets. How Stem-and-Leaf Plots Work:

  ▪ **Stem:** The 'stem' represents the leading digit(s) of each data value. These are typically the most significant digits.
  ▪ **Leaf:** The 'leaf' consists of the final digit of each data value.
  ▪ **Arrangement:** Data values are split into stems and leaves, and the leaves are listed in ascending order next to their corresponding stems.

- Creating a Stem-and-Leaf Plot Step-by-Step Guide:

  ▪ **Sort Data:** Arrange your data in ascending order.
  ▪ **Determine Stems:** Decide how many digits will form the stem.
  ▪ **Create Stems:** List the stems in a vertical column.
  ▪ **Add Leaves:** Write the leaf next to the appropriate stem.
  ▪ **Order Leaves:** Arrange the leaves in ascending order for each stem.
  ▪ **Analyze:** Interpret the plot to understand the distribution of your data.

Example:

A teacher wants to create a stem-and-leaf plot to analyze the distribution of scores from a recent math test. The test scores of the 20 students are as follows:

$$71, 85, 92, 69, 74, 91, 88, 83, 76, 95, 81, 72, 84, 90, 77, 89, 73, 86, 82, 94$$

The teacher aims to understand the general performance of the class and identify any patterns in the scores.

Solution: First, arrange the scores in ascending order:

$$69, 71, 72, 73, 74, 76, 77, 81, 82, 83, 84, 85, 86, 88, 89, 90, 91, 92, 94, 95$$

Here, the stems will be the tens place, and the leaves will be the units place of each score.
Create the Stem-and-Leaf Plot:

Analyze the Plot: The plot shows a concentration of scores in the 80s, indicating that most students scored in this range.

There's a noticeable gap in the 70s, with no students scoring between 77 and 81, suggesting a division in the class performance.

Stems	Leaves
6	9
7	1 2 3 4 6 7
8	1 2 3 4 5 6 8 9
9	0 1 2 4 5

The higher end of the scores (90s) is less populated but consistent, with no outliers.

The lowest score is in the high 60s, and the highest scores are mid-90s.

Histograms

- A histogram is a type of bar graph used to represent the frequency distribution of numerical data. It is one of the most common ways to visualize data distributions.

- Key Features:
    - The x −axis represents the intervals or bins into which the data is grouped.
    - The y −axis shows the frequency of data points in each bin.
    - Adjacent bars touch each other to indicate that the data is continuous.

- Creating Histograms Step-by-Step:
    - Collect and Sort Data: Gather your data and sort it into a range of classes or intervals.
    - Calculate Frequencies: Count how many data points fall into each class.
    - Draw the axes.
    - Label the x −axis with the classes and the y −axis with the frequency.
    - Draw bars for each class where the height represents the frequency.

Example:

A meteorologist is studying the annual rainfall in a particular region over the last 20 years. The rainfall (in inches) recorded for each year is as follows:

$$28, 34, 32, 37, 30, 35, 33, 31, 36, 38, 29, 40, 42, 39, 41, 33, 34, 35, 36, 37$$

The meteorologist wants to create a histogram to visualize the distribution of annual rainfall.

Solution: Arrange the rainfall data in ascending order:

$$28, 29, 30, 31, 32, 33, 33, 34, 34, 35, 35, 36, 36, 37, 37, 38, 39, 40, 41, 42$$

Determine suitable intervals for the data. Since the range is from 28 to 42 inches, we can create intervals of inches: $28 − 32, 33 − 37, 38 − 42$.

Count Frequencies:

$28 − 32$: 5, $33 − 37$: 10, $38 − 42$: 5

Draw the Histogram:

x −axis: Label the class intervals ($28 − 32, 33 − 37, 38 − 42$).

y − axis: Mark the frequency of each interval.

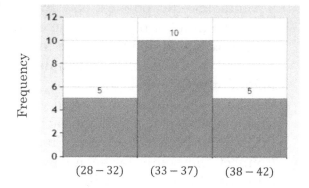

Bars: Draw bars for each class interval. The height of each bar corresponds to the frequency of the interval.

Frequency Polygons

- A frequency polygon is a line graph used to depict the distribution of a dataset. It can be constructed from a histogram or independently.

- Unlike histograms, frequency polygons are line graphs, making them less visually cluttered and easier to interpret when comparing multiple distributions.

- Creating a Frequency Polygon Step-by-Step:
  - Collect and Organize Data: Gather your dataset and organize it into a frequency table with class intervals.
  - Calculate Midpoints: For each class interval, calculate the midpoint by averaging the upper and lower limits.
  - Plot the Midpoints: On a graph with the $x-$axis representing the midpoints and the $y-$axis representing the frequencies, plot the points for each class.
  - Connect the Points: Draw straight lines between consecutive points.
  - Interpret the Graph: Analyze the shape and spread of the polygon to understand the distribution of your data.

Example:

A teacher wants to compare the test scores of two different classes using a frequency polygon. The scores for each class are out of 100 and are as follows:
Class A Scores: $55, 60, 62, 63, 64, 70, 75, 76, 77, 80, 85, 85, 90, 91, 92$
Class B Scores: $58, 63, 68, 73, 77, 78, 78, 79, 81, 82, 83, 86, 88, 89, 94$
The teacher aims to visualize and compare the distribution of scores between the two classes.

Solution: Given the range of scores (55 to 94), suitable intervals could be every 5 points: $55 - 59, 60 - 64, 65 - 69, 70 - 74, 75 - 79, 80 - 84, 85 - 89, 90 - 94$.
Tally the number of scores from each class that fall into each interval.

Calculate the midpoint of each interval for the $x-$axis. For example, the midpoint of $55 - 59$ is 57.
On the $x-$axis (midpoints) and $y-$axis (frequencies), plot points for each class interval for both Class A and Class B.
Connect the points for each class with straight lines. You will have two polygons on the same graph, one for each class.

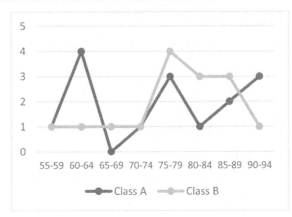

Mean, Median, Mode, and Range of the Given Data

- **Mean:** The average of all data points. Calculated by summing all values and dividing by the number of values. $M = \dfrac{sum\ of\ the\ data}{total\ number\ of\ data\ entires}$

- **Mode:** The most frequently occurring value in a data set. A data set can have one mode, more than one mode, or no mode at all.

- **Median:** The middle value in a data set when the values are arranged in ascending or descending order. If there is an even number of values, the median is the average of the two middle numbers.

- **Range:** the difference between the largest value and smallest value in the list

$$Range = Maximum\ Value - Minimum\ Value$$

Examples:

Example 1. What is the mode of these numbers? 5, 6, 8, 6, 8, 5, 3, 5

Solution: Mode: the value in the list that appears most often.

Therefore, the mode is number 5. There are three number 5 in the data.

Example 2. What is the median of these numbers? 6, 11, 15, 10, 17, 20, 7

Solution: Write the numbers in order: 6, 7, 10, 11, 15, 17, 20

The median is the number in the middle. Therefore, the median is 11.

Example 3. What is the mean of these numbers? 7, 2, 3, 2, 4, 8, 7, 5

Solution: Use this formula: Mean $= \dfrac{sum\ of\ the\ data}{total\ number\ of\ data\ entires}$.

Therefore: Mean $= \dfrac{7+2+3+2+4+8+7+5}{8} = \dfrac{38}{8} = 4.75$

Example 4. What is the range in this list? 3, 7, 12, 6, 15, 20, 8

Solution: The range is the difference between the largest value and the smallest value in the list. The largest value is 20 and the smallest value is 3.

Then: $20 - 3 = 17$

Quartiles and Percentiles of the Given Data

- **Quartiles:**
  - First Quartile (Q_1): This is the median of the lower half of the data. It marks the 25th percentile.
  - Second Quartile (Q_2): This is the median of the dataset and marks the 50th percentile.
  - Third Quartile (Q_3): This is the median of the upper half of the data. It marks the 75th percentile.
  - Interquartile Range (IQR): The difference between Q_3 and Q_1, representing the middle 50% of the data.

- **Calculate Quartiles:**
  - Find the median (Q_2).
  - For Q_1, find the median of the data points below Q_2.
  - For Q_3, find the median of the data points above Q_2.

- **Percentiles:** are values below which a certain percentage of the data falls. For example, the 20th percentile is the value below which 20% of the data can be found. For calculate the percentiles use the formula:
$$\text{Percentile rank} = \frac{P(N+1)}{100}$$
Where P is the desired percentile and N is the number of data points.

Examples:

Example 1. Find the quartiles for the following data set:
$$3, 7, 8, 5, 12, 14, 21, 13, 18$$

Solution: Arrange Data: $3, 5, 7, 8, 12, 13, 14, 18, 21$.

Q_2 (Median): 12. Q_1: Median of $3, 5, 7, 8$ is 6. Q_3: Median of $13, 14, 18, 21$ is 16.

IQR: $16 - 6 = 10$

Example 2. Find the 30th and 70th percentiles of the following data set:
$$15, 20, 35, 40, 50, 55, 60$$

Solution: 30th Percentile: $\frac{30(7+1)}{100} = 2.4$. The 30th percentile is between the 2nd and 3rd values, so it's approximately 20.

70th Percentile: $\frac{70(7+1)}{100} = 5.6$. The 70th percentile is between the 5th and 6th values, so it's approximately 55.

Three Standard Deviations

- Standard deviation (σ) is a measure of the amount of variation or dispersion in a set of values. A low standard deviation means that the values tend to be close to the mean (μ), while a high standard deviation indicates that the values are spread out over a wider range.

- The Empirical Rule ($68 - 95 - 99.7$ Rule): The empirical rule, also known as the $68 - 95 - 99.7$ rule, is a statistical rule which states that for a normal distribution:

  ▪ Approximately 68% of the data falls within one standard deviation of the mean.

  ▪ Approximately 95% of the data falls within two standard deviations of the mean.

  ▪ Approximately 99.7% of the data falls within three standard deviations of the mean.

- Understanding Three Standard Deviations: Three standard deviations from the mean (3σ) encompasses about 99.7% of the data. This range is calculated as follows:

  ▪ Lower limit: $\mu - 3\sigma$
  ▪ Upper limit: $\mu + 3\sigma$

Example:

Suppose a set of test scores in a class are: $82, 76, 90, 86, 88$. Calculate the range that covers three standard deviations from the mean.

Solution: Mean (μ): $\frac{82+76+90+86+88}{5} = 84.4$

Deviations: $82 - 84.4 = -2.4$, $76 - 84.4 = -8.4$, $90 - 84.4 = 5.6$, $86 - 84.4 = 1.6$, $88 - 84.4 = 3.6$,

Squared Deviations: $(-2.4)^2 = 5.76$, $(-8.4)^2 = 70.56$, $(5.6)^2 = 31.36$, $(1.6)^2 = 2.56$, $(3.6)^2 = 12.96$

Variance: $\sigma^2 = \frac{5.76+70.56+31.36+2.56+12.96}{5} = 24.64$

Standard Deviation (σ): $\sqrt{\text{Variance}} = \sigma \approx 4.96$

3σ Range: $\mu \pm 3\sigma$

Lower limit: $\mu - 3\sigma = 84.4 - (3 \times 4.96) = 69.52$

Upper limit: $\mu + 3\sigma = 84.4 + (3 \times 4.96) = 99..28$

The final step provides the range within which approximately 99.7% of the data in a normal distribution would fall.

Measures of Data Location

- Measures of data location, also known as measures of central tendency, are statistical tools used to describe the center of a data set. They provide a single value that is representative of the entire data set, helping to summarize and understand large amounts of information.

- Calculating Measures of Data Location Step-by-Step:

  - Organize Your Data: Arrange the data in ascending order.

  - Calculate the Mean: Add all the values together and divide by the number of values.

  - Find the Median: If the number of data points is odd, the median is the middle value. If it's even, average the two middle values.

  - Determine the Mode: Identify the value(s) that occur most frequently.

  - Calculate Quartiles and Percentiles: For quartiles, divide the data set into four equal parts. For percentiles, use a percentile rank formula or a statistical tool.

Example:

A teacher wants to evaluate the performance of a class in a recent exam. The scores of ten students are as follows: $72, 88, 95, 80, 67, 79, 90, 85, 75, 83$. Calculate the mean, median, mode, and the first and third quartiles of these salaries.

Solution: Calculate the Mean: Mean $= \frac{72+88+95+80+67+79+90+85+75+83}{10} = 81.4$

Find the Median: Arranged Scores: $67, 72, 75, 79, 80, 83, 85, 88, 90, 95$

Since there are 10 scores, the median is the average of the 5th and 6th scores: Median $= \frac{80+83}{2} = 81.5$

Determine the Mode: There are no repeating scores, so this data set does not have a mode.

Calculate the First Quartile (Q_1): The first half (after sorting) is: $67, 72, 75, 79, 80$

Since there are 5 numbers, the median (and Q_1) is the middle number, which is 75.

Calculate the Third Quartile (Q_3): The second half (after sorting) is: $83, 85, 88, 90, 95$

Since there are 5 numbers here as well, the median (and Q_3) is the middle number, which is 88.

Mean deviation

- Mean deviation, also known as the average deviation, is a statistical measure that describes the average distance of all data points from the mean of the dataset. It provides a clear picture of dispersion or variability in the data.

- Mean Deviation Step-by-Step:

- Calculating Mean: First, calculate the mean $\bar{x}$ of the dataset by summing all the values x_i and dividing by the number of values n. Formula: $\bar{x} = \frac{\sum x_i}{n}$

- Calculating Mean Deviation: Subtract the mean from each data point, take the absolute value of these differences, sum them up, and then divide by the number of data points. Formula:

$$\text{Mean deviation} = \frac{1}{n} \sum |x_i - \bar{x}|$$

Examples:

Example 1. Calculate the mean deviation for the dataset: 5, 10, 15, 20, 25

Solution: Mean Calculation: $\bar{x} = \frac{5+10+15+20+25}{5} = 15$

Mean Deviation $= \frac{|5-15|+|10-15|+|15-15|+|20-15|+|25-15|}{5} = \frac{10+5+0+5+10}{5} = 6$

Mean Deviation Interpretation: The mean deviation in this example is 6. This indicates that, on average, each data point is 6 units away from the mean of the dataset.

Example 2. A class of six students took a math test, and their scores out of 100 were $68, 72, 77, 80, 82, 85$. Calculate the mean deviation of their scores.

Solution: Calculating the Mean: $\bar{x} = \frac{68+72+77+80+82+85}{6} = 77.33$

First, calculate the absolute differences from the mean: $|68 - 77.33| + |72 - 77.33| + |77 - 77.33| + |80 - 77.33| + |82 - 77.33| + |85 - 77.33| = 30$

Calculating the Mean Deviation: $= \frac{.33+5.33+0.33+2.67+4.67+7.67}{6} = 5$

Mean Deviation Interpretation: The mean deviation of 5 suggests that, on average, the scores of the students deviate from the mean score by 5 points. This indicates a moderate level of consistency in the scores. A lower mean deviation would have indicated more uniform scores, while a higher mean deviation would have suggested greater variability among the students' performance.

Two Types of Variance

- Sample Variance: sed when dealing with a sample of a population. It estimates the variance based on a sample. And typically used in inferential statistics.

$$s^2 = \frac{1}{n-1} \sum (x_i - \bar{x})^2$$

- Population Variance: Used when the entire population is available for analysis. It gives the variance of the whole population. Used in descriptive statistics.

$$\sigma^2 = \frac{1}{N} \sum (x_i - \mu)^2$$

- Variance is a fundamental statistical measure used to assess the spread or dispersion of a dataset around its mean.

Examples:

Example 1. A small survey was conducted to find out the number of hours spent on social media daily by a group of high school students. The data collected from 5 students were as follows: $2, 3, 4, 5, 6$ hours. Calculate the sample variance of the data.

Solution: Calculating the Mean: $\bar{x} = \frac{2+3+4+5+6}{5} = 4$ hours

Calculating the Sample Variance (s^2):
$$s^2 = \frac{(2-4)^2+(3-4)^2+(4-4)^2+(5-4)^2+(6-4)^2}{5-1} = \frac{10}{4} = 2.5 \text{ hours square}$$

The sample variance of 2.5 hours squared indicates that, on average, the number of hours spent on social media by the students varies by 2.5 hours squared from the mean.

Example 2. Consider a population of five plants in a garden and their heights in centimeters: $30, 35, 40, 45, 50$. Calculate the population variance of the plant heights.

Solution: Calculating the Mean: $\mu = \frac{30+35+40+45+50}{5} = 40$ hours

Calculating the population Variance (σ^2):
$$\sigma^2 = \frac{(30-40)^2+(35-40)^2+(40-40)^2+(45-40)^2+(50-40)^2}{5} = \frac{250}{5} = 50 \text{ cm}^2$$

The population variance of $50 \ cm^2$ suggests that the heights of the plants vary considerably around the average height, indicating a diverse range of plant heights in the garden.

Measures of Dispersion

- Measures of dispersion provide insights into the spread or variability of data. Understanding these measures is crucial for accurate data interpretation.

- Step-by-Step Interpretative Measures of Dispersion:

    ▪ Range Interpretation: Indicates the total spread of data. Larger range signifies more variability.
    ▪ Interquartile Range (IQR) Interpretation: Measures the spread in the middle 50% of the data, reducing the impact of outliers.
    ▪ Mean Deviation (Average Deviation) Interpretation: Reflects the average distance of each data point from the mean.
    ▪ Variance Interpretation: Measures the average squared deviation from the mean. Higher variance indicates more spread.
    ▪ Standard Deviation Interpretation: Provides the average distance of each data point from the mean, in the same units as the data.

Example:

A teacher records the scores of 7 students in a math test out of 100. The scores are as follows: 60, 65, 70, 75, 80, 85, 90. Calculate the range, interquartile range (IQR), mean deviation, variance, and standard deviation of these scores. Interpret the results.

Solution: Range (30): The scores are spread across a range of 30 marks. This indicates a moderate variability in the performance of the students.

IQR (20): The middle 50% of the scores are within a 20 −point range, suggesting that most students scored relatively close to each other.

Mean Deviation (10): On average, each student's score deviates from the mean score by about 10 marks.

Variance (116.67) and Standard Deviation (10.8): These indicate that the scores are somewhat spread out from the mean, with a standard deviation of approximately 10.8 marks. The standard deviation being close to the mean deviation suggests a relatively uniform spread around the mean.

This data suggests that while there is some variability in the students' performance, most students scored within a relatively close range, as indicated by the IQR and the mean deviation. The standard deviation being higher than the IQR points to a few scores that are more distant from the mean, affecting the overall spread.

Box-and-Whisker Plots

- The Box and Whisker plot consists of the following parts:
  - **Median:** This shows the middle point of the data and is represented by a line that divides the box into two parts. Half of the values are greater than or equal to this value and half are less.
  - **First Quartile (Q_1):** This indicator shows the value that 25% of the data is smaller than. This value makes the left body of the box by a vertical line.

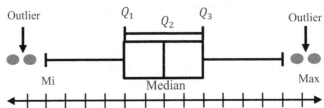

  - **Third Quartile (Q_3):** This indicator shows the value that 75% of the data is smaller than. This indicator is also used to display the right side of the box.
  - **Interquartile Range (IQR):** The distance between the first and third quartiles is shown by this index. The length of the other sides of the box is determined by this index.
  - **Whiskers:** These lines fill the gap between the first quartile and the lowest value as well as the highest value.
  - **Maximum:** In this plot, the maximum is the largest value that is at most 1.5 times the interquartile range away from the third quartile.
  - **Minimum:** In this plot, the minimum is the lowest value that is at most 1.5 times the interquartile range away from the first quartile.
  - **Outlier data:** Data that is smaller than the minimum or larger than the maximum is considered an outlier.

Example:

According to the following data, draw the related box-and-whisker plots.

$$10, 15, 18, 21, 22, 24, 25, 29, 31, 35$$

Solution: According to the data, the median is equal to the average of the two numbers 22 and 24: $\frac{22+24}{2} = 23$. In this boxplot, the minimum is equal to 10 and the maximum is equal to 35. Also, $Q_1 = 18$, $Q_3 = 29$, and $IQR = 29 - 18 = 11$.

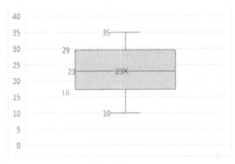

Skewness

- Skewness measures the degree of asymmetry of a distribution. A perfectly symmetrical data distribution has a skewness of 0. There are two types of skewness:

- **Positive Skewness:** The tail on the right side of the distribution is longer or fatter than the left side.

- **Negative Skewness:** The tail on the left side of the distribution is longer or fatter than the right side.

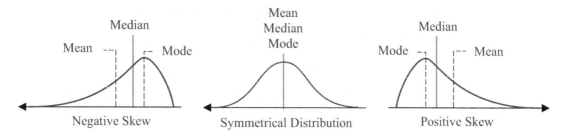

- The formula for skewness (Sk) is: $Sk = \frac{\sum_{i=1}^{n}(x_i - \bar{x})^3}{(n-1) \cdot s^3}$

  where x_i represents each value in the dataset, $\bar{x}$ is the mean of the dataset, n is the number of observations, and s is the standard deviation.

Example:

Given a dataset: $2, 3, 4, 8, 10$, calculate its skewness.

Solution: Calculate the mean $\bar{x}$: $\bar{x} = \frac{2+3+4+8+10}{5} = \frac{27}{5} = 5.4$

The standard deviation is the square root of the variance. First, we calculate the variance. So, calculating $\sum(x_i - \bar{x})^2$ for each data point: $(2 - 5.4)^2 = 11.56$, $(3 - 5.4)^2 = 5.76$, $(4 - 5.4)^2 = 1.96$, $(8 - 5.4)^2 = 6.76$, $(10 - 5.4)^2 = 21.16$

$Variance = \frac{\sum(x_i - \bar{x})^2}{n-1} = \frac{11.56+5.76+1.96+6.76+21.16}{4} = \frac{47.2}{4} = 11.8$

Thus, the standard deviation (s) is the square root of 11.8: $s = \sqrt{11.8} \approx 3.435$

Calculating $(x_i - \bar{x})^3$ for each data point

$(2 - 5.4)^3 = -39.304$, $(3 - 5.4)^3 = -13.824$, $(4 - 5.4)^3 = -2.744$,

$(8 - 5.4)^3 = 17.576$, $(10 - 5.4)^3 = 97.336$

Now, we use the skewness formula:

$$SK = \frac{-39.304 - 13.824 - 2.744 + 17.576 + 97.336}{(4) \cdot (3.435)^3} = \frac{59.04}{162.1213515} \approx 0.364$$

Therefore, the skewness of the dataset $2, 3, 4, 8, 10$ is approximately 0.364. This indicates a slight positive skewness.

Kurtosis

- Kurtosis measures the 'tailedness' of a data distribution, indicating how the tails of a distribution differ from the tails of a normal distribution. Kurtosis can be categorized as follows:
  - **Leptokurtic ($K > 3$):** The distribution has heavy tails and a sharp peak.
  - **Mesokurtic ($K = 3$):** The distribution resembles a normal distribution.
  - **Platykurtic ($K < 3$):** The distribution has light tails and a flat peak.
- To calculating the kurtosis (K), we provided two formulas:
  - Sample Kurtosis (Simplified Formula): $K = \frac{\sum_{i=1}^{n}(x_i - \bar{x})^4}{(n-1)\cdot s^4} - 3$
  - Excess Kurtosis (Using Adjusted Fisher's Definition):
  $$K = \frac{n(n+1)}{(n-1)(n-2)(n-3)} \sum_{i=1}^{n} \left(\frac{x_i - \bar{x}}{s}\right)^4 - \frac{3(n-1)^2}{(n-2)(n-3)}$$

For large data sets, both formulas will give similar results. However, for small samples, the adjusted Fisher's definition is preferred for its accuracy.

Example:

For the dataset (In the Skewness example) $2, 3, 4, 8, 10$, calculate its kurtosis using both formulas and compare the results.

Solution: First, calculate the Mean $\bar{x}$ and Standard Deviation (s). From the previous calculations, we have: $\bar{x} = 5.4$ and $s \approx 3.435$

- Simplified Kurtosis Formula: Calculate the fourth power of the summation of each term's deviation from the mean.
  $\sum (x_i - 5.4)^4 = (2 - 5.4)^4 + (3 - 5.4)^4 + (4 - 5.4)^4 + (8 - 5.4)^4 + (10 - 5.4)^4 =$
  $133.6336 + 33.1776 + 3.8416 + 45.6976 + 447.7456 = 664.096$

Then, we have: $K = \frac{\sum_{i=1}^{5}(x_i - 5.4)^4}{(4) \times (3.435)^4} - 3 = \frac{664.096}{556.887} - 3 \approx 1.192 - 3 \approx -1.808$

- Adjusted Fisher's Definition: Calculate the summation of the fourth power of each term's deviation from the mean, normalized by the standard deviation.
  $\sum \left(\frac{x_i - \bar{x}}{s}\right)^4 = \left(\frac{2-5.4}{3.435}\right)^4 + \left(\frac{3-5.4}{3.435}\right)^4 + \left(\frac{4-5.4}{3.435}\right)^4 + \left(\frac{8-5.4}{3.435}\right)^4 + \left(\frac{10-5.4}{3.435}\right)^4 \approx 4.77$

Then, we have: $K = \frac{5 \times (6)}{4 \times 3 \times 2} \times \sum_{i=1}^{5} \left(\frac{x_i - 5.4}{3.435}\right)^4 - \frac{3 \times (4)^2}{3 \times 2} = \frac{30}{24} \times 4.77 - \frac{48}{6} \approx -2.038$

The simplified formula (-1.808) is easier to calculate but can be biased, especially for small sample sizes. The adjusted Fisher's definition provides a more accurate measure of kurtosis (-2.038) by correcting for bias, making it more reliable, particularly for small datasets.

This negative value indicates a platykurtic distribution, meaning the distribution has lighter tails and a flatter peak compared to a normal distribution.

Chapter 2: Practices

✍ **Answer two questions based on the data provided.**

1) You conducted a survey on the number of hours students in your school spend on homework per week. The results were as follows: $1, 4, 3, 7, 2, 4, 5, 6, 4, 3, 2, 1, 7, 4, 6$. Create a frequency distribution table.

2) Using the frequency distribution from Question 1, create a bar chart.

✍ **For each of the following data sets, create a stem plot and identify any outliers.**

3) For the following data set of ages of participants in a survey.
   Ages: 22, 23, 23, 24, 24, 25, 25, 26, 27, 27, 27, 28, 29, 30, 30, 31, 32, 33, 34, 35, 36, 37, 40, 41, 42

4) for the following set of scores from a math test.
   Scores: 55, 57, 58, 60, 62, 63, 64, 65, 65, 66, 67, 68, 70, 72, 73, 75, 76, 78, 80, 82, 85, 88, 90

5) Given the following data set of daily temperatures (in degrees Celsius) over a month.
   Temperatures: 21, 22, 22, 23, 24, 24, 25, 25, 26, 27, 27, 27, 28, 29, 29, 30, 31, 31, 32, 33, 33, 34, 35, 36, 38, 39, 40

6) For the following data set of the number of books read by students in a year.
   Books Read: 1, 2, 2, 3, 3, 4, 4, 5, 5, 6, 7, 7, 8, 9, 10, 10, 11, 12, 13, 14, 15, 16, 18, 20, 24

✎ **Answer the questions based on the data provided.**

7)   The table below shows the frequency distribution of test Scores for 150 students?

Scores	21 − 30	31 − 40	41 − 50	51 − 60	61 − 70	71 − 80	81 − 90	91 − 100
Number of Students	12	17	19	28	30	23	13	8

Draw a cumulative frequency polygon for the above distribution by more than method.

8)   The given temperature distribution over a 60 −day period is:

Temperature ($c°$)	0 − 5	5 − 10	10 − 15	15 − 20	20 − 25	25 − 30	30 − 35	35 − 40
Number of days	1	6	16	18	16	1	1	1

Draw a CDF graph and obtain the median temperature.

9)   The graph depicts the cumulative probability distribution for the amount of rainfall (in millimeters) recorded in a particular region during the monsoon season. The x −axis shows the rainfall amount, and the y −axis indicates the cumulative probability of receiving that amount of rainfall or less on any given day.

Using the cumulative probability distribution graph, determine the probability that on a randomly chosen day, the rainfall in the region was 35 millimeters or less.

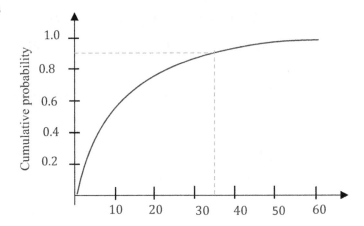

✎ **For each of the following data sets, create a stem plot and identify any outliers.**

10) In a study about sleep habits, 50 people were asked how many hours they sleep per night. The results are as follows:

Hours of Sleep	Frequency
5	8
6	15
7	20
8	7

Use the data to construct a line graph. How does the frequency of people's hours of sleep distribute?

11) A library recorded the number of books checked out by patrons each day for a week. The results are tabulated below:

Construct a line graph using this data. What trend in book checkouts does the graph show over the course of the week?

Day of the Week	Books Checked Out
Monday	30
Tuesday	45
Wednesday	40
Thursday	50
Friday	20

12) During a fitness challenge, participants reported the number of steps they walked each day. The average number of steps for the group is listed below:
Create a line graph from this data.

Day	Average Steps
1	3,000
2	5,000
3	7,500
4	10,000
5	12,500

What does the graph indicate about the participants' progress in the challenge?

13) A coffee shop tracked the number of customers it received at different hours of the day. The data collected is as follows:
Use the data to construct a line graph. What can you infer from the graph about the coffee shop's busiest and slowest times?

Hour of Day	Number of Customers
8 AM	25
10 AM	40
12 PM	37
2 PM	30
4 PM	20

✍ Construct a bar graph.

14) In a gym, the number of new memberships purchased each quarter of the year was recorded. The data is as follows:

Quarter	New Memberships
Q1	20
Q2	35
Q3	25
Q4	30

Construct a bar graph to show the new memberships per quarter.

15) A local bookstore tracked the number of books sold in different genres last month. The results are:

Genre	Books Sold
Fiction	40
Non-Fiction	30
Educational	20
Biographies	30

Use this data to construct a bar graph showing the number of books sold by genre.

16) A high school cafeteria counted the number of students purchasing lunch each day of the week. The data collected is:

Day	Students
Monday	150
Tuesday	120
Wednesday	160
Thursday	110
Friday	130

Construct a bar graph to show the number of students buying lunch each day.

17) A park recorded the number of visitors at different times of the day. The observations are.

Time of Day	Visitors
Morning	75
Afternoon	125
Evening	100

Construct a bar graph to display the number of visitors based on the time of day.

✎ **Complete the table and answer the question. Then sketch the histogram.**

Sixty health club members were surveyed about the number of days they work out in a week. Ten members said they work out two days; fifteen work out three days; twenty work out four days; ten work out five days; five work out six days.

Data Value (Days)	Frequency	Relative Frequency	Cumulative Relative Frequency

18) Complete the table

19) What does the frequency column in the workout frequency table sum to? Why?

20) What does the relative frequency column in the workout frequency table sum to? Why?

21) What is the difference between relative frequency and frequency for each data value in the workout frequency table?

22) What is the difference between cumulative relative frequency and relative frequency for each data value?

23) To construct the histogram for the workout frequency data, determine appropriate minimum and maximum x and y values and the scaling. Sketch the histogram. Label the horizontal and vertical axes with words. Include numerical scaling.

Complete the table and answer the question. Then sketch the histogram.

Seventy-five students were asked how many books they read over the summer. Five students read one book; twenty read two books; twenty-five read three books; fifteen read four books; ten read five books.

Data Value (Books)	Frequency	Relative Frequency	Cumulative Relative Frequency

24) Complete the table.

25) What does the frequency column in the reading frequency table sum to? Why?

26) What does the relative frequency column in the reading frequency table sum to? Why?

27) What is the difference between relative frequency and frequency for each data value in the reading frequency table?

28) What is the difference between cumulative relative frequency and relative frequency for each data value?

29) To construct the histogram for the reading frequency data, determine appropriate minimum and maximum x and y values and the scaling. Sketch the histogram. Label the horizontal and vertical axes with words. Include numerical scaling.

✎ **Construct a frequency polygon for the following:**

30)

Pulse Rates for Women	Frequency
60– 69	11
70– 79	16
80– 89	19
90– 99	3
100– 109	0
110– 119	2
120– 129	1

31)

Daily Range to visit the park	Frequency
Monday	14
Tuesday	11
Wednesday	20
Thursday	17
Friday	28
Saturday	46
Sunday	38

✎ **The following data on the number of public libraries opened per 100,000 people and the literacy rate in a region from 2000 to 2012.**

Public Libraries per 100k People (2000 − 2012)		Literacy Rate (2000 − 2012)	
year	Libraries per 100k	year	Literacy Rate (%)
2000	10	2000	70
2001	11	2001	72
2002	12	2002	74
2003	13	2003	75
2004	14	2004	77
2005	16	2005	79
2006	18	2006	81
2007	19	2007	83
2008	20	2008	85
2009	21	2009	87
2010	22	2010	89
2011	23	2011	91
2012	25	2012	93

32) Construct a double time series graph using a common x −axis for both sets of data:

33) Which variable increased the fastest? Explain:

34) Did the increase in the number of public libraries have an impact on the literacy rate? Explain:

✍ **Find the values of the given data.**

35) 6, 11, 5, 3, 6

    Mode: _____ Range: _____

    Mean: _____ Median: _____

37) 10, 3, 6, 10, 4, 15

    Mode: _____ Range: _____

    Mean: _____ Median: _____

36) 4, 9, 1, 9, 6, 7

    Mode: _____ Range: _____

    Mean: _____ Median: _____

38) 12, 4, 8, 9, 3, 12, 15

    Mode: _____ Range: _____

    Mean: _____ Median: _____

✍ **Given the following data set representing the scores of a class in a math test:**

$$34, 45, 50, 53, 56, 60, 62, 64, 67, 69, 72, 75, 78, 80, 82$$

39) Calculate the first quartile (Q_1):

40) The median (second quartile, Q_2):

41) The third quartile (Q_3):

✍ **Answer the questions.**

Consider two students, Alex and Jordan, who want to compare their test scores to the class average.

Test Scores Comparison			
Student	Test Score	Class Average Score	Class Standard Deviation
Alex	82	85	3
Jordan	88	90	2

42) Which student had the higher test score when compared to his class?

Use the Table to find the value that is three standard deviations.

43) Above the mean:

44) Below the mean:

✎ Answer the questions.

Listed are 32 numbers representing the total books read by students during the summer break, arranged in ascending order:

1, 1, 2, 3, 4, 4, 5, 6, 6, 7, 7, 8, 9, 9, 10, 11, 12, 13, 14, 15, 16, 17, 18, 19, 20, 21, 22, 23, 24, 25, 26, 27

45) Find the percentile of 9 books read.

46) Find the percentile of 23 books read.

Listed are 29 times for runners completing a $10k$ race, in order from fastest to slowest.

28, 31, 33, 35, 36, 38, 40, 41, 43, 45, 48, 49, 52, 53, 56, 59, 61, 63, 65, 68, 70, 72, 75, 77, 79, 81, 83, 85, 88

47) Find the $40th$ percentile for the race times.

48) Find the $78th$ percentile for the race times.

49) In a local marathon, Michelle finished $85th$ out of 400 participants. At what percentile is Michelle's finish?

50) For students taking a standardized test, a high score means a better result. The top scorers in a test have the highest marks. Is it more desirable to have a test score with a high or a low percentile in the context of academic performance?

51) The $20th$ percentile of scores on a math test is 68 out of 100. Write a sentence interpreting the $20th$ percentile in the context of the situation.

52) A student in the $90th$ percentile of a national science exam scored 95 out of 100. Is this student among the highest or lowest scorers in the exam? Write a sentence interpreting the $90th$ percentile in the context of the situation.

Answer the questions.

53) Calculate the mean deviation of the following data set: $5, 7, 9, 10, 12$

54) The scores of five students in a test were $60, 62, 65, 68, 70$. Find the mean deviation.

55) Why is the mean deviation always non-negative?

56) How does mean deviation differ from standard deviation?

Answer the questions.

57) What are the two types of variances in statistics, and how do they differ?

58) Calculate the population variance for the data set $4, 6, 8, 10, 12$.

59) Why is the denominator in the sample variance formula $n - 1$ instead of n?

60) Find the sample variance of the data set $3, 5, 7, 9$.

Answer the questions based on the following scenarios:

Sixty-five customers were asked how many times they visit their favorite restaurant in a month. The responses were as follows:

- Six people visited once.
- Twenty people visited twice.
- Eighteen people visited three times.
- Thirteen people visited four times.
- Eight people visited five times.

61) Construct a box plot for the data.

62) Describe the concentration of the data based on the box plot.

Sixty-five gym-goers were asked how many days per week they work out. The responses were:

- Five people worked out one day.
- Twenty people worked out two days.
- Twenty-five people worked out three days.
- Ten people worked out four days.
- Five people worked out five days.

63) Create a box plot for the workout data.

64) Comment on the distribution of workout days among gym-goers.

Sixty-five people were surveyed about the number of books they read over a year. Here are the results:

- Ten people read two books.
- Fifteen people read four books.
- Twenty-five people read six books.
- Ten people read eight books.
- Five people read ten books.

65) Construct a box plot for the reading data.

66) Analyze the spread of the data from the box plot.

Sixty-five students were asked about the number of extracurricular activities they participate in. The responses were:

- Ten students participate in one activity.
- Fifteen students participate in two activities.
- Twenty students participate in three activities.
- Ten students participate in four activities.
- Ten students participate in five activities.

67) Generate a box plot for the data on extracurricular activities.

68) Assess the concentration of the data points on the box plot.

✍ **According to the box plot, answer the questions (Final exam scores for high school students).**

69) Which score range shows the smallest spread of data? What is that spread?

70) Which score range shows the largest spread of data? What is that spread?

71) Find the interquartile range (IQR).

72) Are there more scores in the range of 70– 90 or 50– 70? How do you know?

73) Which score range has the fewest data in it?

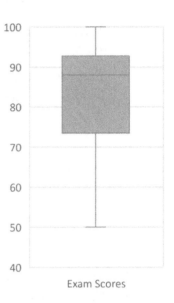
Exam Scores

✍ **According to the box plot, answer the questions (The amount of time spent on the website by visitors).**

74) During which time interval do we see the smallest spread of visitor numbers? What is that spread?

75) During which time interval do we see the largest spread of visitor numbers? What is that spread?

76) Find the interquartile range (IQR).

77) Are there more visitors in the interval of 20– 30 or 35– 45? How do you know?

78) Which visitor number range has the fewest data in it?

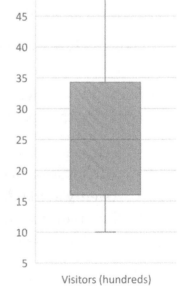
Visitors (hundreds)

✎ **Use the following information to answer the questions.**

Sixty-five customers were asked how many cups of coffee they purchase in a week. Twelve customers said they purchase two cups; twenty customers purchase three cups; fifteen purchase four cups; eleven purchase five cups; seven purchase six cups.

79) Sample mean: $\bar{x} =$ ____

80) Median:

81) Mode:

✎ **State whether the data are symmetrical, skewed to the left, or skewed to the right.**

Consider a fitness tracker report showing the number of steps taken daily by an individual over 20 days:

82) 3000, 3000, 3000, 4000, 4000, 4000, 4000, 5000, 5000, 5000, 5000, 5000, 5000, 5000, 5000, 6000, 6000, 6000, 7000, 7000

Here are the test scores out of 100 for a class on a particular exam:

83) 55, 60, 60, 65, 65, 65, 65, 65, 70

84) 92, 92, 92, 92, 92, 93, 94, 94, 95, 96

✎ **Answer the questions.**

85) When the data are skewed left, what is the typical relationship between the mean and median?

86) When the data are symmetrical, what is the typical relationship between the mean and median?

87) What word describes a distribution that has two modes.

88) Referring to the answer in Question 87, describe the shape of this distribution.

✎ **According to the histogram answer the questions.**

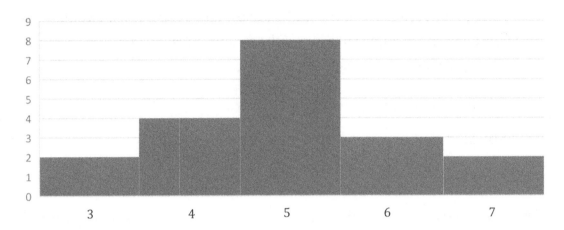

89) Describe the relationship between the mode and the median of this distribution.

90) Are the mean and the median the exact same in this distribution? Why or why not?

91) Describe the shape of this distribution.

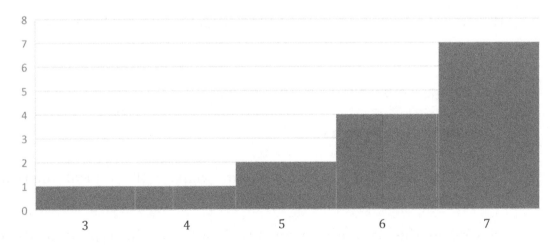

92) Describe the relationship between the mode and the median of this distribution.

93) Describe the relationship between the mean and the median of this distribution.

94) Describe the shape of this distribution.

Use the following information to answer the next two questions.

The following data are the new set of data for 20 customers, that customers wait for service at a bank (in minutes):

$$5, 7, 8, 10, 12, 15, 16, 16, 18, 20, 20, 22, 23, 23, 25, 27, 30, 35, 40, 45$$

95) Calculate the standard deviation of the wait times and round to the nearest tenth.

96) Find the wait time that is one standard deviation below the mean wait time.

Answer the questions.

97) How does kurtosis relate to the presence of outliers in a data set.

98) Consider the daily high temperatures (in degrees Celsius) recorded over a week in a city: $20, 22, 23, 21, 20, 17, 24$. Calculate the excess kurtosis of this temperature data set using the first formula.

Identify the type of kurtosis.

99)

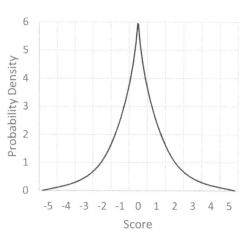

100)

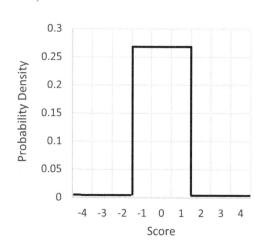

Chapter 2: Answers

1)

Hours of Homework	Frequency
1	2
2	2
3	2
4	4
5	1
6	2
7	2

2)

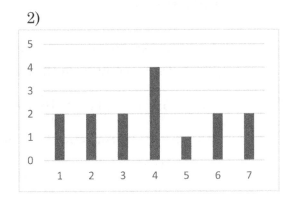

3) The ages of 40, 41, and 42 could be considered outliers as they are distinctly separate from the main cluster of data (ages 22 to 37).

Stems	Leaves
2	2 3 3 4 4 5 5 6 7 7 7 8 9
3	0 0 1 2 3 4 5 6 7
4	0 1 2

4) There are no apparent outliers in this data set.

Stems	Leaves
5	5 7 8
6	0 2 3 4 5 5 6 7 8
7	0 2 3 5 6 8
8	0 2 5 8
9	0

5) There are no apparent outliers in this data set.

Stems	Leaves
2	1 2 2 3 4 4 5 5 6 7 7 7 8 9 9
3	0 1 1 2 3 3 4 5 6 8 9
4	0

6) The number 24 books read stands out as an outlier. It's much higher than the majority of the data points.

Stems	Leaves
0	1 2 2 3 3 4 4 5 5 6 7 7 8 9
1	0 0 1 2 3 4 5 6 8
2	0 4

7) Here's the calculation for cumulative frequency:

$21 - 30$: 12(cumulative frequency is just the frequency of the first interval)

$31 - 40$: $12 + 17 = 29$

$41 - 50$: $29 + 19 = 48$

$51 - 60$: $48 + 28 = 76$

$61 - 70$: $76 + 30 = 106$

$71 - 80$: $106 + 23 = 129$

$81 - 90$: $129 + 13 = 142$

$91 - 100$: $142 + 8 = 50$

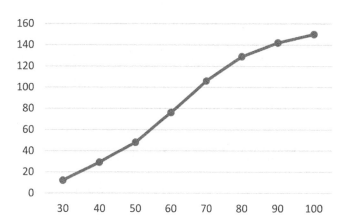

Plot the points and connect them to form the polygon:

We plot the points using the upper limit of each score range (30, 40, 50, etc.) and the corresponding cumulative frequency.

We then connect these points with straight lines to form the polygon.

This graph visually represents the accumulation of frequencies across the score ranges.

8) Let's calculate the cumulative frequency:

$0 - 5°C$: 1 day

$6 - 10°C$: $1 + 6 = 7$ days

$11 - 15°C$: $7 + 16 = 23$ days

$16 - 20°C$: $23 + 18 = 41$ days

$26 - 25°C$: $41 + 16 = 57$ days

$26 - 30°C$: $57 + 1 = 58$ days

$31 - 35°C$: $58 + 1 = 59$ days

$36 - 40°C$: $59 + 1 = 60$ days

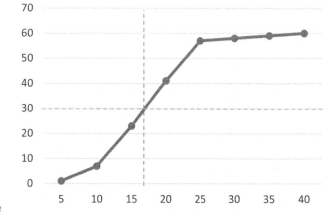

We'll plot these cumulative frequencies against the upper boundary of each temperature range.

The median temperature is the value separating the higher half from the lower half of a data sample. For our dataset of 60 days, the median will be ($\frac{60+1}{2} = 30.5$) between $30th$ and $31th$ day's temperatures. We'll find this value using the graph.

To find the median temperatures between $30th$ and $31th$ day's (x), first calculate the slope with the two ordered pairs $(15, 23)$ and $(20, 41)$: $m = \frac{y_2 - y_1}{x_2 - x_1}$

Calculate the Slop: $m = \frac{y_2 - y_1}{x_2 - x_1} = \frac{41 - 23}{20 - 15} = 3.6$

To find the point of $(x, 30.5)$, use the slope-intercept form formula:

$$y = mx + b$$

First, calculate b from point $(15, 23)$:

$$y = mx + b \rightarrow b = 23 - (3.6 \times 15) = -31$$

Now, we can calculate the x:

$$y = mx + b \rightarrow 30.5 = 3.6x - 31 \rightarrow x = \frac{61.5}{3.6} \approx 17.08$$

This graph illustrates how the cumulative number of days increases with the temperature. Using this graph, we have calculated the median temperature. The median temperature, which is the temperature at the midpoint of the 60 −day period, is approximately $17.08°C$.

This value can be visually confirmed on the cumulative frequency graph where the green dashed line (median day) intersects with the graph curve and the corresponding blue dashed line represents the median temperature on the temperature axis.

9) To solve this, we find the point corresponding to 35 millimeters on the x −axis and trace a line vertically up to the curve. From the point where it intersects the curve, we draw a horizontal line to the y −axis. The value on the y −axis at this intersection gives us the cumulative probability for 35 millimeters of rain or less. Let's analyze the graph to determine this probability.

Upon examining the graph, we can observe that the vertical line from the 35 millimeters point on the x −axis intersects the cumulative probability curve at a point that corresponds to a cumulative probability on the y −axis. The dashed lines on the graph suggest that this intersection occurs at a cumulative probability of approximately 0.9 (or 90%).

Therefore, based on the graph, the probability that on a randomly selected day the rainfall was 35 millimeters or less is 90%.

10) The graph shows the frequency of hours of sleep, indicating that most people surveyed sleep 7 hours a night.

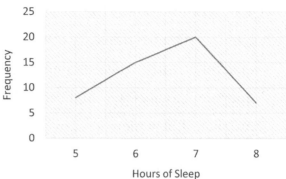

11) The graph illustrates the number of books checked out on each day of the week, with a peak on Thursday.

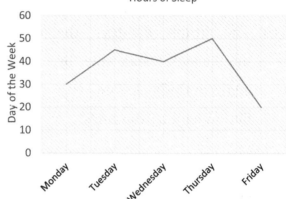

12) The graph depicts the average number of steps taken each day during the fitness challenge, showing a clear upward trend.

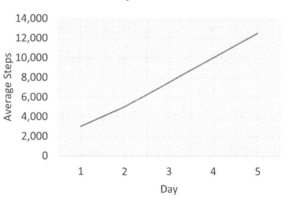

13) The graph shows the number of customers at different hours of the day at a coffee shop, with the highest patronage at 10 AM and lowest patronage at 4 PM.

14) The graph shows the new gym memberships per quarter, with the second quarter having the highest number of new memberships.

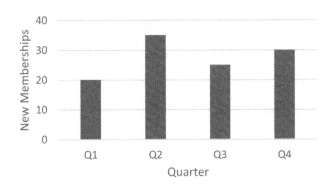

15) The graph displays the number of books sold by genre in the bookstore, with fiction leading the sales.

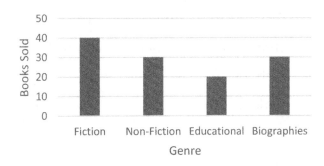

16) The graph presents the number of students buying lunch each day at the high school cafeteria, with Wednesday being the busiest day.

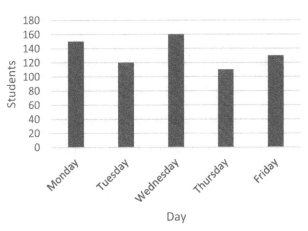

17) The graph illustrates the number of visitors to the park based on the time of day, with the afternoon being the most popular time for visits.

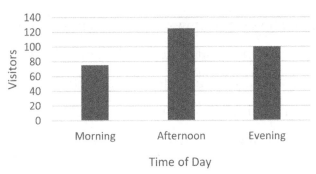

18)

Data Value (Days)	Frequency	Relative Frequency	Cumulative Relative Frequency
2	10	0.1667	0.1667
3	15	0.2500	0.4167
4	20	0.3333	0.7500
5	10	0.1667	0.9167
6	5	0.0833	1.0000

19) The frequency column sums to 60 because that's the total number of surveyed members.

20) The relative frequency column sums to 1 or 100% because it represents the proportion of the total count.

21) Frequency is the count of occurrences of each data value; relative frequency is that count divided by the total number of data points, expressing each count as a proportion of the total.

22) Cumulative relative frequency is the running total of relative frequencies, adding up from the first to the current data value; it's different from relative frequency, which is individual for each data value.

23) The histogram would have the number of days on the x−axis and the number of members on the y−axis, with scaling appropriate to the data values (2 to 6 days) and in the graph for three days, the frequency should be 15 (5 to 20 members).

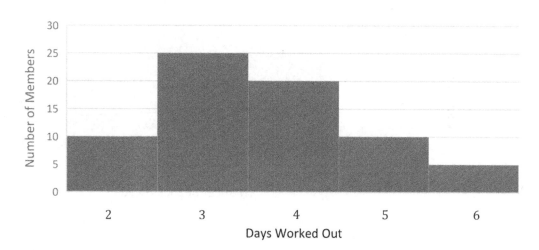

24)

Data Value (Books)	Frequency	Relative Frequency	Cumulative Relative Frequency
1	5	0.0667	0.0667
2	20	0.2667	0.3333
3	25	0.3333	0.6667
4	15	0.2000	0.8667
5	10	0.1333	1.0000

25) The frequency column sums to 75 because that's the total number of surveyed students.

26) The relative frequency column sums to 1 or 100% because it represents the complete proportion of the surveyed population.

27) Frequency is how many students reported each quantity of books read; relative frequency is the percentage of the total responses that each quantity represents.

28) Cumulative relative frequency accumulates the relative frequencies from the first data value through to the current data value; it differs from relative frequency, which does not accumulate.

29) The histogram would have the number of books on the x−axis and the number of students on the y−axis, with scaling fitting the data values (1 to 5 books) and frequencies (5 to 25 students).

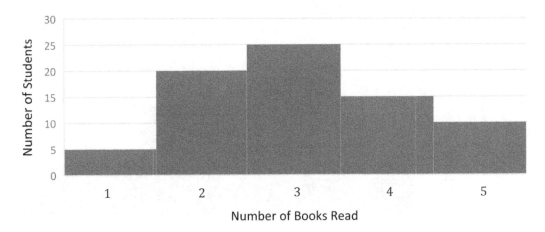

30)

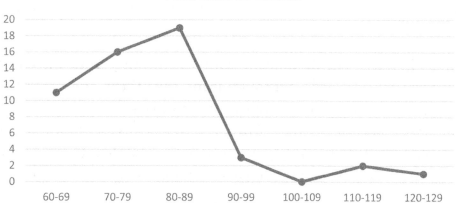

31)

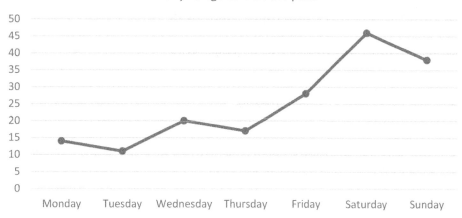

32)

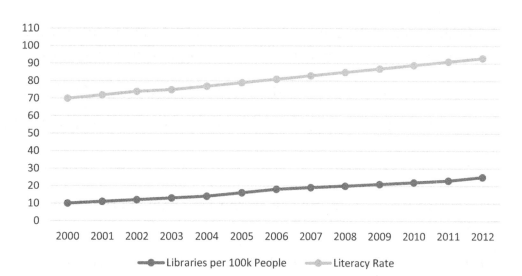

33) If the literacy rate line shows a steeper slope than the public libraries line, it would suggest that the literacy rate increased faster over the years than the number of libraries did.

34) If both lines rise in tandem with the literacy rate increasing as more libraries are opened, one could argue that there is a positive correlation, suggesting that the increase in libraries may have supported the improvement in literacy rates. However, as with any such analysis, correlation does not imply causation, and further investigation would be required to determine the impact of libraries on literacy rates.

35) Mode: 6, Range: 8, Mean: 6.2, Median: 6

36) Mode: 9, Range: 8, Mean: 6, Median: 6.5

37) Mode: 10, Range: 12, Mean: 8, Median: 8

38) Mode: 12, Range: 12, Mean: 9, Median: 9

39) 53   40) 64   41) 75

42) To compare the students' scores to their class averages, we can calculate the z−scores for both Alex and Jordan.
For Alex: $z = \frac{82-85}{3} = -1$
For Jordan: $z = \frac{88-90}{2} = -1$
Both Alex and Jordan have a z−score of -1, which means they both scored one standard deviation below their respective class averages.

43) For Alex's class: $85 + (3 \times 3) = 94$. For Jordan's class: $90 + (3 \times 2) = 96$.

44) For Alex's class: $85 - (3 \times 3) = 76$. For Jordan's class: $90 - (3 \times 2) = 84$.

45) $\frac{12}{32} \times 100 = 37.5\%$ 46) $\frac{27}{32} \times 100 = 84.375\%$

47) $0.4 \times 29 = 11.6 \approx 12$. We look at the $12th$ value in the ordered list, which is 49 minutes.

48) $0.78 \times 29 = 22.62 \approx 23.$. We look at the $23rd$ value in the ordered list, which is 75 minutes.

49) $\frac{400-85}{400} \times 100 = 78.75\%$

50) A high percentile. because this means the student scored better than a larger percentage of their peers.

51) The 20th percentile score of 68 means that 20% of the students scored 68 or lower on the math test.

52) The student is among the highest scorers in the exam. Being in the 90th percentile means that they scored higher than 90% of the students who took the national science exam.

53) 2.08   54) 3.2

55) The mean deviation involves taking the absolute value of the differences between each data point and the mean.

56) Mean deviation is the average of the absolute differences between each data point and the mean, whereas standard deviation is the square root of the average of the squared differences from the mean. Standard deviation gives more weight to outliers than mean deviation does.

57) The two types of variances are population variance and sample variance. Population variance σ^2 is used when considering the entire population, while sample variance (s^2) is used when dealing with a sample of that population. The formula for sample variance includes a correction factor dividing by $n-1$ instead of n to account for the bias in estimating the population variance from a sample.

58) 8

59) Using $n-1$ in the denominator of the sample variance formula corrects for the bias in estimating the population variance from a sample. It compensates for the fact that a sample tends to be less varied than the population, providing a more accurate estimate.

60) 6.67

61)

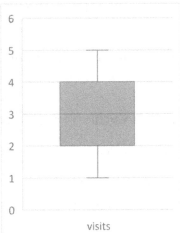

62) The box plot shows a median around three visits, with the data fairly evenly distributed, indicating that most customers visit their favorite restaurant a few times a month.

63)

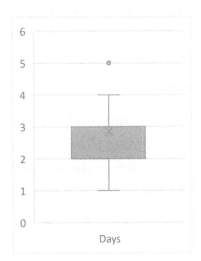

64) The median is around three days. Based on the box plot, the median is closer to Q_3 than Q_1 ($Q_2 = Q_3 = 3$), it indicates that more people work out on the higher end of the scale. and the spread is quite even.

65)

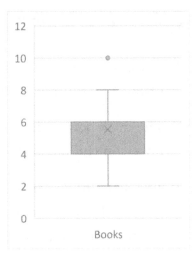

66) This plot has a median around six books, with a slightly larger spread ($Q_2 = Q_3 = 6$), suggesting a variety in the number of books read by the students.

67)

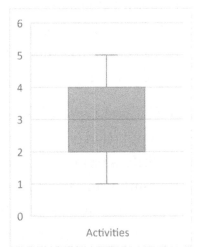

68) The median is close to three activities, with the interquartile range being quite tight, indicating that students tend to participate in a few extracurricular activities.

69) The smallest spread is between the maximum and the 75th percentile ($Q_3 \approx$ 93), which is approximately 7 points ($10 - 93 = 7$).

70) The largest spread is between the minimum and the 25th percentile ($Q_1 \approx$ 73) which is about 23 points ($73 - 50 = 23$).

71) The IQR is approximately 20 points, between 73 and 93.

72) The range from 70 to 90 covers the box (from Q_1 to Q_3), which contains the middle 50% of the data. The range from 50 to 70, on the other hand, includes part of the lower whisker and extends just to Q_1. Since the box itself represents a more concentrated area where 50% of the scores lie, there are more scores in the range of 70–90.

73) The smallest range, indicating the highest data density and thus the fewest data points per unit length, is 88 to 93 (Median to Q_3). Therefore, the range with the fewest data points per unit length is 5.

74) The smallest spread indicates that the visitor numbers are more consistent and less variable. When the spread is small, it means most of the data points (visitor numbers) are closer to each other. Here, the smallest spread is between the minimum and the 25th percentile ($Q_1 \approx 16,000$), which is about 6,000 visitors ($16 - 10 = 6$ hundred).

75) The largest spread indicates that the visitor numbers are more diverse and variable. A larger spread means the data points are more spread out, showing greater variability in visitor numbers. Here, the largest spread is between the maximum and the 75th percentile ($Q_3 \approx 34,000$), which is approximately 16,000 visitors ($50 - 34 = 16$ hundred).

76) The *IQR* is the range between Q_1 (16) and Q_3 (34). Thus, the *IQR* is $34 - 16 = 18$ hundreds of visitors.

77) There are more visitors in the interval of 20–30 because this interval falls entirely within the interquartile range, which contains the middle 50% of the data. The interval 35–45 is in the whisker, indicating fewer data points.

78) The smallest range, indicating the highest data density and thus the fewest data points per unit length, is 10 to 16 (Minimum to Q_1). Thus, the range with the fewest data points per unit length is 6 hundred.

79) Sample mean = 3.71 cups of coffee per week.

80) 4 cups of coffee per week.   81) 3 cups of coffee per week.

82) The distribution is skewed to the right, as there are more low values and the higher values tail off to the right.

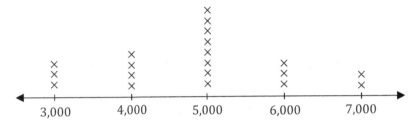

83) The distribution is skewed to the left, as there are more high values and the lower values tail off to the left.

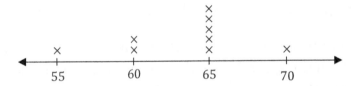

84) The distribution is skewed to the right, as there are more low values and the higher values tail off to the right.

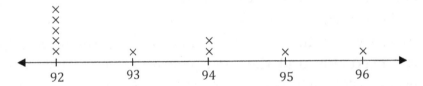

85) When the data are skewed left, the mean is typically less than the median.

86) When the data are symmetrical, the mean is typically very close to or the same as the median.

87) A distribution that has two modes is described as bimodal.

88) The shape of a bimodal distribution typically features two distinct peaks or high points, each representing a mode. This shape indicates two different clusters of data points within the distribution.

89) The mode of this distribution is the value that appears most frequently, which is 5, as it has the highest frequency (tallest bar). The median is the middle value when all values are listed in order, and given the somewhat symmetric shape of the histogram, the median is likely to be near the mode, possibly the same if the number of observations is odd and the distribution is perfectly symmetric.

90) The mean and median are not necessarily the same in this distribution. The mean is the average value and is affected by the magnitude of each value and its frequency. If the distribution is perfectly symmetric, the mean and median could be the same. However, since there is a slight asymmetry with more data on the left of the mode, the mean might be slightly lower than the mode (and potentially the median).

91) The shape of the distribution appears to be roughly symmetric with a slight skew to the left. This can be deduced from the fact that the bars on the left side of the mode are slightly taller than those on the right, indicating a larger frequency of values below the mode.

92) Mode is the value with the highest frequency, which is 7 (frequency = 7). Median is the middle value when the data is ordered. Since we have 15 data points, the median is the 8th value.
Ordered data: 3, 4, 5, 5, 6, 6, 6, $\boxed{6}$, 7, 7, 7, 7, 7, 7, 7. Thus: Median = 6.
Relationship: The mode (7) is higher than the median (6).

93) The histogram shows a left-skewed or negatively skewed distribution. This means that the data has more frequent higher values, with fewer lower values extending the tail to the left.
Characteristics: The bars are higher on the right side. The tail on the left side (towards lower values) is longer. Most of the data points are concentrated on the right side (higher values). The frequencies decrease as the values decrease, peaking at the highest value (7). The mean will be smaller or equal than the median.

94) The distribution is left-skewed (Negatively skewed), as evidenced by the longer tail on the left side of the histogram, where there are lower values with lower frequency. The bulk of the data is concentrated on the left side, with frequencies tapering off as the values increase.

95) 10.7   96) 10.1

97) Kurtosis is related to the presence of outliers because higher kurtosis indicates more of the variance is due to rare, extreme deviations (outliers) from the mean. In contrast, lower kurtosis suggests that extreme values are less frequent and less extreme.

98) Dataset: $x_i = \{17, 20, 20, 21, 22, 23, 24\}$, $\bar{x} = 21$, $S \approx 2.31$.
Kurtosis Formula (use adjusted Fisher's definition because samples are small): $K = \frac{n(n+1)}{(n-1)(n-2)(n-3)} \sum_{i=1}^{n} \left(\frac{x_i - \bar{x}}{s}\right)^4 - \frac{3(n-1)^2}{(n-2)(n-3)}$
First calculate the summation of the fourth power of each term's deviation from the mean, normalized by the standard deviation:
$$\sum \left(\frac{x_i - 21}{2.31}\right)^4 = \left(\frac{-4}{2.31}\right)^4 + \left(\frac{-1}{2.31}\right)^4 + \left(\frac{-1}{2.31}\right)^4 + \left(\frac{0}{2.31}\right)^4 + \left(\frac{1}{2.31}\right)^4 + \left(\frac{2}{2.31}\right)^4 + \left(\frac{3}{2.31}\right)^4$$
$$\approx 12.50$$
Now, calculate the Kurtosis value:
$$K = \frac{7 \times 8}{6 \times 5 \times 4} \times \sum_{i=1}^{7} \left(\frac{x_i - 21}{2.31}\right)^4 - \frac{3 \times 6^2}{5 \times 4} = \frac{56}{120} \times 12.50 - \frac{108}{20} \approx 0.43$$
So, the excess kurtosis of the temperature data set is approximately 0.43. The excess kurtosis of approximately 0.430 indicates that the temperature data set has a slight positive kurtosis, suggesting a distribution with slightly heavier tails and a sharper peak compared to a normal distribution.

99) This graph shows a distribution with a sharp peak and heavy tails, which means the distribution has a positive kurtosis value, implying it is more peaked than a normal distribution.

100) This graph shows a distribution with a flat top and lighter tails compared to a normal distribution., which means the distribution has a negative kurtosis value, implying it is less peaked than a normal distribution.

CHAPTER

3 Probability

Topics that you'll learn in this chapter:

- ☑ Basics of Probability
- ☑ Theoretical Probability
- ☑ Experimental Probability
- ☑ Probability Rules and Laws
- ☑ Mutually Exclusive Events
- ☑ Independent and Dependent Events
- ☑ Compound Events
- ☑ Conditional and Binomial Probabilities
- ☑ Probability Problems
- ☑ Types of Probability Distributions
- ☑ Permutations and Combinatorics
- ☑ Systematic List of Outcomes and Set Notation
- ☑ Tree Diagrams
- ☑ Venn Diagrams
- ☑ Contingency Tables

83

Basics of Probability

- Probability is a fundamental concept in statistics that measures the likelihood of an event occurring. It ranges from 0 (the event will not occur) to 1 (the event will certainly occur).

  - **Random Experiment:** An experiment whose outcome cannot be predicted with certainty.

  - **Sample Space (S):** The set of all possible outcomes of a random experiment.

  - **Event (E):** A specific outcome or a set of outcomes within the sample space.

  - **Probability of an Event ($P(E)$):** The measure of the likelihood that the event will occur.

  - **Range of Probability:** $0 \leq P(E) \leq 1$

    A probability of 0 means the event will not occur, and 1 means it will certainly occur.

  - **Probability of the Sample Space:** $P(S) = 1$

    The probability of the sample space (all possible outcomes) is always 1.

Example:

A fair die is rolled. What is the probability of rolling a 4?

Solution: The probability of an event is calculated by dividing the number of favorable outcomes by the total number of possible outcomes. In this case, the event is rolling a 4, which can happen in only one way (rolling the face with the number 4). The total number of possible outcomes is 6 (since there are 6 faces on the die). Therefore, the probability P of rolling a 4 is:

Sample Space, $S = \{1, 2, 3, 4, 5, 6\}$

Event E (rolling a 4), $E = \{4\}$

Probability, $P(E) = \frac{Number\ of\ favorable\ outcomes}{Total\ number\ of\ outcomes} = \frac{1}{6}$

So, the probability of rolling a 4 with a fair die is $\frac{1}{6}$ or approximately 0.1667 (when converted to a decimal).

Theoretical Probability

- Theoretical probability is an approach in probability theory and its usage is for the calculation of the probability of a particular event occurrence. Probability theory is a branch of math that's involved with finding the chance of the occurrence of a random event. It tells us about what ought to occur in a perfect situation without conducting any experiments.

- The probability that an event can occur lies between zero and one. If the probability is nearer to zero, it means that the event is less likely to happen. Similarly, if the probability is nearer to one it implies that the event has more of a chance of happening.

- To find the theoretical probability of an event, divide the number of favorable outcomes by the number of total outcomes.

Examples:

Example 1. The letters of the word "PROBABILITY" are put in a bag. What is the probability of pulling out the letter "B" from the bag?

Solution: First count the total number of letters in the word "PROBABILITY": there are 11 letters in this word. Now count the number of the letter "B" in this word: there are 2 letters "B" in this word. The theoretical probability of an event $= \frac{The\ number\ of\ favorable\ outcomes}{The\ number\ of\ total\ outcomes} = \frac{2}{11}$.

Example 2. We have written the numbers 0, 2, 8, 7, 9, and 10 separately on 6 cards and put them in a bag. What is the probability that the number we will pick out is greater than 5?

Solution: We know the total number of cards is 6. Now count the number of the cards with numbers greater than 5: there are 4 cards with numbers greater than 5. The theoretical probability of an event $= \frac{The\ number\ of\ favorable\ outcomes}{The\ number\ of\ total\ outcomes} = \frac{4}{6} = \frac{2}{3}$.

Example 3. The Environmental Protection Organization predicts that there is a 30% chance that half of the world's vegetation will disappear in the next 20 years. What is the probability that this will not happen?

Solution: $p(event) + p(complement\ of\ event) = 100\%$ or 1

$\rightarrow 30\% + p(complement\ of\ event) = 100\%$

$\rightarrow p(complement\ of\ event) = 100\% - 30\% = 70\% \rightarrow \frac{70}{100} = \frac{7}{10} = 0.7$.

Experimental Probability

- The chance or occurrence of a specific event is termed its probability. The value of a probability lies between zero and one. It means if it's an impossible event, the probability is zero and if it's a definite event, the probability is one.

- Experimental probability is a kind of probability that occurs based on a series of experiments. A random experiment is completed and repeated over and over to see their likelihood and every single repetition is considered a trial. The experiment is conducted to find the possibility of an occurrence occurring or not occurring. It could be coin-tossing, die-rolling, or spinner-rotating.

- In math terms, the probability of an event = the number of times an occurrence occurred ÷ the entire number of trials.

- To find the experimental probability you can follow these steps:
  - 1st step: Conduct an experiment and pay attention to the number of times the event happens and also the total number of trials.
  - 2nd step: Divide these 2 numbers to get the Experimental Probability.

Examples:

Example 1. A bookstore recently sold 12 books, 6 of which were novels. What is the experimental probability that the next book will be a novel?

Solution: We know that the experimental probability of an event = The number of times an occurrence occurred ÷ The entire number of trials. We also know that out of the 12 books sold, 6 were novels. Therefore, the experimental probability that the next book will be a novel is $= \frac{6}{12}$. Write the fraction in the simplest form: $\frac{1}{2}$.

Example 2. A manufacturer of smartwatches, after testing 100 smartwatches, finds that 95 smartwatches are not defective. What is the experimental probability that a smartwatch chosen at random has no defects?

Solution: We know that the experimental probability of an event = The number of times an occurrence occurred ÷ The entire number of trials.

So, the experimental probability that a smartwatch chosen at random has no defects $= \frac{95}{100}$. Write the fraction in the simplest form: $\frac{19}{20}$.

Probability Rules and Laws

- Probability rules and laws are the foundational principles that guide the calculation and interpretation of probability in various scenarios.
- **Key Probability Rules and Laws**
  - The Law of Total Probability: This law is used when dealing with a set of mutually exclusive and exhaustive events. If $B_1, B_2, \ldots, B_n$ are mutually exclusive and exhaustive events, then for any event A:
  $$P(A) = P(A \text{ and } B_1) + P(A \text{ and } B_2) + \ldots + P(A \text{ and } B_n)$$
  - Additive Rule: For any two events, A and B:
  $$P(A \text{ or } B) = P(A) + P(B) - P(A \text{ and } B)$$
  If A and B are mutually exclusive (cannot occur at the same time), this simplifies to: $P(A \text{ or } B) = P(A) + P(B)$
  - Multiplicative Rule: For any two independent events, A and B (the occurrence of one does not affect the occurrence of the other):
  $$P(A \text{ and } B) = P(A) \times P(B)$$
  - Complementary Rule: The probability of the complement of an event A (event A not occurring) is: $P(\text{not } A) = 1 - P(A)$
  - Conditional Probability: The probability of an event A given that event B has occurred is denoted by $P(A|B)$ and is calculated as: $P(A|B) = \frac{P(A \text{ and } B)}{P(B)}$

    This is applicable when the occurrence of B affects the probability of A.
  - Bayes' Theorem: A fundamental theorem in probability, it is used to revise probabilities given new information. Bayes' Theorem states:
  $$P(A|B) = \frac{P(A \cap B)}{P(B)} = \frac{P(B|A) \times P(A)}{P(B)}$$

Example:

In a deck of cards, what is the probability of drawing either a heart or a queen?

Solution: First, let's calculate the number of favorable outcomes for each event: $P(heart) = \frac{1}{4}$, $P(queen) = \frac{4}{52}$, $P(heart \text{ and } queen) = \frac{1}{52}$
However, we must consider that one of the queens is also a heart (the Queen of Hearts). Therefore, this card is counted in both categories and should not be double-counted. The total number of favorable outcomes for drawing either a heart or a queen is the sum of the individual favorable outcomes, minus the overlap (the Queen of Hearts): $P(heart \text{ or } queen) = \frac{1}{4} + \frac{4}{52} - \frac{1}{52} = \frac{4}{13}$
So, the probability of drawing either a heart or a queen from a standard deck of cards is $\frac{4}{13}$.

Mutually Exclusive Events

- Mutually exclusive events are events that cannot occur at the same time. Their occurrence is exclusive of each other in a single trial of an experiment.

- **Characteristics of Mutually Exclusive Events**

  - **Non-Overlap:** If two events are mutually exclusive, the occurrence of one event precludes the occurrence of the other in the same trial. Their intersection is empty, meaning they have no outcomes in common.

  - **Additive Rule:** For mutually exclusive events, the probability of either event occurring is the sum of their individual probabilities. If A and B are mutually exclusive, then: $P(A\ or\ B) = P(A) + P(B)$

  - **Limitations:** Mutually exclusive events are distinct from independent events. Independent events can occur simultaneously, and the occurrence of one does not affect the probability of the other. However, mutually exclusive events cannot occur at the same time.

Examples:

Example 1. In a single roll of a fair six-sided die, what is the probability of rolling either a 2 or a 5?

Solution: The events of rolling a 2 and rolling a 5 are mutually exclusive because both cannot happen at the same time in a single roll.
$P(rolling\ a\ 2) = \frac{1}{6}, P(rolling\ a\ 5) = \frac{1}{6}$
Therefore, $P(rolling\ a\ 2\ or\ 5) = \frac{1}{6} + \frac{1}{6} = \frac{1}{3}$

Example 2. What is the probability of drawing either a heart or a queen from a standard deck of cards?

Solution: The events of drawing a heart and drawing a queen are not mutually exclusive (since there is a queen of hearts). To calculate the probability correctly, we need to adjust for the overlap (See the answer in the example from the "Probability Rules and Laws").

Independent and Dependent Events

- Dependent events affect the likelihood of other events -or their likelihood of happening is influenced by different events.

- Independent events don't have an effect on each other and don't increase or decrease the likelihood of another event happening.

- To identify dependent events or independent events, you can follow these steps:

  - 1st step: Determine whether it's possible for the events to occur in any order or not. If the answer is yes, go to the 2nd step.
  - 2nd step: Determine if one event influences the result of the other event If the answer is yes, go to the 3rd step.
  - 3rd step: If the event is independent, use the formula of independent events and find the answer: $P(A \cap B) = P(A) \cdot P(B)$.
  - 4th step: If the event is dependent, use the formula of dependent events and find the answer: $P(B \ and \ A) = P(A) \times P(B \ after \ A)$.

Examples:

Example 1. In a factory, out of 12 products, 2 of them are defective. If the manufacturer chooses 2 products, what is the probability that both are defective?

Solution: The probability that the manufacturer selects a defective product is equal to the number of defective products divided by the total number of products: $\frac{2}{12}$. Once the manufacturer selects a product, only 11 products remain. There is also one less defective product because the manufacturer is not going to choose the same defective product twice. Therefore, the probability that the manufacturer chooses the second defective product is equal to: $\frac{1}{11}$. Therefore, the probability that the manufacturer chooses products in such a way that both are defective is: $\frac{2}{12} \times \frac{1}{11} = \frac{2}{132} = \frac{1}{66}$.

Example 2. In a survey, it was found that 4 out of 8 people read books in their free time. If 3 people are randomly selected with replacements, what is the probability that all 3 people read books in their free time?

Solution: If 3 people are randomly selected with replacements who read books, then the probability that all 3 people read books is: P(person 1 reads books) $= \frac{4}{8}$, P(person 2 reads books) $= \frac{4}{8}$, P(person 3 reads books) $= \frac{4}{8}$.
P(person 1 and person 2 and person 3 read books) $= \frac{4}{8} \times \frac{4}{8} \times \frac{4}{8} = \frac{1}{8}$.

Compound Events

- The compound probability of compound events is defined as the possibility of 2 or more independent events happening together. An independent event is one whose outcome isn't influenced by the result of other events.

- Compound probability can be determined for 2 sorts of compound events: mutually exclusive compound events and mutually inclusive compound events. The formulas to determine the compound probabilities for each sort of event are different. A mutually inclusive event is a situation where one event can occur with the other, whereas a mutually exclusive event is when 2 events cannot happen at the same time. The compound probability will always be between zero and one.

- To find a compound probability you can follow these steps:

  - 1st step: Read the question and determine if the compound event is a mutually exclusive compound event or a mutually inclusive compound event.

  - 2nd step: List the given information and probabilities.

  - 3rd step: Choose the right compound probability formula: The mutually exclusive events compound probability formula is $P(A \, or \, B) = P(A) + P(B)$ and the mutually inclusive events compound probability formula is: $P(A \, or \, B) = P(A) + P(B) - P(A \, and \, B)$.

  - 4th step: Find the value of $P(A)$ and $P(B)$.

  - 5th step: Put the values into the respective formula to find the answer.

Examples:

Example 1. We have thrown a coin 6 times. What is the probability that we obtain at least one tail?

Solution: First, find the total number of outcomes. we have thrown a coin 6 times so the total number of outcomes is equal to 2^6: $2 \times 2 \times 2 \times 2 \times 2 \times 2 = 2^6 = 64$. Now we should find the desired outcomes (at least one tail): 63. The final step is to find the required probability: $\frac{63}{64}$.

Example 2. If we roll two dice, what is the probability that their sum is 3 or less?

Solution: When we roll a dice, for each roll there are 6 possible outcomes. So, the total number of outcomes is equal to 6^2: $6 \times 6 = 6^2 = 36$. In the next step we should find favorable outcomes: 3. The final step is to find the required probability: $\frac{3}{36} = \frac{1}{12}$.

Conditional and Binomial Probabilities

- The conditional probability for events A and B:

$$P(B|A) = \frac{P(A \cap B)}{P(A)}$$

where $P(A) \neq 0$.

- Binomial probability is the probability of exactly x successes in n repeated trials in an experiment with two possible outcomes. For $0 \leq x \leq n$, where p is the probability of success and $1 - p$ is the probability of failure, it is obtained using the following formula:

$$P = {}_nC_x p^x (1-p)^{n-x} \quad \text{or} \quad P = \binom{n}{x} p^x (1-p)^{n-x}$$

Examples:

Example 1. A bag contains 3 black, 5 grey, and 8 white marbles. Two marbles are randomly selected. Find the probability that the second marble is black given that the first marble is grey. (Assume that the first marble is not replaced.)

Solution: Use the conditional probability formula: $P(B|A) = \frac{P(A \cap B)}{P(A)}$.

The probability of selecting a grey marble: $P(grey) = \frac{5}{3+5+8} = \frac{5}{16}$.

The probability of selecting a black marble: $P(black) = \frac{3}{3+4+8} = \frac{3}{15}$.

The probability of selecting a grey marble: $P(grey \ and \ black) = \frac{5}{16} \times \frac{3}{15} = \frac{1}{16}$.

Therefore, $P(black) = \frac{P(grey \ and \ black)}{P(grey)} = \frac{\frac{1}{16}}{\frac{5}{16}} = \frac{1}{5}$.

Example 2. What is the probability of getting 4 tails when you toss a coin 7 times?

Solution: Considering that there are two outcomes for a coin toss experiment, and assuming equal probability in the coin toss, i.e., the probability is $\frac{1}{2}$. Let $n = 7$ be the number of repeated trials, $x = 4$ the number of successful trials. Use the formula for binomial probability $P = {}_nC_x p^x (1-p)^{n-x}$. Therefore:

$$P = {}_7C_4 \left(\frac{1}{2}\right)^4 \left(1 - \frac{1}{2}\right)^{7-4} \rightarrow P = \binom{7}{4}\left(\frac{1}{2}\right)^4 \left(\frac{1}{2}\right)^3 \rightarrow P = \frac{7!}{4!(7-4)!}\left(\frac{1}{2}\right)^7 \rightarrow P = \frac{35}{128}$$

So, the probability is: $P \approx 0.27$

Probability Problems

- Probability is the likelihood of something happening in the future. It is expressed as a number between zero (Can never happen) to 1 (Will always happen).

- Probability can be expressed as a fraction, a decimal, or a percent.

- Probability formula: $Probability = \frac{number\ of\ desired\ outcomes}{number\ of\ total\ outcomes}$.

Examples:

Example 1. Anita's trick–or–treat bag contains 10 pieces of chocolate, 16 suckers, 16 pieces of gum, 22 pieces of licorice. If she randomly pulls a piece of candy from her bag, what is the probability of her pulling out a piece of sucker?

Solution: Use this formula:

$$Probability = \frac{number\ of\ desired\ outcomes}{number\ of\ total\ outcomes}.$$

Probability of pulling out a piece of sucker $= \frac{16}{10+16+16+22} = \frac{16}{64} = \frac{1}{4}$.

Example 2. A bag contains 20 balls: four green, five black, eight blue, one brown, one red and one white. If 19 balls are removed from the bag at random, what is the probability that a brown ball has been removed?

Solution: If 19 balls are removed from the bag at random, there will be one ball in the bag. The probability of choosing a brown ball is 1 out of 20. Therefore, the probability of not choosing a brown ball is 19 out of 20 and the probability of having not a brown ball after removing 19 balls is the same.

The answer is: $\frac{19}{20}$.

Types of Probability Distributions

Probability distributions describe how probabilities are distributed over the values of a random variable.

- **Discrete Probability Distributions:** These are used when the set of possible outcomes is discrete (countable). Common examples include:

  - Binomial Distribution: Used for scenarios with a fixed number of trials, two possible outcomes, and a constant probability of success.
  - Poisson Distribution: Applies to situations where events occur independently at a constant rate within a given interval of time or space.
  - Geometric Distribution: Models the number of trials needed to get the first success in repeated, independent Bernoulli trials.

- **Continuous Probability Distributions:** These are used when the set of possible outcomes is a continuous range. Common examples include:

  - Normal Distribution: Represents a symmetric, bell-shaped distribution of a continuous random variable.
  - Uniform Distribution: All outcomes in the range are equally likely.
  - Exponential Distribution: Used to model the time between events in a process where events occur continuously and independently at a constant average rate.

Examples:

Example 1. Scenario: Suppose we toss a fair coin 5 times. We want to determine the probability distribution type for the number of heads that appear.

Solution: There are a fixed number of trials (5 coin tosses). Each trial has only two possible outcomes (head or tail). The probability of success (getting a head) is constant (0.5) for each trial. Each toss is independent of the others. Type of Distribution: The scenario fits the criteria of a "Binomial Distribution", where the number of trials is 5, and the probability of getting a head in each trial is 0.5.

Example 2. Scenario: Consider a bus stop where buses arrive randomly but at an average rate of 4 buses per hour. We want to determine the probability distribution type for the time until the next bus arrives.

Solution: The event (bus arrival) happens independently. The rate of occurrence (4 buses/hour) is constant. We are interested in the time between events (bus arrivals). Type of Distribution: This scenario is best modeled by an "Exponential Distribution". The exponential distribution is used to model the time between independent events that occur at a constant average rate.

Permutations and Combinations

- **Factorials** are products, indicated by an exclamation mark. For example, $4! = 4 \times 3 \times 2 \times 1$. (Remember that $0!$ is defined to be equal to 1.)

- **Permutations:** The number of ways to choose a sample of k elements from a set of n distinct objects where order does matter, and replacements are not allowed. For a permutation problem, use this formula:

$$nP_k = \frac{n!}{(n-k)!}$$

- **Combination:** The number of ways to choose a sample of r elements from a set of n distinct objects where order does not matter, and replacements are not allowed. For a combination problem, use this formula:

$$nC_r = \frac{n!}{r!(n-r)!}$$

Examples:

Example 1. How many ways can the first and second place be awarded to 7 people?

Solution: Since the order matters, (The first and second place are different!) we need to use a permutation formula where n is 7 and k is 2.

Then:

$$\frac{n!}{(n-k)!} = \frac{7!}{(7-2)!} = \frac{7!}{5!} = \frac{7 \times 6 \times 5!}{5!},$$

remove 5! from both sides of the fraction.

Then:

$$\frac{7 \times 6 \times 5!}{5!} = 7 \times 6 = 42.$$

Example 2. How many ways can we pick a team of 3 people from a group of 8?

Solution: Since the order doesn't matter, we need to use a combination formula where n is 8 and r is 3.

Then:

$$\frac{n!}{r!(n-r)!} = \frac{8!}{3!(8-3)!} = \frac{8!}{3!(5)!} = \frac{8 \times 7 \times 6 \times 5!}{3!(5)!} = \frac{8 \times 7 \times 6}{3 \times 2 \times 1} = \frac{336}{6} = 56.$$

Systematic List of Outcomes and Set Notation

- The sample space is the set of all possible outcomes of a random experiment. Two effective ways to represent a sample space are through a systematic list of outcomes and using set notation.

- **Systematic List of Outcomes:** This method involves listing all possible outcomes of a random experiment in an organized and systematic manner. It is most effective for experiments with a finite and small number of outcomes.

- Advantages: Straightforward and easy to understand. Clearly shows each individual outcome.

- **Set Notation:** Set notation uses mathematical symbols to succinctly describe the sample space. It's useful for both simple and complex experiments, especially when dealing with a large or infinite number of outcomes.

- Advantages: Concise and can easily represent large or complex sample spaces.

- Useful for theoretical analysis and mathematical manipulations.

Example:

Show the systematic list of outcomes and set notation sample space.

Scenario: Consider the experiment of drawing a single card from a standard deck of 52 playing cards. We want to represent the sample space of drawing a card from the suits: hearts or clubs.

Solution: Systematic List of Outcomes:

List all the hearts and clubs: {2♥, 3♥, 4♥, ..., A♥, 2♣, 3♣, 4♣, ..., A♣}

Set Notation:

Represent the sample space as a set: $S = \{Hearts, Clubs \times \{2, 3, 4, \ldots, A\}$

Here, "×" denotes the Cartesian product, indicating that the sample space consists of all combinations of the suit (hearts or clubs) and the rank (2 through Ace).

Tree Diagrams

- A tree diagram is a branching diagram that represents all the possible outcomes of a series of events. Each branch represents a possible outcome, and subsequent branches show further possible outcomes.

- **Uses:** Ideal for representing sequential events and calculating their probabilities. Helpful in breaking down complex probability problems into simpler, sequential steps.

- **Structure:**

  - Starts with a single point, branching out to represent different outcomes.

  - Each branch is labeled with the probability of that outcome.

  - Subsequent branches represent further developments from each outcome.

Example:

Scenario: A customer is choosing an ice cream flavor (chocolate or vanilla) and then a topping (sprinkles or nuts). We want to use a tree diagram to illustrate all possible combinations.

Solution: First Level (Ice Cream Flavor): Two branches: Chocolate (C) and Vanilla (V). Second Level (Topping): Two branches from each flavor: Sprinkles (S) and Nuts (N). The tree diagram will have four final branches. The possible combinations are: {CS, CN, VS, VN}.

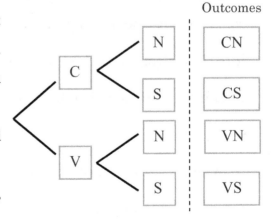

Each outcome, like "CS", represents choosing chocolate ice cream with sprinkles.

Venn Diagrams

- A Venn diagram uses overlapping circles to illustrate the logical relationships between two or more sets of items. It is useful for visualizing the intersections and unions of different events or categories.

- **Structure:**
    - Circles or other shapes represent different sets or events.
    - Overlapping areas indicate where sets intersect.
    - The universal set is often represented by a rectangle enclosing all other shapes.
    - Venn Diagram: Key Area

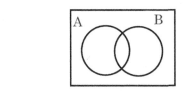 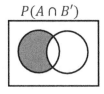 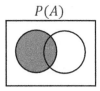 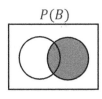

  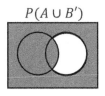 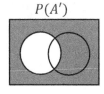 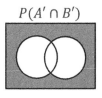

Example:

Scenario: In a survey of 100 people, 60 said they like movies, 50 like books, and 30 like both movies and books. Represent this information using a Venn diagram.

Solution: Two Circles: One circle for people who like movies (M). Another circle for people who like books (B).

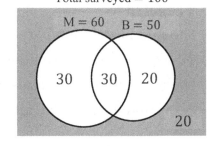

Overlap Area: The area where both circles overlap represents people who like both movies and books.

People who only like movies: 60 (total who like movies) −30 (like both) = 30

People who only like books: 50 (total who like books) −30 (like both) = 20

People who like neither:

100 (total surveyed) −30 (only movies) −20 (only books) −30 (like both) = 20

The Venn diagram will have 30 in the movies-only part, 20 in the books-only part, and 30 in the overlapping part, with 20 outside both circles.

Contingency Tables

- Contingency tables, also known as cross-tabulation or two-way tables, are a type of table in a matrix format that displays the frequency distribution of the variables. They are widely used in statistics to analyze the relationship between two or more categorical variables.

- **Structure of a Contingency Table**

  - Dimensions: Typically, contingency tables are two-dimensional, with each dimension representing a categorical variable. The rows represent the categories of one variable, and the columns represent the categories of the other variable.

  - Cells: Each cell in the table shows the count or frequency of occurrences for a specific combination of categories from both variables.

  - Margins: The rightmost column and the bottom row, known as marginal totals, show the total counts across each row and column, respectively.

  - Total: The bottom-right cell of the table shows the grand total, representing the total number of observations.

Example:

Scenario: A study was conducted to understand the relationship between pet ownership and allergies in a group of people. Out of 100 individuals, 40 own pets, 35 have allergies, and 15 have both pets and allergies.

Solution: The number of individuals who have allergies but do not own pets is calculated as: 35 (total with allergies) −15 (both allergies and pets) = 20.
The number of individuals who do not have allergies and own pets is: 40 (total pet owners) −15 (both allergies and pets) = 25.
The number of individuals who neither have allergies nor own pets is: 100 (total individuals) −35 (have allergies) −40 (pet owners) +15 (both) = 40.

Contingency Table

	Own Pets	Do Not Own Pets	Total
Have Allergies	15	20	35
No Allergies	25	40	65
Total	40	60	100

Chapter 3: Practices

✍ Answer the questions according to the information.

Imagine a shelf with six different books, each uniquely numbered from 1 to 6. The number represents a unique feature of the book (e.g., genre, author, etc.). We will identify various events as subsets of this sample space and calculate the probability of each event.

1) Event T = choosing the book with feature number two.

2) Event A = choosing a book with an even-numbered feature.

3) Event B = choosing a book with a feature number less than four.

4) The complement of A (choosing a book with an odd-numbered feature).

5) A GIVEN B (choosing an even-numbered book given it's one with a feature number less than four).

6) B GIVEN A (choosing a book with a feature number less than four given it's an even-numbered book).

7) A AND B (choosing a book that is both even-numbered and has a feature number less than four).

8) A OR B (choosing a book that is either even-numbered or has a feature number less than four).

9) A OR B' (choosing a book that is either even-numbered or has a feature number greater than or equal to four).

10) Event N = choosing a book with a prime-numbered feature.

11) Event I = choosing a book with feature number seven (impossible in this scenario).

✎ **Calculate each probabilities.**

A library with a collection of 150 books in different genres.

-   Total books = 150
-   Romance $(R) = 22$
-   Mystery $(Y) = 38$
-   Science Fiction $(G) = 20$
-   Historical $(P) = 28$
-   Fantasy $(B) = 26$
-   Others $(O) = 150 - (22 + 38 + 20 + 28 + 26) = 16$

Let's define the events based on the genres:

-   B = selecting a Fantasy book
-   G = selecting a Science Fiction book
-   O = selecting a book from Others
-   P = selecting a Historical book
-   R = selecting a Romance book
-   Y = selecting a Mystery book

Then:

12) $P(B) =$ 14) $P(P) =$ 16) $P(Y) =$

13) $P(G) =$ 15) $P(R) =$ 17) $P(O) =$

✎ **Solve.**

18) A class conducted an experiment by flipping a coin 100 times. The coin landed on heads 57 times. What is the experimental probability of the coin landing on heads?

19) In a school's science fair, a student rolled a six-sided die 60 times. The die landed on a 3 a total of 15 times. Calculate the experimental probability of rolling a 3.

20) During a basketball practice session, a player attempts 80 free throws and makes 56 of them. What is the experimental probability that the player makes a free throw?

21) A biology class is studying the genetics of pea plants. They find that out of 200 pea plants, 48 have yellow peas. What is the experimental probability of a pea plant having yellow peas?

✍ Answer the questions.

Consider a library with a collection of books numbered from 1 to 19. Each number represents a unique book. We will identify various events as subsets of this sample space.

Event A = books with even numbers.
Event B = books with numbers greater than 13.

22) $S =$

23) $A =$, $B =$

24) $P(A) =$, $P(B) =$

25) A And $B =$, A OR $B =$

26) $P(A \text{ and } B) =$, $P(A \text{ or } B) =$

27) $A' =$, $P(A') =$

28) $P(A) + P(A') =$

29) $P(A|B) =$, $P(B|A) =$, and are the probabilities equal?

✍ Solve.

30) In a music concert, choosing to attend the classical music performance (Event M) and the rock music performance (Event N) are mutually exclusive. If $P(M) = 0.7$ and $P(N) = 0.2$, find $P(M \mid N)$.

Given U and V are mutually exclusive events with $P(U) = 0.26$ and $P(V) = 0.37$. Find:

31) $P(U \text{ AND } V) =$ 32) $P(U|V) =$ 33) $P(U \text{ OR } V) =$

In a game, choosing a red card (Event A) and choosing a black card (Event B) are mutually exclusive events. $P(A) = 0.5$; $P(B) = 0.5$. Find:

34) $P(A \text{ AND } B) =$ 35) $P(A|B) =$ 36) $P(A \text{ OR } B) =$

Let's consider drawing cards from a standard 52 –card deck. Define several events and determine their probabilities, as well as whether they are mutually exclusive.

Draw two cards from a standard 52 –card deck with replacement. Analyze the following events:

37) Let Event F = drawing a heart or a diamond (at most one spade or club).

38) Let Event G = drawing two cards of the same suit.

39) Let Event H = drawing a heart as the first card followed by any card as the second.

40) Determine if F and G are mutually exclusive.

41) Let Event J = drawing all spades. Are J and H mutually exclusive?

 Answer the questions according to the Scenario.

Imagine you have a basket containing 36 pieces of fruit, divided into four types: apples (A), bananas (B), oranges (O), and grapes (G). Each type has 9 fruits labeled from 1 to 9.

Which of the following questions did you sample with replacement, and which did you sample without replacement?

42) Suppose you pick four fruits, but do not put any fruits back into the basket. Your fruits are $A9$, $B1$, $G1$, $O9$

43) Suppose you pick four fruits and put each fruit back before you pick the next fruit. Your fruits are $B8$, $G7$, $G6$, $B2$.

✍ **Answer the questions.**

44) In a survey, liking science fiction movies (Event A) and enjoying outdoor sports (Event B) are independent. $P(A) = 0.5$, and $P(A\ AND\ B) = 0.2$. Find $P(B)$.

45) In a classroom, the probability that a student prefers mathematics (Event X) is 0.6, and the probability that a student prefers mathematics and plays a musical instrument (Event Y) is 0.18. Find $P(Y)$, assuming X and Y are independent.

46) In a pouch with 5 green and 7 red marbles, what is the likelihood of first picking a red marble followed by a green marble, given that the initially selected marble is not returned to the pouch?

✍ **Solve.**

47) What is the likelihood of obtaining 2 heads when flipping a coin 6 times?

48) In a workshop, among 10 items, 3 of them are faulty. If the producer selects 2 items, what is the likelihood that both are faulty?

✍ **Answer the questions according to the Scenario.**

Bag A contains 8 red marbles and 6 green marbles. Bag B contains 5 black marbles and 7 orange marbles.

49) What is the probability of selecting a green marble at random from bag A?

50) What is the probability of selecting a black marble at random from Bag B?

✎ **Solve.**

51) A weighted die is rolled. The probability of rolling an even number is $\frac{3}{5}$, and the probability of rolling an odd number is $\frac{2}{5}$. What is the probability of rolling three odd numbers in a row, followed by one even number?

52) A biased die is thrown. The chance of landing on an even number is $\frac{4}{7}$, while the chance of landing on an odd number is $\frac{3}{7}$. What is the probability of achieving two successive odd numbers and then one even number?

53) A coin has been tossed 5 times. What is the probability that at least one toss results in a tail?

54) Three cards are drawn at random from a deck of 52 cards. What is the probability that at least one of the cards drawn is an Ace?

55) A fair die is rolled three times. What is the probability that at least one roll results in a 6?

56) What is the probability of rolling a number less than 3 when a fair 6 −sided die is rolled?

57) What is the probability of a leap year having 52 Sundays?

58) In a bag, there are 3 blue, 5 red, and 8 white marbles. Two marbles are drawn without replacement. If the first marble drawn is red, what is the probability that the second marble drawn is blue?

59) A jar contains 7 red candies, 9 blue candies, and 14 green candies. Two candies are chosen at random without replacement. Given that the first candy is red, what is the probability that the second candy is also red?

✎ **Solve.**

60) Susan is baking cookies. She uses sugar, flour, butter, and eggs. How many different orders of ingredients can she try? _____

61) Jason is planning for his vacation. He wants to go to a museum, go to the beach, and play volleyball. How many different ways of ordering are there for him? _____

62) In how many ways can a team of 6 basketball players choose a captain and co-captain? _____

63) How many ways can the first and second place be awarded to 11 people? _____

64) A professor is going to arrange her 5 students in a straight line. In how many ways can she do this? _____

65) In how many ways can a teacher choose 12 out of 15 students? _____

✎ **Answer the questions.**

66) What is a Binomial Distribution and in what type of scenarios is it used?

67) Define a Normal Distribution and give an example of where it might be observed.

68) What is a Poisson Distribution and when is it applicable?

69) Describe a Uniform Distribution and provide an instance where it might be used.

✍ **Identify types of Probability Distributions based on the scenarios.**

70) In a game, a player rolls a six-sided die 60 times and records the number of times the die lands on a six. What type of probability distribution does this scenario represent?

71) A researcher is studying the height of adult men in a large city. She collects data from thousands of individuals. Which probability distribution is likely to describe the distribution of heights in this population?

72) A call center records the number of calls received every hour. They notice that the calls come independently of each other and at a steady average rate. What type of probability distribution best describes the number of calls received per hour?

73) A factory produces light bulbs, and a quality control test is conducted to ensure uniform quality. Each light bulb from the production line has an equal chance of being selected for testing. What type of probability distribution does this scenario represent?

✍ **Answer the Permutations and Combinatorics questions.**

74) How many different ways can the letters of the word "STATS" be arranged?

75) In a class of 30 students, how many ways can a president, vice president, and secretary be elected?

76) A team of 4 needs to be formed from a group of 10 people. How many different teams can be formed?

77) How many different 3 − letter words can be formed from the word "APPLE" assuming that each letter can be used only once?

78) A code consists of 4 digits followed by 2 letters. How many such codes are possible if repetitions are not allowed?

79) How many ways can 5 books be arranged on a shelf?

✎ **List all possible subsets of each set.**

80) If you flip a coin and roll a six-sided die, list the possible outcomes using set notation.

81) List all possible subsets of the set $A = \{a, b, c\}$.

82) For a single toss of a fair coin, create a systematic list of outcomes and represent the event 'getting tails' using set notation.

83) If two dice are rolled, how can you represent the event of getting a sum of 7 using set notation?

✎ **Compute the probabilities based on the tree diagram structure provided.**

A classroom setting where there are 52 students, 12 of whom are seniors (S) and the rest are not seniors (Ns). You are selecting two students, one at a time, without replacement to represent the class in a school committee.

84) Find $P(SNs \text{ or } NsS)$.

85) Find $P(Ns|S)$.

86) Find $P(\text{at most one senior})$.

87) Find $P(\text{at least one senior})$.

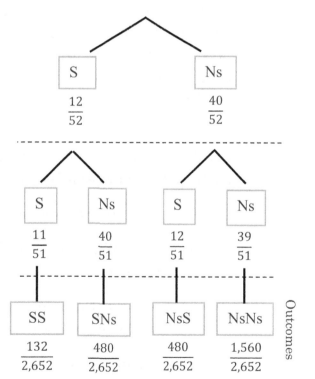

✍ **Illustrate all possible combinations using a tree diagram.**

88) A customer is choosing a pet (dog or cat) and then a collar (red or blue). Illustrate all possible combinations using a tree diagram.

89) A student council election has three candidates running for president and two candidates running for vice-president. Construct a tree diagram to represent all the possible outcomes of the election for these two positions. How many outcomes are possible?

90) A sandwich shop offers 3 types of meat, 2 types of bread, and the option of having cheese or not. Use a tree diagram to represent the different sandwich combinations a customer can choose. How many different sandwich combinations are there?

✍ **Answer the corresponding questions.**

In a company, 40% of employees have management training (M) and 50% have participated in a professional development program (PD). Five percent of the employees have both management training and participated in a professional development program.

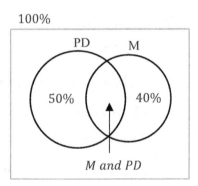

Let M = employee has management training and PD = employee has participated in professional development.

91) The probability that an employee has management training.

92) The probability that an employee has participated in professional development.

93) The probability that an employee has both management training AND participated in professional development.

94) The probability that an employee has management training given that the employee has participated in professional development.

95) The probability that an employee has management training OR has participated in professional development.

✎ **Answer the corresponding questions**.

In a classroom, 51% of students are proficient in mathematics (*M*), and an average of 7.5% are proficient in science (*S*). Four percent of the students are proficient in both subjects and are members of the science club.

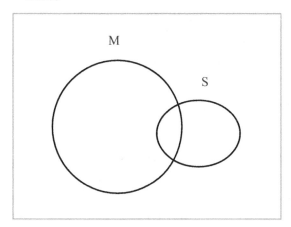

The "*M*" circle represents the students proficient in mathematics. The "*S*" oval represents the students proficient in science.

96) $P(M) =$

97) $P(S) =$

98) $P(M \ AND \ S) =$

99) $P(M \ OR \ S) =$

100) In the Venn Diagram, describe the overlapping area using a complete sentence.

101) In the Venn Diagram, describe the area in the rectangle but outside both the circle and the oval using a complete sentence.

✍ **Use the information in the Table to answer the next eight questions.**

The table shows the participation of students in two extracurricular activities, Math Club (*MC*) and Science Club (*SC*), at a school with 67 students in June 2012. Students are scheduled to participate in competitions in November 2014 and November 2016.

	Math Club	Science Club	Other	Total
November 2014	20	13	0	33
November 2016	10	24	0	34
Total	30	37	0	67

102) What is the probability that a randomly selected student is in an "Other" club?

103) What is the probability that a randomly selected student is scheduled for a competition in November 2016?

104) What is the probability that a randomly selected student is in the Math Club and scheduled for a competition in November 2016?

105) What is the probability that a randomly selected student is in the Science Club or is scheduled for a competition in November 2014?

106) Given that a student is scheduled for a competition in November 2016, what is the probability that this student is in the Math Club?

107) Knowing that a student is in the Science Club, what is the probability that they are scheduled for a competition in November 2014?

108) The events "Science Club" and "Up for competition in 2016" are:

    a. mutually exclusive.
    b. independent.
    c. both mutually exclusive and independent.
    d. neither mutually exclusive nor independent.

109) The events "Other" club and "Up for competition in November 2016" are:

    a. mutually exclusive.
    b. independent.
    c. both mutually exclusive and independent.
    d. neither mutually exclusive nor independent.

🖙 **Use the information in the Table to answer the next seven questions.**

The table below identifies a group of 215 students by their interest in one of four extracurricular activities: Math, Science, Arts, and Sports.

Student Type	Math	Science	Arts	Sports	Totals
Enthusiast	30		18	0	73
Non-enthusiast	50	55		15	
Totals		80			215

110) Complete the table.

111) What is the probability that a randomly selected student is interested in Arts?

112) What is the probability that a randomly selected student is a Sports enthusiast?

113) What is the probability that a randomly selected student is either a Math enthusiast or interested in Science?

114) What is the probability that a randomly selected student is a Non-enthusiast in Science, given that the student is interested in Sports?

115) If E is the event of a student having an interest in Math, find the probability of the complement of E.

116) In words, what does the complement of E represent?

Chapter 3: Answers

1) $T = \{2\}, P(T) = \frac{1}{6}$

2) $A = \{2, 4, 6\}, P(A) = \frac{1}{2}$

3) $B = \{1, 2, 3\}, P(B) = \frac{1}{2}$

4) $A' = \{1, 3, 5\}, P(A') = \frac{1}{2}$

5) $A|B = \{2\}, P(A|B) = \frac{1}{3}$

6) $B|A = \{2\}, P(B|A) = \frac{1}{3}$

7) $A \text{ AND } B = \{2\}, P(A \text{ AND } B) = \frac{1}{6}$

8) $A \text{ OR } B = \{1, 2, 3, 4, 6\}, P(A \text{ OR } B) = \frac{5}{6}$

9) $A \text{ OR } B' = \{2, 4, 5, 6\}, P(A \text{ OR } B') = \frac{2}{3}$

10) $N = \{2, 3, 5\}, P(N) = \frac{1}{2}$

11) As there are only six books, the probability of choosing a book with feature number seven is $P(7) = 0$.

12) $P(B) = \frac{26}{150}$ 14) $P(P) = \frac{28}{150}$ 16) $P(Y) = \frac{38}{150}$

13) $P(G) = \frac{20}{150}$ 15) $P(R) = \frac{22}{150}$ 17) $P(O) = \frac{16}{150}$

18) The experimental probability of the coin landing on heads is $\frac{57}{100}$ or 57%.

19) The experimental probability of rolling a 3 is $\frac{15}{60}$ or 25%.

20) The experimental probability of making a free throw is $\frac{56}{80}$ or 70%.

21) The experimental probability of a pea plant having yellow peas is $\frac{48}{200}$ or 24%.

22) $S = \{1, 2, 3, 4, 5, 6, 7, 8, 9, 10, 11, 12, 13, 14, 15, 16, 17, 18, 19\}$, The set of books numbered.

23) $A = \{2, 4, 6, 8, 10, 12, 14, 16, 18\}$, The set of even-numbered books.

$B = \{14, 15, 16, 17, 18, 19\}$, The set of books numbered greater than 13.

24) $P(A) = \frac{9}{19}$, Probability of selecting an even-numbered book.

$P(B) = \frac{6}{19}$, Probability of selecting a book numbered greater than 13.

25) A AND $B = \{14, 16, 18\}$, Books that are both even-numbered and greater than 13.

A OR $B = \{2, 4, 6, 8, 10, 12, 14, 15, 16, 17, 18, 19\}$, Books that are either even-numbered or numbered greater than 13.

26) $P(A \ and \ B) = \frac{3}{19}$, Probability of a book being both even-numbered and greater than 13.

$P(A \ or \ B) = 12/19$, Probability of a book being either even-numbered or greater than 13.

27) $A' = \{1, 3, 5, 7, 9, 11, 13, 15, 17, 19\}$, Books that are not even-numbered

$P(A') = \frac{10}{19}$, Probability of selecting a book that is not even-numbered.

28) $P(A) + P(A') = 1 (\frac{9}{19} + \frac{10}{19} = 1)$

29) $P(A|B) = \frac{3}{6}$, Probability of selecting an even-numbered book given it's numbered greater than 13,

$P(B|A) = \frac{3}{9}$, Probability of selecting a book numbered greater than 13 given it's even-numbered.

And these probabilities are not equal.

30) Since M and N are mutually exclusive, $P(M \mid N) = 0$.

31) Since U and V are mutually exclusive, $P(U \ AND \ V) = 0$.

32) Since U and V are mutually ex clusive, $P(U|V) = 0$.

33) $P(U \, OR \, V) = P(U) + P(V) = 0.26 + 0.37 = 0.63$.

34) $P(A \, AND \, B) = 0$, as A and B cannot occur together.

35) $P(A|B) = 0$, as the occurrence of B rules out A.

36) $P(A \, OR \, B) = P(A) + P(B) = 0.5 + 0.5 = 1$.

37) Drawing a heart or a diamond (F) occurs when we draw either of these suits. Since there are 26 hearts and diamonds in total. $P(F) = \frac{26}{52} \times \frac{26}{52} = \frac{1}{4}$

38) Two cards of the same suit (G) can be any suit. There are 4 suits, and the probability of drawing two cards of the same suit with replacement. $P(G) = 4 \times \frac{13}{52} \times \frac{13}{52} = \frac{1}{4}$

39) Drawing a heart first (H) followed by any card. as there are 13 hearts and any card can follow: $P(H) = \left(\frac{13}{52}\right) \times 1 = \frac{1}{4}$

40) F and G share the possibility of drawing two hearts or two diamonds, so $P(F \, AND \, G)$ is not zero. F and G are not mutually exclusive.

41) Since we are drawing with replacement, the probabilities are independent of each other. Probability of drawing a spade on the first draw is $\frac{13}{52}$. Probability of drawing a spade on the second draw is $\frac{13}{52}$. Therefore, the probability of both events occurring (drawing two spades) is: $P(J) = \frac{13}{52} \times \frac{13}{52} = \frac{1}{16}$

Drawing all spades (J) does not share any outcomes with drawing a heart first (H). Thus, $P(J \, AND \, H) = 0$. J and H are mutually exclusive.

42) Without replacement, you didn't put the fruits back after picking them.

43) With replacement, you returned each fruit to the basket before picking the next one.

44) $P(B) = \frac{P(A \, AND \, B)}{P(A)} = \frac{0.2}{0.5} = 0.4$.

45) $P(Y) = \frac{P(X \, AND \, Y)}{P(X)} = \frac{0.18}{0.6} = 0.3$.

46) To find the probability of first picking a red marble followed by a green marble without replacement, we can use the formula:

$$P(B \text{ and } A) = P(A) \times P(B \text{ after } A)$$

In this case, event A is picking a red marble, and event B is picking a green marble after a red marble has been picked.

$P(A)$ = Probability of picking a red marble first:

$$P(A) = \frac{(Number\ of\ red\ marbles)}{(\text{Total number of marbles})} = \frac{7}{12}$$

Once a red marble has been picked, there are 11 marbles remaining in the pouch, with 5 of them being green.

$P(B \text{ after } A)$ = Probability of picking a green marble after picking a red marble:

$$P(B \text{ after } A) = \frac{(Number\ of\ green\ marbles\ remaining)}{(\text{Total number of marbles remaining})} = \frac{5}{11}$$

Now we can calculate the probability of both events occurring:

$$P(B \text{ and } A) = P(A) \times P(B \text{ after } A) = \frac{7}{12} \times \frac{5}{11} = \frac{35}{132}$$

Therefore, the likelihood of first picking a red marble followed by a green marble without replacement is $\frac{35}{132}$.

47) To find the probability of obtaining 2 heads when flipping a fair coin 6 times, we can use this probability formula:

$$P = {}_nC_k p^k (1-p)^{n-k}$$

In this case, n is the number of trials (flips), k is the number of successful outcomes (getting heads), and p is the probability of success on a single trial.

$n = 6$ (Flipping the coin 6 times)

$k = 2$ (Wanting to get 2 heads)

$p = 0.5$ (Probability of getting a head in a single flip, since the coin is fair)

First, we need to calculate the binomial coefficient ${}_nC_k = C(n,k)$, which can be found using the formula:

$$C(n,k) = \frac{n!}{(k!(n-k)!)} \rightarrow C(6,2) = \frac{6!}{(2!(6-2)!)} = \frac{6!}{2! \times 4!} \rightarrow C(6,2) = 15$$

Now, we can calculate the probability:

$$P = C(6,2) \times 0.5^2 \times (1-0.5)^{6-2} \rightarrow P = 15 \times 0.25 \times (0.5)^4 \rightarrow P = 0.234375$$

48) To find the probability of selecting both faulty items from a total of 10 items, of which 3 are faulty, we can use combinations:

$$P(A) = \frac{(Number\ of\ favorable\ outcomes)}{(Total\ possible\ outcomes)}$$

The number of ways to choose 2 items from 3 faulty items (favorable outcomes) can be found using combinations:

$$C(n,k) = \frac{n!}{(k!(n-k)!)} \rightarrow C(3,2) = \frac{3!}{(2!(3-2)!)} \rightarrow C(3,2) = 3$$

Now we need to find the total number of ways to choose 2 items from the 10 items (total possible outcomes):

$$C(10,2) = \frac{10!}{(2!(10-2)!)} \rightarrow C(10,2) = 45$$

Now we can find the probability:

$$P(A) = \frac{(Number\ of\ favorable\ outcomes)}{(Total\ possible\ outcomes)} = \frac{3}{45} = \frac{1}{15}$$

49) Probability of Selecting a Green Marble from Bag A:

Total marbles in Bag A = 8 red +6 green = 14 marbles.

Number of green marbles in Bag A = 6.

$$Probability = \frac{Number\ of\ green\ marbles}{Total\ marbles\ in\ Bag\ A} = \frac{6}{14}\ or\ \frac{3}{7}$$

50) Probability of Selecting a Black Marble from Bag B:

Total marbles in Bag B = 5 black +7 orange = 12 marbles.

Number of black marbles in Bag B = 5.

$$Probability = \frac{Number\ of\ black\ marbles}{Total\ marbles\ in\ Bag\ B} = \frac{5}{12}$$

51) To find the probability of rolling three odd numbers in a row, followed by one even number, we simply multiply the individual probabilities together:

Probability of rolling an odd number (first roll) $= \frac{2}{5}$

Probability of rolling an odd number (second roll) $= \frac{2}{5}$

Probability of rolling an odd number (third roll) $= \frac{2}{5}$

Probability of rolling an even number (fourth roll) $= \frac{3}{5}$

Total probability $= \frac{2}{5} \times \frac{2}{5} \times \frac{2}{5} \times \frac{3}{5} = \frac{24}{625}$

52) To find the probability of achieving two successive odd numbers and then one even number when the die is thrown, you simply multiply the probabilities of each individual event:

Probability of two odd numbers in a row: $\frac{3}{7} \times \frac{3}{7}$

Probability of one even number: $\frac{4}{7}$

Now, multiply the probabilities together: $\frac{3}{7} \times \frac{3}{7} \times \frac{4}{7} = \frac{36}{343}$

So, the probability of achieving two successive odd numbers and then one even number is $\frac{36}{343}$.

First, find the total number of outcomes. we have thrown a coin 5 times so the total number of outcomes is equal to 2^5: $2 \times 2 \times 2 \times 2 \times 2 = 2^5 = 32$

Now we should find the desired outcomes (at least one tail): $32 - 1 = 31$

The final step is to find the required probability: $\frac{31}{32}$

53) The probability that none of the three cards drawn are Aces can be calculated as follows:

The probability of drawing a non-Ace card on the first draw is $\frac{48}{52}$, since there are 48 non-Ace cards out of 52 cards total. Similarly, the probability of drawing a non-Ace card on the second draw, after one non-Ace card has already been drawn, is $\frac{47}{51}$. Finally, the probability of drawing a non-Ace card on the third draw, after two non-Ace cards have already been drawn, is $\frac{46}{50}$.

Therefore, the probability that all three cards drawn are non-Aces is:

$$\frac{48}{52} \times \frac{47}{51} \times \frac{46}{50} = \frac{103,776}{132600} = \frac{4,324}{5,525}$$

Therefore, the probability of getting at least one Ace: $P = 1 - \frac{4,324}{5,525} = \frac{1,201}{5,525}$

54) The probability of not getting a 6 in one roll is $\frac{5}{6}$, so the probability of not getting a 6 in three rolls is $\left(\frac{5}{6}\right)^3 = \frac{125}{216}$.

Therefore, the probability of getting at least one 6: $P = 1 - \frac{125}{216} = \frac{91}{216}$

55) There are two possible outcomes that satisfy the condition (rolling a 1 or 2), and there are a total of six possible outcomes (rolling any number from 1 to 6). Therefore, the probability of rolling a number less than 3 is:

$$Probability = \frac{2\ favorable\ outcomes}{6\ possible\ outcomes} = \frac{1}{3}$$

56) The total number of events is: 7 (number of days in a week).

A leap year has 366 days, which is equal to 52 weeks and 2 days. And two days could be any days amongst Sunday, Monday, Tuesday, Wednesday, Thursday, Friday or Saturday.

So, $7 - 2 = 5$ is number of favorable outcomes. Therefore, the probability of a leap year having 52 Sundays is: $Probability = \frac{5\ favorable\ outcomes}{7\ possible\ outcomes} = \frac{5}{7}$

57) The bag has a total $3 + 5 + 8 = 16$ marbles.

There are 5 red marbles in the bag, and if one of them is drawn first, there will be a total of $16 - 1 = 15$ marbles remaining in the bag. And out of these 15 marbles, 3 marbles will be blue (Reducing the number of red marbles does not affect the number of blue marbles).

Therefore, the probability that the second marble drawn is blue, given that the first marble drawn was red, is: $Probability = \frac{3\ blue\ marbles}{15\ total\ marbles} = \frac{1}{5}$

58) The jar has a total $7 + 9 + 14 = 30$ candies.

There are 7 red candies in the jar, so if one of them is drawn first, there will be a total of 29 candies remaining in the jar. Out of these 29 candies, there will be 6 red candies remaining. Therefore, the probability that the second candy drawn is also red: $Probability = \frac{6\ red\ candies}{29\ total\ candies} = \frac{6}{29}$

59) $4! = 4 \times 3 \times 2 \times 1 = 24$ ways.

60) $3! = 3 \times 2 \times 1 = 6$ ways.

61) $P(6, 2) = \frac{6!}{(6-2)!} = 6 \times 5 = 30$ ways.

62) $P(11, 2) = \frac{11!}{(11-2)!} = 11 \times 10 = 110$.

63) $5! = 5 \times 4 \times 3 \times 2 \times 1 = 120$ ways.

64) $C(15, 12) = \frac{15!}{12! \times (15-12)!} = 455$ ways.

65) A Binomial Distribution is used in scenarios with a fixed number of independent trials, each with only two possible outcomes (success or failure). It's used to determine the probability of a specific number of successes in a set number of trials.

66) A Normal Distribution, also known as Gaussian distribution, is a continuous probability distribution characterized by its bell-shaped curve. It's symmetric around the mean. An example is the distribution of heights in a large population.

67) A Poisson Distribution is used for counting the number of times an event occurs within a fixed interval of time or space. It is applicable in scenarios like counting the number of emails received in an hour or the number of cars passing through a checkpoint.

68) A Uniform Distribution is a type of probability distribution where all outcomes are equally likely. Each event in the sample space has an equal chance of occurring. An instance where it might be used is rolling a fair six-sided die; each face has an equal chance of landing up.

69) This scenario represents a Binomial Distribution, as each roll is an independent trial with a success (landing on six) or failure (not landing on six), and the number of trials is fixed.

70) This scenario is likely to follow a Normal Distribution, as the height of adult men in a large population tends to be normally distributed with a specific mean and standard deviation.

71) This scenario best fits a Poisson Distribution, as it involves counting the number of events (calls) occurring within a fixed interval of time, with the events happening independently at a constant rate.

72) This scenario represents a Uniform Distribution, as each light bulb has an equal and constant probability of being selected, indicating uniformity across the sample space.

73) The word "STATS" has 5 letters with 'S' and 'T' each repeating twice. The number of arrangements is $\frac{5!}{2! \times 2!} = 30$ ways.

74) This is a permutation problem. The number of ways is $P(30,3) = \frac{30!}{(30-3)!} = 24,360$ ways.

75) This is a combination problem. The number of teams is $C(10,4) = \frac{10!}{4! \times (10-4)!} = 210$ ways.

76) "APPLE" has 5 unique letters. The number of 3 −letter words is $P(4,3) = \frac{4!}{(4-3)!} = 24$ ways.

77) The number of codes is (assuming 10 digits and 26 letters):
$$P(10,4) \times P(26,2) = \frac{10!}{(10-4)!} \times \frac{26!}{(26-2)!} = 5040 \times 650 = 3276000 \text{ ways}$$

78) The number of arrangements is $5! = 5 \times 4 \times 3 \times 2 \times 1 = 120$ ways.

79) The possible outcomes can be represented as: $\{(H,1), (H,2), (H,3), (H,4),$ $(H,5), (H,6), (T,1), (T,2), (T,3), (T,4), (T,5), (T,6)\}$, where H represents heads, T represents tails, and the numbers represent the face of the die.

80) The subsets of A are: $\{\ \}, \{a\}, \{b\}, \{c\}, \{a,b\}, \{a,c\}, \{b,c\}, \{a,b,c\}$. The empty set is also a subset of any set.

81) The systematic list of outcomes is $\{H, T\}$. The event 'getting tails' can be represented as $\{T\}$.

82) The event of getting a sum of 7 can be represented as $\{(1,6), (2,5), (3,4),$ $(4,3), (5,2), (6,1)\}$, where each pair represents the numbers on the two dice.

83) $P(SNs) = \left(\frac{12}{52}\right) \times \left(\frac{40}{51}\right), P(NsS) = \left(\frac{40}{52}\right) \times \left(\frac{12}{51}\right)$
$P(SNs \text{ OR } NsS) = P(SNs) + P(NsS) = \left(\frac{12}{52} \times \frac{40}{51}\right) + \left(\frac{40}{52} \times \frac{12}{51}\right) = \frac{480}{2652} + \frac{480}{2652}$
$P(SNs \text{ OR } NsS) = \frac{960}{2652}$

84) $P(Ns|S) = \frac{40}{51}$ (as directly given in the tree diagram for the second draw after selecting a senior).

85) $P(\text{at most one senior}) = P(NsNs) + P(SNs) + P(NsS)$
$P(NsNs) = \left(\frac{40}{52}\right) \times \left(\frac{39}{51}\right), P(SNs) = \left(\frac{12}{52}\right) \times \left(\frac{40}{51}\right), P(NsS) = \left(\frac{40}{52}\right) \times \left(\frac{12}{51}\right)$
$P(\text{at most one senior}) = \left(\frac{40}{52}\right) \times \left(\frac{39}{51}\right) + \left(\frac{12}{52}\right) \times \left(\frac{40}{51}\right) + \left(\frac{40}{52}\right) \times \left(\frac{12}{51}\right) = \frac{2520}{2652}$

86) $P(\text{at least one senior}) = 1 - P(\text{no seniors})$
$P(\text{no seniors}) = P(NsNs) = \left(\frac{40}{52}\right) \times \left(\frac{39}{51}\right) = \frac{1560}{2652}$
$P(\text{at least one senior}) = 1 - \frac{1560}{2652} = \frac{1092}{2652}$

87)

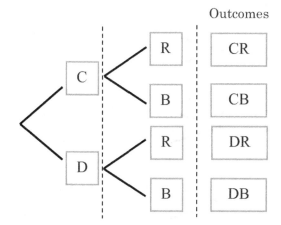

88) 6 outcomes are possible .

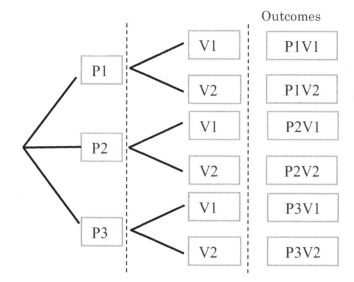

89) There are 12 different sandwich combinations.   Outcomes

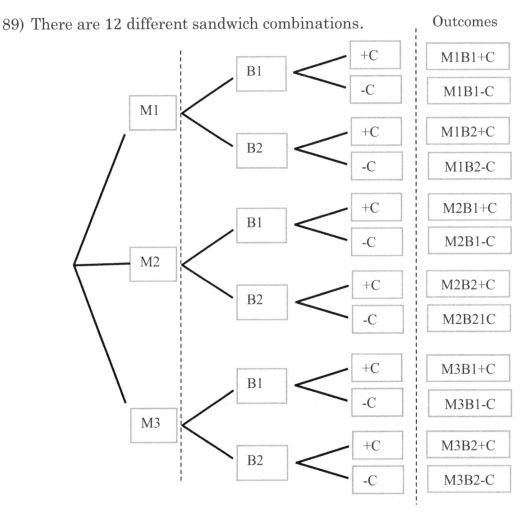

90) $P(M) = 0.40$

91) $P(PD) = 0.50$

92) $P(M \ AND \ PD) = 0.05$

93) $P(M|PD) = \frac{P(M \ AND \ PD)}{P(PD)} = \frac{0.05}{0.50} = 0.10$

94) $P(M \ OR \ PD) = P(M) + P(PD) - P(M \ AND \ PD) = 0.40 + 0.50 - 0.05 = 0.85$

95) $P(M) = 0.51$

96) $P(S) = 0.075$

97) $P(M \ AND \ S) = 0.04$

98) $P(M \ OR \ S) = P(M) + P(S) - P(M \ AND \ S) = 0.51 + 0.075 - 0.04 = 0.545$

99) In the Venn Diagram, the overlapping area represents students who are proficient in both mathematics and science.

100) In the Venn Diagram, the area in the rectangle but outside both the circle and the oval represents students who are neither proficient in mathematics nor science.

101) 0

102) $\frac{34}{67}$

103) $\frac{10}{67}$

104) $\frac{57}{67}$

105) $\frac{10}{34}$

106) $\frac{13}{37}$

107) d. neither mutually exclusive nor independent.

108) a. mutually exclusive.

109)

Student Type	Math	Science	Arts	Sports	Totals
Enthusiast	30	**25**	18	0	73
Non-enthusiast	50	55	**22**	15	**142**
Totals	**80**	80	**40**	15	215

110) $P(Arts) = \frac{Total\ Arts}{Total\ Students} = \frac{40}{215}$

111) $P(Sports\ Enthusiast) = \frac{Number\ of\ Enthusiast\ Sports}{Total\ Students} = \frac{0}{215}$ (since there are no enthusiast sports students).

112) $P(Math\ Enthusiast\ or\ Science\ Interest) = \frac{Math\ Enthusiasts+Science\ Interest-Both}{Total\ Students} = \frac{30+80-25}{215} = \frac{17}{43}$

113) $P(Non-enthusiast\ Science|Sports\ Interest) = \frac{Number\ of\ Non-enthusiast\ Science\ with\ Sports\ Interest}{Total\ Sports\ Interested} = \frac{15}{15} = 1$

114) $P(Not\ Math\ Interest) = 1 - P(Math\ Interest) = 1 - \left(\frac{Total\ Math}{Total\ Students}\right)$

$P(Not\ Math\ Interest) = 1 - \left(\frac{80}{215}\right) = \frac{27}{43}$

115) The complement of E represents the probability that a student does not have an interest in Math.

CHAPTER

4 Discrete Random Variable

Topics that you'll learn in this chapter:

- ☑ Probability Mass Functions
- ☑ Mean and Standard Deviation
- ☑ Mean or Expected Value and Variance of Discrete Random Variables
- ☑ Bernoulli Distributions
- ☑ Binomial Distributions
- ☑ Poisson Distribution
- ☑ Hypergeometric Distribution
- ☑ Geometric Distribution
- ☑ Negative Binomial Distribution
- ☑ Identifying the Type of Discrete Distribution

Probability Mass Functions

- A discrete random variable is one that can take on distinct, separate values (like counting numbers). The (PMF) assigns a probability to each of these possible discrete values.

Key Characteristics of PMFs

- Discreteness: PMFs are only used for discrete random variables.
- Probability Range: The probability for any value x (i.e., $P(X = x)$) lies between 0 and 1, inclusive.
- Normalization: The sum of the probabilities over all possible values of X equals 1.

Probability Mass Functions Step-by-Step:

- Identify the Discrete Random Variable: Recognize the variable X whose probabilities you want to find.

- List Possible Values: Enumerate all possible values x that X can take.

- Calculate Probabilities: Determine $P(X = x)$ for each value of x.

- Check Normalization: Ensure that the sum of all $P(X = x)$ equals 1.

Examples:

Example 1. Suppose there is a bag with 3 red, 2 blue, and 5 green marbles. If a marble is chosen at random, what is the PMF for the color of the marble?

Solution: Random Variable X: The color of the chosen marble.
Possible Values: Red, Blue, Green.
Calculating Probabilities: $P(X = Red) = \frac{3}{10}$, $P(X = Blue) = \frac{2}{10}$, $P(X = Green) = \frac{5}{10}$
Normalization: $\frac{3}{10} + \frac{2}{10} + \frac{5}{10} = 1$.
By understanding and applying the concept of PMFs, one can analyze and interpret the likelihood of various outcomes in a given discrete distribution.

Example 2. A six-sided die is rolled. What is the PMF of the outcome?

Solution: Random Variable X: The outcome of the die roll.
Possible Values: $1, 2, 3, 4, 5, 6$
Calculating Probabilities: Since the die is fair, $P(X = x) = \frac{1}{6}$ for $x = 1, 2, 3, 4, 5, 6$.
Normalization: The sum of probabilities is $6 \times \frac{1}{6} = 1$, which is correct.

Mean and Standard Deviation

- The mean, often denoted as μ for a population or $\bar{x}$ for a sample, is the average of all data points. For a set of values $x_1, x_2, \ldots, x_n$, the mean $\bar{x}$ is calculated as:

$$\bar{x} = \frac{1}{n} \sum_{i=1}^{n} x_i$$

where n is the number of data points.

- Standard deviation, denoted as σ for a population or s for a sample, measures the amount of variation or dispersion in a set of values. A low standard deviation indicates that the values tend to be close to the mean, while a high standard deviation indicates that the values are spread out over a wider range.

- The standard deviation is calculated as the square root of the variance. For a sample, it's given by:

$$s = \sqrt{\frac{1}{n-1} \sum_{i=1}^{n} (x_i - \bar{x})^2}$$

Example:

Calculate the mean and standard deviation for the data set $2, 4, 6, 8, 10$.

Solution: Data Points: $2, 4, 6, 8, 10$

Mean: $\bar{x} = \frac{2+4+6+8+10}{5} = 6$

Deviations: $-4, -2, 0, 2, 4$

Squared Deviations: $16, 4, 0, 4, 16$

Sum: $16 + 4 + 0 + 4 + 16 = 40$

Variance: $\frac{40}{5-1} = 10$

Standard Deviation: $s = \sqrt{10} \approx 3.16$

Mean or Expected Value and Variance of Discrete Random Variables

- The mean (or expected value) of a discrete random variable is a measure of its central tendency. It's calculated as the weighted average of all possible values, with probabilities as weights. For a discrete random variable X taking values $x_1, x_2, \ldots, x_n$ with probabilities $P(X = x_i)$, the mean μ is given by:

$$\mu = E(X) = \sum_{i=1}^{n} x_i P(X = x_i)$$

- Variance measures the spread of a probability distribution. It is the expected value of the squared deviation of X from its mean μ. For the same discrete random variable X, the variance σ^2 is:

$$\sigma^2 = Var(X) = \sum_{i=1}^{n} (x_i - \mu)^2 P(X = x_i)$$

Examples:

Example 1. A fair six-sided die is rolled. Calculate the mean and variance of the outcome.

Solution: Values and Probabilities: $1, 2, 3, 4, 5, 6$ each with a probability of $\frac{1}{6}$.

Mean: $E(X) = \frac{1}{6}(1 + 2 + 3 + 4 + 5 + 6) = 3.5$

Variance: Squared deviations: $(1 - 3.5)^2, (2 - 3.5)^2, \ldots, (6 - 3.5)^2$

$$Var(X) = \frac{1}{6}((1 - 3.5)^2 + (2 - 3.5)^2 + \ldots + (6 - 3.5)^2) = \frac{17.5}{6} \approx 2.92$$

Example 2. If a coin is tossed three times, calculate the mean and variance of the number of heads.

Solution: Values and Probabilities: $0, 1, 2, 3$ heads with respective probabilities $\frac{1}{8}, \frac{3}{8}, \frac{3}{8}, \frac{1}{8}$.

Mean: $E(X) = 0 \times \frac{1}{8} + 1 \times \frac{3}{8} + 2 \times \frac{3}{8} + 3 \times \frac{1}{8} = 1.5$

Variance: Compute $(x_i - 1.5)^2$ for $x_i = 0, 1, 2, 3$

$$Var(X) = \frac{1}{8}(0 - 1.5)^2 + \frac{3}{8}(1 - 1.5)^2 + \frac{3}{8}(2 - 1.5)^2 + \frac{1}{8}(3 - 1.5)^2 = 0.75$$

Bernoulli Distributions

- A Bernoulli distribution represents the outcome of a single trial that can result in either success (with probability p) or failure (with probability $1 - p$).

- Probability Mass Function (PMF):

$$P(X = x) = p^x(1 - p)^{1-x} \text{ for } x = 0, 1$$

Here, X is a random variable that represents the outcome (success or failure).

- **Characteristics:**

  - It has only two possible outcomes.

  - Commonly used for experiments like flipping a coin, where the outcome is either heads or tails.

Example:

Suppose a basketball player has a 70% chance of making a free throw (success). If she takes one free throw, what is the probability that she makes the shot (success) and the probability that she misses the shot (failure)?

Solution: Probability of Success (making the shot):

Given $p = 0.70$ (70% chance of making the shot)

Since it's a single trial, it's a Bernoulli trial.

Probability of success $P(X = 1) = p = 0.70$

Probability of Failure (missing the shot):

Probability of failure $P(X = 0) = 1 - p = 1 - 0.70 = 0.30$

Interpretation: The basketball player has a 70% chance of making the free throw and a 30% chance of missing it in a single attempt.

Binomial Distributions

- A Binomial distribution extends the Bernoulli distribution to multiple independent trials. It represents the number of successes in n independent Bernoulli trials.

- Probability Mass Function (PMF): $P(X = k) = \binom{n}{k} p^k (1-p)^{n-k}$

  Where $\binom{n}{k}$ is the binomial coefficient, n is the number of trials, k is the number of successes, and p is the probability of success on each trial.

- **Comparing Bernoulli and Binomial Distributions**

  - Bernoulli Distribution is a special case of the Binomial Distribution with $n = 1$.

  - Binomial Distribution can be thought of as the sum of outcomes of multiple Bernoulli trials.

- **Notice:** The calculation of the mean (μ), variance (σ^2), and standard deviation (σ) for a binomial probability distribution can be efficiently performed using the following shortcut formulas:

- Mean: $\mu = np$, Variance: $\sigma^2 = np(1-p)$, Standard Deviation: $\sigma = \sqrt{np(1-p)}$

- These formulas provide a quick and straightforward method for determining key statistical parameters of a binomial distribution.

Example:

A factory's machine produces bolts, and 5% of the bolts are defective. If 10 bolts are randomly selected, what is the probability that exactly 2 of them are defective?

Solution: Probability of finding a defective bolt (success in this context) $p = 0.05$
Number of trials $n = 10$
Number of successes (defective bolts) $k = 2$
Binomial Probability Calculation:
Using the formula for Binomial distribution: $P(X = k) = \binom{n}{k} p^k (1-p)^{n-k}$

$$P(X = 2) = \binom{10}{2} (0.05)^2 (0.95)^8 = \frac{10!}{2!(10-2)!} \times 0.05^2 \times 0.95^8$$
$$= 45 \times 0.0025 \times 0.66342 \approx 0.0746$$

Interpretation: There is approximately a 7.46% chance that exactly 2 out of the 10 randomly selected bolts will be defective.

Poisson Distribution

- The Poisson Distribution is a discrete probability distribution that expresses the probability of a given number of events occurring in a fixed interval of time or space, provided these events occur with a known constant mean rate and independently of the time since the last event.

- Characteristics of Poisson Distribution

- Events Occur Independently: The occurrence of one event does not affect the probability of another event.

- Constant Mean Rate: The average rate at which events occur is constant.

- Random and Rare Events: Typically used for modeling rare events in a large sample space.

- The probability of observing k events in an interval is given by:

$$P(X = k) = \frac{e^{-\lambda} \lambda^k}{k!}$$

- Where:

  - λ is the average number of events per interval

  - e is Euler's number (approximately 2.71828)

  - k is the number of occurrences of an event

  - $k!$ denotes the factorial of k

- Notation for the Poisson: $X \sim P(\lambda)$

  X is a random variable with a Poisson distribution. The parameter is λ (or μ); λ = the mean for the interval of interest.

Example:

A customer service center receives an average of 3 calls per hour. What is the probability of receiving exactly 5 calls in an hour?

Solution: Given, $\lambda = 3$ (average rate is 3 calls per hour)

We want to find $P(X = 5)$

Using the Poisson formula:

$$P(X = 5) = \frac{e^{-3} \cdot 3^5}{5!} = \frac{2.71828^{-3} \cdot 243}{120} \approx 0.1008$$

Interpretation: The probability of receiving exactly 5 calls in an hour at this customer service center is approximately 10.08%.

Hypergeometric Distribution

- The population or set from which samples are drawn is finite.

- Each draw is done without replacing the previous item, altering the composition of the population for subsequent draws.

- The number of items categorized as 'successes' in the population is fixed.

- Hypergeometric probability function: $P(X = k) = \dfrac{\binom{M}{k}\binom{N-M}{n-k}}{\binom{N}{n}}$

  - $\binom{a}{b}$ is a binomial coefficient representing the number of ways to choose b items from a items.
  - M is the total number of successes in the population.
  - N is the total number of items in the population.
  - n is the number of draws.
  - k is the number of observed successes.

- Notation for the hypergeometric: $X \sim H(N, M, n)$

  X is a random variable with a hypergeometric distribution.

- Mean (Average): $\mu = n \times \dfrac{M}{N}$

- Standard Deviation: $\sigma = \sqrt{n \times \dfrac{M}{N} \times \left(1 - \dfrac{M}{N}\right) \times \dfrac{N-n}{N-1}}$

Example:

In a batch of 20 products, there are 5 defective items. If 6 products are randomly selected for inspection, what is the probability that exactly 2 of them are defective?

Solution: Total number of items, $N = 20$. Number of successes in the population (defective items), $M = 5$. Number of draws, $n = 6$. Number of observed successes (defective items found), $k = 2$.

Using the Hypergeometric formula:

$$P(X = 2) = \frac{\binom{5}{2}\binom{20-5}{6-2}}{\binom{20}{6}} = \frac{\left(\frac{5!}{2!\,(5-2)!}\right)\left(\frac{15!}{4!\,(15-4)!}\right)}{\left(\frac{20!}{6!\,(20-6)!}\right)} = \frac{10 \times 1365}{38760} \approx 0.3522$$

There is approximately a 35.22% chance of finding exactly 2 defective products when 6 are randomly selected from this batch.

Geometric Distribution

- **Key Characteristics**

  - Binary Outcome: Each trial has only two outcomes - success or failure.
  - Independent Trials: The outcome of one trial does not affect the outcome of another.
  - Constant Probability of Success: The probability of success (denoted by p) remains the same for each trial.
  - First Success: The focus is on determining the probability of achieving the first success on the k −th trial.

- The probability that the first success occurs on the k −th trial is given by:

$$P(X = k) = (1 - p)^{k-1}p$$

- Where:

  - X is the random variable representing the number of trials until the first success.
  - p is the probability of success on each trial.
  - k is the number of trials needed to achieve the first success.

- The mean: $\mu = \frac{1}{p}$, and standard deviation: $\sigma = \frac{\sqrt{1-p}}{p}$

Example:

A baseball player has a batting average of 0.300, meaning he has a 30% chance of hitting the ball each time he bats. What is the probability that his first hit will occur on his fourth turn at bat?

Solution: Given probability of success (hitting the ball), $p = 0.300$.

We want to find the probability that the first hit occurs on the 4th turn, $k = 4$.

Using the Geometric Distribution formula:

$$P(X = 4) = (1 - 0.300)^{4-1} \times 0.300 = 0.7^3 \times 0.300 = 0.343 \times 0.300 = 0.1029$$

There is approximately a 10.29% chance that the baseball player will get his first hit on his fourth turn at bat.

Negative Binomial Distribution

- **Key Characteristics**
  - Number of Successes: This distribution counts the number of trials needed to achieve a predetermined number of successes, denoted by r.
  - Probability of Success: Each trial has the same probability of success, denoted by p.
  - Independent Trials: Each trial is independent of others.

- The probability of achieving the r −th success on the $k - th$ trial is given by:

$$P(X = k) = \binom{k-1}{r-1} p^r (1-p)^{k-r}$$

- Where:
  - X is the random variable representing the number of trials needed.
  - $\binom{k-1}{r-1}$ is a binomial coefficient.
  - p is the probability of success on each trial.
  - k is the total number of trials.
  - r is the number of required successes.
- Mean (Expected Value) of the Negative Binomial Distribution: $\mu = \dfrac{r}{p}$

- Standard Deviation of the Negative Binomial Distribution: $\sigma = \sqrt{\dfrac{r \times (1-p)}{p^2}}$

Example:

A biologist is observing a rare bird species. The probability of observing this bird on any given day is 10%. What is the probability that the biologist will need to wait 7 days to observe the bird three times?

Solution: Here, $r = 3$ (3 observations needed), $p = 0.10$ (probability of observing the bird), and $k = 7$ (7 days in total).

Using the Negative Binomial Distribution formula:

$$P(X = 7) = \binom{7-1}{3-1}(0.10)^3(0.90)^{7-3} = \binom{6}{2}(0.001)(0.6561) = 15 \times 0.001 \times 0.6561$$
$$= 0.0098415$$

There is approximately a 0.984% chance that the biologist will need to observe for 7 days to see the rare bird three times.

Identifying the Type of Discrete Distribution

- Common Types of Discrete Distributions: Bernoulli Distribution, Binomial Distribution, Poisson Distribution, Geometric Distribution, Hypergeometric Distribution, Negative Binomial Distribution.

- **Identifying the Correct Distribution**

  ▪ Number of Trials: If the number of trials is fixed, consider Binomial or Hypergeometric distributions.

  ▪ Independence: For independent trials with a constant probability of success, think of Bernoulli or Binomial distributions.

  ▪ Sampling Without Replacement: If the sampling is without replacement from a finite population, the Hypergeometric distribution might be the right choice.

  ▪ Rare Events Over Time/Space: The Poisson distribution is usually used for modeling the occurrence of rare events over a continuous interval.

  ▪ First Success: If the focus is on the trial number of the first success, the Geometric distribution is appropriate.

  ▪ Multiple Successes: For scenarios counting the number of trials until a specific number of successes, use the Negative Binomial distribution.

Examples:

Example 1. A quality control manager is inspecting light bulbs from a production line. The probability that any light bulb is defective is 2%. The manager selects 15 light bulbs at random. What type of discrete distribution is appropriate to model the number of defective light bulbs in this scenario?

Solution: Since we are dealing with a fixed number of independent trials (15 light bulbs), each having two possible outcomes (defective or not defective), with a constant probability of success (defective), this scenario is appropriately modeled by a Binomial Distribution.

Example 2. A call center receives an average of 5 calls per hour. What type of discrete distribution would be suitable to model the number of calls received in a two-hour period?

Solution: The appropriate model for this scenario is the Poisson Distribution. This is because we are dealing with the count of events (calls) happening at a known average rate over a fixed interval of time (two hours), and the events (calls) occur independently of each other.

Chapter 4: Practices

✎ **Answer the questions based on the given information.**

A study is being conducted on the frequency of customer service calls received by a tech company's support center during their peak hours. For a random sample of 50 calls, the following data was collected. Let X represent the number of calls a support agent receives in peak hours. For this scenario, $x = 0, 1, 2, 3, 4, 5$. $P(x)$ is the probability that X is equal to x.

X	$P(x)$
0	$\frac{4}{50}$
1	$\frac{8}{50}$
2	$\frac{16}{50}$
3	$\frac{14}{50}$
4	$\frac{6}{50}$
5	$\frac{2}{50}$

1) Why would this be considered a discrete probability distribution function?

A local gardener is planning how many flower bouquets to prepare for a weekend market. She wants to prepare a sufficient number to meet demand without having excess. She has estimated the probability distribution for the demand based on past sales data.

X	$P(x)$
1	0.15
2	0.35
3	0.4
4	0.1

2) Define the random variable X.

3) What is the probability the gardener will sell more than one bouquet? $P(X > 1)$

4) What is the probability the gardener will sell exactly one bouquet? $P(X = 1)$

5) On average, how many bouquets should the gardener prepare?

✍ **Solve.**

6) A high school basketball player makes an average of 15 points per game with a standard deviation of 3 points. In a particularly good game, he scores 24 points. How many standard deviations above the mean is this score?

7) The test scores for a history class are normally distributed with a mean of 75 and a standard deviation of 10. If a student scores 95 on the test, how does her score compare to the class average?

8) For a set of data, the mean age of participants is 22 years, and the standard deviation is 4 years. If the data is normally distributed, between what ages do approximately 68% of the participants fall?

9) A class of students takes a standardized test, and the results have a mean score of 500 and a standard deviation of 100. If the scores are normally distributed, what percentage of students scored between 400 and 600?

✍ **Answer the questions based on the scenarios.**

10) A mobile app developer wants to know the average number of in-app purchases per user during the first week after launch. They collected the following data from a random sample of 100 users:

Number of Purchases	Number of Users
0	30
1	40
2	20
3	10

11) A survey is conducted to find out how many online articles a person reads per day. For a sample of 150 people, the results are:

Number of Articles	Number of People
0	60
1	45
2	30
3	10
4	5

12) Imagine you're at a carnival, playing a ball toss game. There are three colored bins: orange, purple, and yellow. If you toss a ball into the orange bin, you lose $5. The purple bin breaks even, and the yellow bin wins you $15. The probabilities are $P(orange) = \frac{3}{9}$, $P(purple) = \frac{4}{9}$, and $P(yellow) = \frac{2}{9}$. Calculate the expected monetary value of playing this game. And complete the following expected value table.

Color	X	$P(x)$	$XP(x)$
Orange	-5		
Purple		$\frac{4}{9}$	
Yellow			$\frac{10}{3}$

13) Consider a raffle at a local event. The tickets are drawn for three prizes. For a red ticket, you win $50, for a silver ticket, you break even, and for a gold ticket, you win $100. The probabilities are $P(red) = \frac{1}{4}$, $P(silver) = \frac{1}{2}$, and $P(gold) = \frac{1}{4}$. What's the expected value of the prize money for a single raffle ticket? Complete the following expected value table.

Ticket Color	X	$P(x)$	$XP(x)$
Red			$\frac{25}{2}$
Silver			0
Gold	100	$\frac{1}{4}$	

✍ **What are the expected value and variance of this Bernoulli distribution?**

14) In a free throw shooting contest, a basketball player has a 70% chance of making a free throw. What are the expected value and variance of this Bernoulli distribution? And create a bar graph to represent this distribution.

15) A student answers a true/false question on a test by guessing. What is the probability of guessing correctly, and how is this represented in a Bernoulli distribution?

16) A light bulb manufacturer finds that 1% of their bulbs are defective. If a bulb is chosen at random, what is the probability distribution and what are the mean and standard deviation? And create a bar graph to represent this distribution.

✍ **Answer the questions based on the scenario.**

Scenario: Around 80 percent of gym members utilize their membership by attending at least once a week. Each member's gym attendance is independent of others. In a gym with 30 members, what is the probability that at least 25 will attend the gym at least once this week? Members are selected randomly.

17) This is a binomial problem because there is only a success or a _____, there are a fixed number of trials, and the probability of a success is 0.80 for each trial.

18) If we are interested in the number of members attending the gym this week, then how do we define Y?

19) What values does y take on?

20) What is a failure, in words?

21) If $p + q = 1$, then what is q?

22) The words at least translate as what kind of inequality for the probability question $P(y \_\_ 25)$?

Scenario: In a survey, 70 percent of students at a high school say they prefer online classes to in-person ones. Let Y be the number of students out of a random sample of 30 who prefer online classes.

23) What is the probability distribution for X?

Use your calculator or the binomial formula to find the following probabilities:

24) The probability that 25 students prefer online classes.

25) The probability that at most 20 students prefer online classes.

26) The probability that more than 30 students prefer online classes.

27) Using the formulas, calculate the (i) mean and (ii) standard deviation of X.

Scenario: The chance of a randomly selected individual being left-handed is approximately 10%. If we randomly sample 100 people, let Y be the number of people who are left-handed.

28) What is the probability distribution for Y?

29) Using the formulas, calculate the (i) mean and (ii) standard deviation of Y.

30) Find the probability that at most eight people are left-handed.

31) Is it more likely that seven or eight people will be left-handed? Justify your answer numerically.

✍ **Based on the given scenario, answer the following 4 questions.**

You observe that a teacher says "um" approximately three times in each lecture. What is the likelihood that the teacher says "um" more than three times in a single lecture?

32) Identifying the type of discrete distribution.

33) What duration are we considering for this analysis?

34) What is the mean number of times the teacher says "um" in a lecture?

35) Define a variable Y. What values can Y assume?

36) What is the specific probability question we are addressing?

✍ **Answer the questions based on the scenario of a customer service center receiving emails. ($e \approx 2.71828$)**

A customer service center receives about 10 emails every half-hour.

37) What is the probability that the center receives exactly 3 emails in the next six minutes? and draw the diagram for this Poisson distribution.

38) What is the probability that the center receives at least 2 emails in the next six minutes?

39) What is the likelihood that no emails are received in the next twelve minutes? and draw the diagram for this Poisson distribution.

40) Calculate the probability of receiving more than 5 emails in the next 15 minutes. and draw the diagram for this Poisson distribution.

✎ **Identify each value based on the scenarios:**

Suppose a sports academy has 20 soccer players and 10 basketball players. A coach is selecting a random team of 8 players for a mixed-sport training session. We are interested in the number of soccer players in the team.

41) In words, define the random variable X.

42) $X \sim$ _____(_____,_____)

43) What values does X take on?

44) On average (μ), how many soccer players would you expect?

45) Find the standard deviation.

✎ **Answer the questions.**

A book club is selecting a discussion panel from 8 fiction and 7 non-fiction readers. If the panel consists of 5 members chosen randomly.

46) What is the probability that 3 of them are fiction readers?

47) How many fiction readers do you expect on the panel?

48) draw the diagram for this hypergeometric distribution.

A technology conference is forming a committee from nine software developers and six hardware engineers. If the committee consists of four members chosen randomly.

49) What is the probability that two of them are software developers?

50) How many software developers do you expect on the committee?

✍ Identify each value based on the scenarios:

Suppose you are searching for an employee in your company who can speak a second language fluently. You know that 40% of the 1,000 employees are bilingual. You randomly approach employees until one confirms they are bilingual. What is the probability that you need to speak to three people?

51) Let X = the number of _____ you must approach _____ one confirms they are bilingual.

52) What values does X take on?

53) What are Probability (p) and Complement (q)?

54) The probability question is $P($_____$)$.

55) What type of probability distribution problem is this? Why?

✍ Solve.

56) A bookstore finds that 70% of the books in a particular section are fiction. If a store worker randomly selects books until they find a fiction book, how many books are they expected to check? What is the standard deviation?

57) A restaurant observes that 60% of orders include a dessert. If a staff member reviews orders until finding one with a dessert, what is the expected number of orders to check? What is the standard deviation?

58) An online survey platform notes that 80% of participants complete the survey. How many participants must be surveyed on average until finding one who completed it? What is the standard deviation?

59) A tech company finds that 90% of its employees prefer to telecommute. How many employees must HR interview to expect to find one who prefers telecommuting? What is the standard deviation?

✎ **Answer the questions.**

The lifetime risk of contracting a rare disease is about one in 100 (1%). Let Y = the number of patients a doctor sees until one is diagnosed with this rare disease. Y follows a geometric distribution: $Y \sim G\left(\frac{1}{100}\right)$ or $Y \sim G(0.01)$.

60) What is the probability that a doctor sees 10 patients before diagnosing one with this rare disease?

61) What is the probability that a doctor must see 20 patients?

62) Find the mean and standard deviation of Y.

The chance of finding a customer who is satisfied with a new product is one in 50 (2%). Let Z = the number of customers surveyed until one expresses satisfaction. Z is a geometrically distributed random variable: $Z \sim G(\frac{1}{50})$ or $Z \sim G(0.02)$.

63) What is the probability that 8 customers are surveyed before finding a satisfied customer?

64) What is the probability that 15 customers need to be surveyed?

65) Determine the mean and standard deviation of Z.

✎ **Use the following information to answer the next six exercises:**

Imagine that a survey was conducted to determine how many people use public transportation for their daily commute in a large city. Out of 150,000 surveyed individuals, 60 percent indicated that they regularly use public transportation. Suppose you randomly speak to individuals from this survey population until you find someone who uses public transportation. You are interested in the number of people you must ask.

66) In words, define the random variable X.

67) $X \sim$ ___(_____).

68) What values does the random variable X take on?

69) Construct the probability distribution function. Stop at $x = 6$. And draw the geometric distribution diagram.

70) On average (μ), how many people would you expect to have to ask until you find someone who uses public transportation?

71) What is the probability that you will need to ask fewer than three people?

✍ Answer the questions.

72) A company's quality control department finds that, on average, there is one defective product in every ten. They inspect products until they find two defective ones. Define the random variable Y for this scenario.

73) If the probability of rain on any given day in April is 0.3, and a farmer needs three rainy days to start planting crops, how would you describe the random variable Z for the number of days until the farmer has the third day of rain?

74) In a sequence of independent basketball free throws, if a player has a 70% chance of making a free throw, what is the probability that the player makes their fifth free throw on the seventh attempt?

75) A biologist is studying a rare species of bacteria that has a 10% chance of being found in a soil sample. How would you calculate the mean number of soil samples that need to be tested before finding four samples with the bacteria?

76) If it's known that a baseball player hits a home run in 10% of their at-bats and the team wants to estimate the variability of at-bats before the player hits their fourth home run, what would be the standard deviation of the number of at-bats needed?

✍ Identifying the type of discrete distribution, based on the scenarios.

77) In a raffle, there are 100 tickets and only one winning ticket. A person keeps buying tickets one after another until they win. Which discrete distribution does this scenario follow?

78) A quality inspector checks smartphones off the assembly line for defects and counts the total number of phones checked at the end of the day. What type of distribution should be used to model the number of defective phones found?

79) A die is rolled repeatedly, and the number of rolls needed to get a six is recorded. What type of discrete distribution does this scenario represent?

80) A basketball player has a free-throw success rate of 75%. If they take 10 free throws, what type of distribution can be used to model the number of successful free throws? Why?

81) A scientist counts the number of bacterial colonies that grow in a Petri dish over a 24 – hour period. Each colony develops from a single bacterium, and they grow at a constant rate. What type of discrete distribution fits this scenario?

82) A surveyor is asking homeowners if they have a fire extinguisher at home. They record the number of homeowners they have to survey before finding three who do have a fire extinguisher. What kind of distribution is this?

Chapter 4: Answers

1) This is considered a discrete probability distribution function for two primary reasons:

   Countable Outcomes: The random variable X can only take on a finite or countable number of values $(0, 1, 2, 3, 4, 5)$, which is typical of a discrete distribution.

   Probability Sum: The sum of all the probabilities $P(x)$ equals 1, which satisfies the requirement for a probability distribution. This means that all possible outcomes are accounted for, and they encompass the entire sample space.

2) Let X be the random variable representing the number of flower bouquets the gardener sells.

3) $P(X > 1) = P(X = 2) + P(X = 3) + P(X = 4) = 0.35 + 0.40 + 0.10 = 0.85$

4) $P(X = 1) = 0.15$

5) To find the average, multiply each value of X by its probability and sum the products:

   $\mu = \sum(X \cdot P(X)) = (1 \times 0.15) + (2 \times 0.35) + (3 \times 0.40) + (4 \times 0.10) = 0.15 + 0.7 + 1.2 + 0.4 = 2.45$

   On average, the gardener should prepare 2.45, or approximately 3 bouquets, when rounded to the nearest whole number to avoid having fractions of a bouquet.

6) To find how many standard deviations above the mean the score is, subtract the mean from the score and divide by the standard deviation: $\frac{24-15}{3} = 3$. The score is 3 standard deviations above the mean.

7) The student's score is $\frac{95-75}{10} = 2$ standard deviations above the mean, meaning she performed significantly better than average.

8) Approximately 68% of the data falls within one standard deviation of the mean in a normal distribution. Therefore, between $22 - 4$ and $22 + 4$, or between 18 and 26 years old.

9) Scores between 400 and 600 are within one standard deviation of the mean on either side. In a normal distribution, approximately 68% of the scores fall within one standard deviation of the mean, so about 68% of students scored between 400 and 600.

10) The expected number of in-app purchases per user is calculated as:

$$E(X) = \left(0 \cdot \frac{30}{100}\right) + \left(1 \cdot \frac{40}{100}\right) + \left(2 \cdot \frac{20}{100}\right) + \left(3 \cdot \frac{10}{100}\right) = 0 + 0.4 + 0.4 + 0.3 = 1.1$$

So, on average, users make 1.1 in-app purchases during the first week after the app's launch.

11) The expected number of articles read per person per day is:

$$E(X) = \left(0 \cdot \frac{60}{150}\right) + \left(1 \cdot \frac{45}{150}\right) + \left(2 \cdot \frac{30}{150}\right) + \left(3 \cdot \frac{10}{150}\right) + \left(4 \cdot \frac{5}{150}\right)$$

$$E(X) = 0 + 0.3 + 0.4 + 0.2 + 0.133 \approx 1.033$$

So, the average person reads about 1.03 articles per day.

12) To find the expected value, multiply the outcome by its probability and sum the results:

Color	X	$P(x)$	$XP(x)$
Orange	-5	$\frac{3}{9}$	$-\frac{5}{3}$
Purple	0	$\frac{4}{9}$	0
Yellow	15	$\frac{2}{9}$	$\frac{10}{3}$

$$EV = \left(\frac{3}{9}\right) \times (-\$5) + \left(\frac{4}{9}\right) \times (\$0) + \left(\frac{2}{9}\right) \times (\$15) = -\frac{\$5}{3} + \$0 + \frac{\$10}{3} = \frac{\$5}{3}$$

So, the expected value of playing the ball toss game is approximately $1.67.

13) Again, the expected value is found by multiplying each outcome by its probability:

Ticket Color	X	$P(x)$	$XP(x)$
Red	50	$\frac{1}{4}$	$\frac{25}{2}$
Silver	0	$\frac{1}{2}$	0
Gold	100	$\frac{1}{4}$	25

$$EV = \left(\frac{1}{4}\right) \times \$50 + \left(\frac{1}{2}\right) \times \$0 + \left(\frac{1}{4}\right) \times \$100 = \$12.50 + \$0 + \$25 = \$37.50$$

The expected value of the prize money for a single raffle ticket is $37.50.

14) The expected value (mean) of a Bernoulli distribution is p, so it would be 0.7 for this player. The variance is $p(1 - p)$, which would be:

$$0.7(1 - 0.7) = 0.7 \times 0.3 = 0.21$$

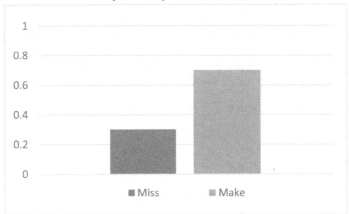

The blue bar represents the probability of missing the free throw: $P(X = 0) = 0.3$.
The orange bar represents the probability of making the free throw: $P(X = 1) = 0.7$.

15) The probability of guessing correctly is $p = 0.5$ since there are only two outcomes. This Bernoulli distribution would have $p = 0.5$ for a correct guess (success) and $q = 0.5$ for an incorrect guess (failure).

16) The probability that the bulb is defective (success) is $p = 0.01$ and not defective (failure) is $q = 0.99$. The mean of this Bernoulli distribution is $p = 0.01$ and the standard deviation is $\sqrt{p(1 - p)} = \sqrt{0.01 \times 0.99} \approx 0.0995$.

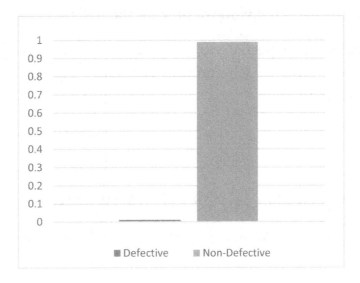

17) Failure

18) Y = the number of gym members who attend at least once this week.

19) $0, 1, 2, \ldots, 30$

20) Failure is defined as a gym member who does not attend the gym at least once this week.
    The probability of a success is $p = 0.80$. The number of trials is $n = 30$.

21) $q = 0.20$

22) ($\geq$), The probability question is $P(y \geq 25)$.

23) The probability distribution for Y is a binomial distribution with parameters $n = 30$ and $p = 0.7$.

24) $P(X = k) = \binom{n}{k} p^k (1-p)^{n-k}$

$P(X = 25) = \binom{30}{25}(0.7)^{25}(0.3)^5 = \frac{30!}{25!(30-25)!} \times 0.7^{25} \times 0.3^5$

$P(X = 25) = 142506 \times 0.000134 \times 0.00243 \approx 0.046$

25) For our calculation, we need to find the cumulative probability $P(Y \leq 20)$, which is the sum of the probabilities of getting 0 up to 20 students who prefer online classes:

$$P(X \leq 20) = \sum_{k=0}^{20} \binom{30}{k}(0.7)^k(0.3)^{30-k}$$

This summation can be quite lengthy to compute by hand, as it involves calculating the binomial probability for each value of k from 0 to 20 and then summing these probabilities. Typically, this kind of calculation is performed using statistical software or a calculator with binomial probability functions, as it is quite complex to do manually.

The final answer, as previously computed, is approximately 0.4112.

26) Since the sample size is 30, it's impossible to have more than 30 students, so $P(Y > 30) = 0$.

27) The mean μ of Y is $\mu = np = 30 \times 0.7 = 21$.
    The standard deviation of Y is $\sigma = \sqrt{np(1-p)} = \sqrt{30 \times 0.7 \times 0.3} \approx 2.51$.

28) This is a binomial distribution, where Y can be described as:
$Y \sim B(100, 0.10)$. ($n = 100$ and $p = 0.1$)

29) (i) Mean: $\mu = n \times p = 100 \times 0.10 = 10$

   (ii) Standard Deviation: $\sigma = \sqrt{n \times p \times (1 - p)} = \sqrt{100 \times 0.10 \times 0.90} = 3$

30) The probability $P(Y \leq 8)$ is approximately 0.3828. This was calculated by summing the probabilities for Y being 0 to 8, using the binomial probability mass function.

31) Using the binomial probability mass function (PMF):
$$P(Y = k) = \binom{100}{k}(0.1)^k(0.9)^{100-k}$$
Let's calculate the probabilities for $P(Y = 7)$ and $P(Y = 8)$:

   Probability for $Y = 7$: $P(Y = 7) = \binom{100}{7}(0.1)^7(0.9)^{93}$

   Probability for $Y = 8$: $P(Y = 8) = \binom{100}{8}(0.1)^8(0.9)^{92}$

   Using a binomial probability calculator or statistical software, we find:
   $P(Y = 7) \approx 0.0901$
   $P(Y = 8) \approx 0.1070$
   It is more likely that eight people will be left-handed than seven people because $P(Y = 8)$ is greater than $P(Y = 7)$.

32) This scenario can be analyzed using a Poisson distribution, as it focuses on counting the number of times "um" is mentioned in a lecture.

33) One lecture.

34) 3

35) Let Y = the number of times the teacher says "um" in a lecture. Y can take values 0, 1, 2, 3, ...

36) $P(Y > 3)$

37) Average rate (λ) = 10 emails per 30 minutes = $\frac{10}{30}$ emails per minute.

   For six minutes, the average rate (λ) would be $\frac{10}{30} \times 6 = 2$ emails.

   Using the Poisson formula: $P(X = k) = \frac{e^{-\lambda}\lambda^k}{k!}$

   Here, $k = 3$, so $P(X = 3) = \frac{e^{-2} \times 2^3}{3!} = \frac{2.71828^{-2} \times 2^3}{1 \times 2 \times 3} \approx 0.1804$

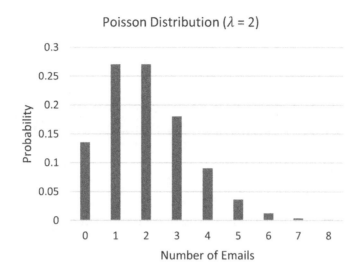

Poisson Distribution (λ = 2)

38) As before, average rate (λ) = 2 emails per 6 minutes.

To find the probability of receiving at least 2 emails, calculate $1 -$ probability of receiving less than 2 emails.

$$P(X \geq 2) = 1 - (P(X = 0) + P(X = 1))$$

$$P(X \geq 2) = 1 - \left(\left(\frac{e^{-2}\times 2^0}{0!}\right) + \left(\frac{e^{-2}\times 2^1}{1!}\right)\right) = 1 - (0.1353 + 0.2706) \approx 0.5941$$

39) For twelve minutes, the average rate (λ) would be $\frac{10}{30} \times 12 = 4$ emails.

$$P(X = 0) = \frac{e^{-4}\times 4^0}{0!} \approx 0.01831$$

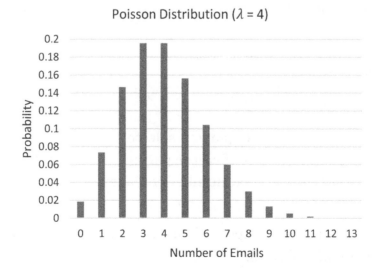

Poisson Distribution (λ = 4)

40) For 15 minutes, the average rate (λ) would be $\frac{10}{30} \times 15 = 5$ emails.

$P(X > 5) = 1 - \big(P(X = 0) + P(X = 1) + P(X = 2) + P(X = 3) + P(X = 4) + P(X = 5)\big)$

$P(X > 5) = 1 - \left(\left(\frac{e^{-5} \times 5^0}{0!}\right) + \left(\frac{e^{-5} \times 5^1}{1!}\right) + \left(\frac{e^{-5} \times 5^2}{2!}\right) + \left(\frac{e^{-5} \times 5^3}{3!}\right) + \left(\frac{e^{-5} \times 5^4}{4!}\right) + \left(\frac{e^{-5} \times 5^5}{5!}\right)\right)$

$P(X > 5) = 1 - (0.00673 + 0.03368 + 0.08422 + 0.14037 + 0.17546 + 0.17546) \approx 0.3840$

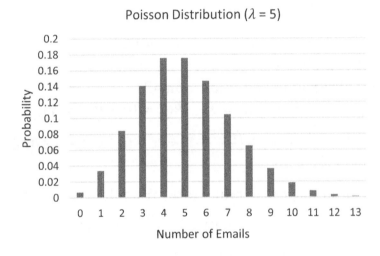

Poisson Distribution ($\lambda = 5$)

41) Random Variable X Definition: The number of soccer players selected in the team.

42) $X \sim (30, 20, 8)$

43) X can take values from 0 to 8.

44) $n = 8$ is the total number of players selected.
$M = 20$ is the total number of soccer players.
$N = 20 + 10 = 30$ is the total number of players.
So, $\mu = n \times \frac{M}{N} = 8 \times \frac{20}{30} = 8 \times \frac{2}{3} \approx 5.33$.

On average, you would expect about 5.33 soccer players in the randomly selected team of 8 players.

45) $\sigma = \sqrt{n \times \frac{M}{N} \times \left(1 - \frac{M}{N}\right) \times \frac{N-n}{N-1}} = \sqrt{8 \times \frac{20}{30} \times \left(1 - \frac{20}{30}\right) \times \frac{30-8}{30-1}} \approx 1.16$

46) Let X = the number of fiction readers on the panel of five. X takes on the values 0, 1, 2, 3, 4, 5, where $N = 15$, $M = 8$, and $n = 5$. $X \sim H(15, 8, 5)$.

$$P(X = 3) = \frac{\binom{M}{k} \binom{N-M}{n-k}}{\binom{N}{n}} = \frac{\binom{8}{3} \binom{15-8}{5-3}}{\binom{15}{5}} = \frac{\left(\frac{8!}{3!(8-3)!}\right) \left(\frac{7!}{2!(7-2)!}\right)}{\left(\frac{15!}{5!(15-5)!}\right)}$$

$$\approx 0.3916$$

47) The expected number of fiction readers on the panel is:
$$\mu = n \times \frac{M}{N} = 5 \times \frac{8}{15} \approx 2.67$$

48)

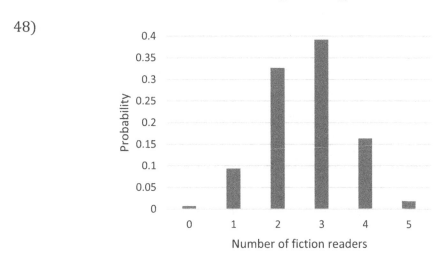

49) Let X = the number of software developers on the committee of four. X takes on the values 0, 1, 2, 3, 4, where $N = 15$, $M = 9$, and $n = 4$. $X \sim H(15, 9, 4)$.

$$P(X = 2) = \frac{\binom{M}{k} \binom{N-M}{n-k}}{\binom{N}{n}} = \frac{\binom{9}{2} \binom{15-9}{4-2}}{\binom{15}{4}} = \frac{\left(\frac{9!}{2!(9-2)!}\right) \left(\frac{6!}{2!(6-2)!}\right)}{\left(\frac{15!}{4!(15-4)!}\right)}$$

$$\approx 0.3956$$

50) The expected number of software developers on the committee is:
$$\mu = n \times \frac{M}{N} = 4 \times \frac{9}{15} \approx 2.4$$

51) Employees, until

52) 1, 2, 3, ..., up to the total number of employees (1,000).

53) $p = 0.40$, $q = 0.60$

54) $P(X = 3)$

55) This is a geometric distribution problem because there could be several failures (non-bilingual employees) before a success (finding a bilingual employee), and the probability of finding a bilingual employee remains constant with each individual approached.

56) $p = 0.70$, Expected number $= \frac{1}{p} = \frac{1}{0.70} \approx 1.43$.

Standard deviation $= \frac{\sqrt{1-p}}{p} = \frac{\sqrt{1-0.7}}{0.7} \approx 0.78$.

57) $p = 0.60$, Expected number $= \frac{1}{p} = \frac{1}{0.60} \approx 1.67$.

Standard deviation $= \frac{\sqrt{1-p}}{p} = \frac{\sqrt{1-0.6}}{0.6} \approx 1.05$.

58) $p = 0.80$, Expected number $= \frac{1}{p} = \frac{1}{0.80} = 1.25$.

Standard deviation $= \frac{\sqrt{1-p}}{p} = \frac{\sqrt{1-0.8}}{0.8} \approx 0.56$.

59) $p = 0.90$, Expected number $= \frac{1}{p} = \frac{1}{0.90} \approx 1.11$.

Standard deviation $= \frac{\sqrt{1-p}}{p} = \frac{\sqrt{1-0.9}}{0.9} \approx 0.35$.

60) $P(X = 10) = (1 - 0.01)^{10-1} \times 0.01 \rightarrow P(X = 10) = 0.00913$

61) $P(X = 20) = (1 - 0.01)^{20-1} \times 0.01 \rightarrow P(X = 20) = 0.00826$

62) Mean: 100, Standard Deviation: $\sqrt{9900} \approx 99.498$.

63) $P(X = 8) = (1 - 0.02)^{8-1} \times 0.02 \rightarrow P(X = 8) = 0.01736$

64) $P(X = 15) = (1 - 0.02)^{15-1} \times 0.02 \rightarrow P(X = 15) = 0.01507$

65) Mean: 50, Standard Deviation: $\sqrt{2,450} \approx 49.497$.

66) X is the number of people you have to ask until you find one who regularly uses public transportation.

67) $X \sim G(0.60)$, X follows a geometric distribution with a probability of success of 0.60.

68) can take on positive integer values starting from 1 $(1, 2, 3, ...)$, as you can't ask a fraction of a person, and there is no upper limit to the number of people you might have to ask.

69)

X	$P(X)$
1	0.6
2	0.24
3	0.096
4	0.0384
5	0.0154
6	0.0061

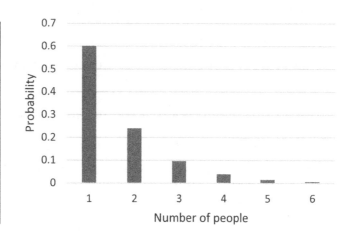

70) $\mu = \frac{1}{0.6} = 1.67$

71) $P(x < 3) = P(x = 1) + P(x = 2) = 0.6 + 0.24 = 0.84$

72) The random variable Y represents the number of products the quality control department must inspect until they find exactly two defective products. It follows a negative binomial distribution because we are looking for the number of trials needed to achieve a fixed number of failures (in this case, two defective products).

73) The random variable Z follows a negative binomial distribution, with Z counting the number of days until the third rainy day occurs. This takes into account both the rainy days and the non-rainy days that pass until the desired number of rainy days is reached.

74) This scenario can be modeled with a negative binomial distribution, where the probability $P(X = 7)$ can be calculated using the formula for the negative binomial distribution, considering $p = 0.7$ (probability of making a free throw) and $r = 5$ (the number of successful free throws desired). We need the fifth success to happen on the seventh trial. So, the calculation

would involve: $P(X = 7) = \binom{7-1}{5-1} \times (0.7)^5 \times (1 - 0.7)^{7-5}$

$$= \left(\frac{6!}{4!(6-4)!}\right) \times (0.7)^5 \times (0.3)^2 \approx 0.22689$$

75) The mean or expected value $E(X)$ of a negative binomial distribution with parameters r (number of successes to be observed) and p (probability of success in each trial) is given by $E(X) = \frac{r}{p}$.

So, for four successes ($r = 4$) with a 10% chance of success ($p = 0.10$), the mean number of soil samples needed would be $E(X) = \frac{4}{0.10} = 40$ samples.

76) The standard deviation of the Negative Binomial Distribution: $\sigma = \sqrt{\frac{r(1-p)}{p^2}}$

For this player, $r = 4$ (the number of home runs needed) and $p = 0.10$ (the probability of hitting a home run). Plugging these into the formula gives:

$$\sigma = \sqrt{\frac{4(1-0.10)}{0.10^2}} = \sqrt{\frac{40.90}{0.01}} = \sqrt{360} \approx 18.97$$

This value represents the variability in the number of at-bats needed for the player to hit four home runs.

77) This scenario follows a geometric distribution, assuming that the person does not replace the winning ticket once it is drawn.

78) Poisson Distribution. If the inspector is counting the number of defects over a continuous interval (the day) and defects occur independently at a constant average rate.

79) Geometric Distribution

80) Binomial Distribution.
Reason: The number of trials (free throws) is fixed (10). Each trial (free throw) has two possible outcomes: success (making the shot) or failure (missing the shot). The probability of success (making a free throw) is constant (75% or 0.75) for each trial. The trials are independent.

81) Poisson Distribution

82) Negative Binomial Distribution.

CHAPTER

5 Continuous Random Variables

Topics that you'll learn in this chapter:

- ☑ Probability Density Functions
- ☑ Continuous Probability Distributions
- ☑ Uniform Distribution
- ☑ Exponential Distribution
- ☑ Normal Distribution and Z −scores
- ☑ Using the Normal Distribution in Real-World

159

Probability Density Functions

- Probability Density Functions (PDFs) are crucial in statistics for understanding the distribution of continuous random variables. A PDF, denoted as $f(x)$, describes the likelihood of a random variable taking on a specific value. The area under the curve of a PDF over an interval represents the probability that the random variable falls within that interval.

- **Key Concepts:**

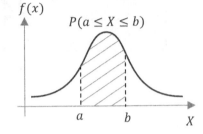

  ▪ Continuous Random Variables: Unlike discrete random variables, continuous variables can take any value within a given range.
  ▪ Area Under the Curve: The total area under the PDF curve is 1 or 100%, representing the total probability space.
  ▪ Probability Calculation: The probability that a variable falls within a specific interval is found by integrating the PDF over that interval.

- **Basic Properties**

  ▪ Non-Negativity: $f(x) \geq 0$ for all x.
  ▪ Normalization: The integral of $f(x)$ over the entire space is 1.
  ▪ Interval Probability: $P(a \leq X \leq b) = \int_a^b f(x)\, dx$.

Examples:

Example 1. Suppose the PDF of a random variable X is given by $f(x) = 2x$ for $0 \leq x \leq 1$. Find the probability that X falls between 0.2 and 0.5.
Solution: First, check normalization: $\int_0^1 2x\, dx = 1$, confirming the PDF is correct. Calculate $P(0.2 \leq X \leq 0.5) = \int_{0.2}^{0.5} 2x\, dx$.
Performing the integration gives $P = [x^2]_{0.2}^{0.5} = 0.5^2 - 0.2^2 = 0.21$.

Example 2. Consider a PDF defined as $f(x) = \frac{1}{4}(4x - x^3)$ for $0 \leq x \leq 2$. Calculate the probability that $X > 1.5$.
Solution: Verify normalization: $\int_0^2 \frac{1}{4}(4x - x^3)\, dx = 1$. confirming the PDF is correctly normalized. Calculate: $P(X > 1.5) = \int_{1.5}^2 \frac{1}{4}(4x - x^3)\, dx = \left[\frac{1}{4}\left(2x^2 - \frac{x^4}{4}\right)\right]_{1.5}^2$

Compute at the upper limit $x = 2$: $\frac{1}{4}\left(2(2)^2 - \frac{4^4}{4}\right) = 1$

Compute at the upper limit $x = 1.5$: $\frac{1}{4}\left(2(1.5)^2 - \frac{1.5^4}{4}\right) = 0.914$

Calculate the difference: $P(X > 1.5) = 1 - 0.914 = 0.086$.

Continuous Probability Distributions

- Unlike discrete distributions that deal with distinct or separate values, continuous distributions cover a continuum of possible values.

- **Properties:**

  ▪ Non-Negativity: $f(x) \geq 0$ for all x.

  ▪ Total Area: The integral of $f(x)$ over its entire range equals 1.

  ▪ Interval Probability: $P(a \leq X \leq b) = \int_a^b f(x)\, dx$.

- **Step-by-Step Guide: Continuous Probability Distributions**

  ▪ Identify the Random Variable: Define the continuous random variable and its range.

  ▪ Determine the Distribution: Find or derive the PDF and CDF.

  ▪ Normalization Check: Ensure the total area under the PDF is 1.

  ▪ Calculating Probabilities:

    For a specific range: Use the PDF to find $P(a \leq X \leq b)$

    For a single point or threshold: Use the CDF to find $P(X \leq x)$.

Examples:

Example 1. Consider a random variable X with a PDF given *by* $f(x) = \frac{1}{2}x$ for $0 \leq x \leq 2$. Calculate the probability that X is less than 1.5.

Solution: Check normalization: $\int_0^2 \frac{1}{2}x\, dx = 1$.

Calculate $P(X < 1.5)$ using the CDF: $\int_0^{1.5} \frac{1}{2}x\, dx = \left[\frac{1}{4}x^2\right]_0^{1.5} = 0.5625$.

Example 2. A random variable Y is uniformly distributed between 3 and 7. Find the probability that Y falls between 4 and 6.

Solution: The PDF of a uniform distribution is $f(y) = \frac{1}{b-a}$ for $a \leq y \leq b$. Here, $a = 3$ and $b = 7$, so $f(y) = \frac{1}{4}$.

Calculate $P(4 \leq Y \leq 6) = \int_4^6 \frac{1}{4}\, dy = \frac{1}{2}$.

Uniform Distribution

- Uniform Distribution is a type of continuous probability distribution where all outcomes are equally likely. It's characterized by two parameters: the minimum value a and the maximum value b.

- This distribution is used to model scenarios where each interval of equal length on the distribution's range is equally probable.

- **Properties**
  - Range: The random variable X takes values in the interval [a, b].
  - Mean: The mean of a uniform distribution is $\mu = \frac{a+b}{2}$.
  - Variance: The variance is $\sigma^2 = \frac{(b-a)^2}{12}$.
  - Percentile Value: $P - value = a + p \times (b - a)$
    Where p is the percentile in decimal form (e.g., 0.90 for the $90th$ percentile).

- **Step-by-Step Guide: Uniform Distribution**
  - Define the Range: Identify the minimum value a and maximum value b.
  - Calculate the PDF: Use $f(x) = \frac{1}{b-a}$ for $a \le x \le b$.
  - Compute the CDF: Apply $F(x) = \frac{x-a}{b-a}$ for $a \le x \le b$.
  - Determine Probabilities: For an interval $[c, d]$ within $[a, b]$, calculate $P(c \le X \le d) = F(d) - F(c)$.

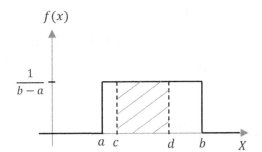

Examples:

Example 1. A random variable X is uniformly distributed between 0 and 10. Find the probability that X is between 3 and 7.

Solution: The PDF is $f(x) = \frac{1}{10-0} = \frac{1}{10}$.

Calculate $P(3 \le X \le 7)$ using the CDF: $F(7) - F(3) = \frac{7-0}{10-0} - \frac{3-0}{10-0} = 0.4$.

Example 2. Suppose Y is uniformly distributed from 20 to 40. Determine the mean and variance.

Solution: The mean μ is $\frac{20+40}{2} = 30$.

The variance σ^2 is $\frac{(40-20)^2}{12} = \frac{400}{12} \approx 33.33$.

Exponential Distribution

- The Exponential Distribution is a continuous probability distribution that is widely used to model the time until an event occurs, such as the lifespan of a machine or the time between customer arrivals. It is characterized by its parameter λ, which is the rate of occurrence of events.

Properties

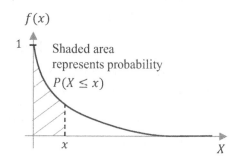

- Rate Parameter λ: Represents the number of events per unit time.

- Mean: The mean of an exponential distribution is $\frac{1}{\lambda}$.

- Variance: The variance is $\frac{1}{\lambda^2}$.

- **Step-by-Step Guide: Exponential Distribution**

  - Identify the Rate: Determine the rate λ of the event occurrence.

  - Calculate the PDF: Use $f(x) = \lambda\, e^{-\lambda x}$ for $x \geq 0$.

  - Compute the CDF: Apply $F(x) = 1 - e^{-\lambda x}$ for $x \geq 0$.

  - Determine Probabilities: For a given value x, calculate $P(X \leq x) = F(x)$.

Example:

If the time between customer arrivals at a store follows an exponential distribution with an average time of 10 minutes, find the probability of the next customer arriving within 5 minutes.

Solution: First, find λ: Since the mean $\mu = \frac{1}{\lambda}$, $\lambda = \frac{1}{10}$ per minute.

The CDF is $F(x) = 1 - e^{-\frac{1}{10}x}$.

Calculate $P(X \leq 5) = F(5) = 1 - e^{-\frac{1}{10} \times 5} \approx 0.393$.

Normal Distribution and Z −scores

- The Normal Distribution, also known as the Gaussian distribution, is a continuous probability distribution that is symmetric around its mean.

- It's one of the most important distributions in statistics, often used to represent real-valued random variables whose distributions are not known.

- **Key Features of Normal Distribution**

  - Symmetry: The distribution is symmetric around the mean, μ.
  - Bell Shape: It has a bell-shaped curve.
  - Mean, Median, Mode: The mean, median, and mode are all equal.
  - Probability Density Function (PDF): $f(x) = \frac{1}{\sigma\sqrt{2\pi}} e^{-\frac{1}{2}\left(\frac{x-\mu}{\sigma}\right)^2}$, where μ is the mean and σ is the standard deviation.
  - Total Area: The total area under the curve is 1.

- A Z −score, or standard score, is a numerical measurement that describes a value's relationship to the mean of a group of values, measured in terms of standard deviations from the mean. The formula for calculating a Z −score is:

  $$Z = \frac{X - \mu}{\sigma}$$

  where X is the value, μ is the mean, and σ is the standard deviation.

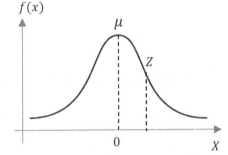

Examples:

Example 1. Suppose test scores are normally distributed with a mean of 70 and a standard deviation of 10. Find the Z −score for a test score of 85.

Solution: Calculate $Z = \frac{85-70}{10} = 1.5$. This score is 1.5 standard deviations above the mean.

Example 2. Given a normal distribution with $\mu = 50$ and $\sigma = 5$, what is the probability of randomly selecting a score less than 45?

Solution: First, find the Z −score for 45: $Z = \frac{45-50}{5} = -1$.

Using a standard normal distribution table, find the probability corresponding to $Z = -1$, which is approximately 0.1587. This is the probability of selecting a score less than 45.

Using the Normal Distribution in Real-World

- The Normal Distribution, often referred to as a bell curve due to its shape. Its ability to represent a wide range of random variables makes it a versatile tool for analysis and decision-making.

- **Characteristics of Normal Distribution**

  - Symmetry Around the Mean: It is symmetrically distributed around its mean.

  - Predictability: Given the mean and standard deviation, the distribution of values can be predicted.

  - Standard Deviation: It determines the spread of the distribution. Most values lie within three standard deviations from the mean.

- Real-World Applications

  - Assessment and Testing: Grades in exams often follow a normal distribution, helping educators identify average and outlier performances.

  - Quality Control: In manufacturing, product dimensions and weights often follow a normal distribution, aiding in quality assurance and control processes.

  - Finance and Economics: Stock market returns frequently exhibit normal distribution characteristics, useful in risk management and investment strategies.

  - Social Science Research: Many human characteristics, like height and IQ, are normally distributed, aiding in sociological studies and research.

Example:

In an IQ test that follows a normal distribution, the mean is 100 with a standard deviation of 15. What percentage of the population is expected to have an IQ between 85 and 115?

Solution: Calculate Z −scores for 85 and 115.

Z −score for 85: $Z = \frac{85-100}{15} \approx -1$.

Z −score for 115: $Z = \frac{115-100}{15} \approx 1$.

he percentage of people with IQs between these Z −scores is about 68%, as per the empirical rule (or $68 - 95 - 99.7$ rule).

Chapter 5: Practices

✍ Answer the questions.

1) Define Probability Density Function (PDF) in the context of continuous random variables.

2) How do you interpret the area under the curve of a PDF?

3) Suppose a random variable X has a PDF given by $f(x) = 2x$ for $0 \le x \le 1$. What is the probability that X is less than 0.5?

4) What is meant by the term 'normalization' in the context of a PDF.

5) Find the probability that a random variable X with a uniform distribution between 2 and 6 (inclusive) takes a value greater than 4.

6) What distinguishes a Probability Density Function from a Probability Mass Function?

7) Describe the typical shape of the PDF of a normal distribution.

8) If a PDF is given by $f(x) = 3x^2$ for $0 \le x \le 1$, what is the mean (expected value) of the random variable?

✍ Solve and draw the graph.

9) Consider the function $g(y) = \frac{1}{6}$ for $0 \le y \le 6$. Draw the graph of $g(y)$ and find $P(1 < y < 5)$.

10) Consider the function $h(z) = \frac{1}{10}$ for $0 \le z \le 10$. Draw the graph of $h(z)$ and find $P(3 < z < 9)$.

11) Consider the function $i(t) = \frac{1}{12}$ for $0 \le t \le 12$. Draw the graph of $i(t)$ and find $P(4 < t < 8)$.

12) Consider the function $j(w) = \frac{1}{15}$ for $0 \le w \le 15$. Draw the graph of $j(w)$ and find $P(5 < w < 10)$.

13) A continuous random variable X has a uniform distribution between 20 and 40. What is the probability that X is between 25 and 35? Draw the graph of the distribution and show the area representing this probability.

14) Consider a continuous random variable Y that follows an exponential distribution with a rate parameter $\lambda = 0.1$. What is the probability that Y is less than 5? Also, draw the graph of this distribution and indicate the area representing this probability.

✒ **Answer the questions based on the scenarios.**

The amount of sugar, in grams, that a chef adds to a cake mixture is uniformly distributed between 50 and 200 grams, inclusive.
15) What is the probability that the chef uses fewer than 180 grams of sugar?

16) On average, how many grams of sugar does the chef use? Find the mean (μ) and the standard deviation (σ).

17) Seventy-five percent of the time, the amount of sugar used falls below what value?

The depth, in meters, at which a scuba diver can find a specific type of coral is uniformly distributed between 5 and 30 meters.
18) What is the probability that this coral is found at a depth less than 25 meters?

19) On average, at what depth is the coral found? Find the mean (μ) and the standard deviation (σ).

20) Eighty percent of the time, the depth at which the coral is found falls below what value?

The time, in hours, it takes to complete a puzzle is uniformly distributed between 1 and 10 hours.
21) What is the probability of completing the puzzle in fewer than 8 hours?

22) On average, how long does it take to complete the puzzle? Find the mean (µ) and the standard deviation (σ).

23) Sixty percent of the time, the time to complete the puzzle falls below what value?

The distance, in kilometers, a bird migrates south is uniformly distributed between 100 and 1000 kilometers.
24) What is the probability that the bird migrates less than 900 kilometers?

25) On average, how far does a bird migrate? Find the mean (μ) and the standard deviation (σ).

26) Eighty-five percent of the time, the migration distance falls below what value?

✎ **Use the following information to answer the next 10 questions.**

The data that follow is the amount of time (in hours) spent on leisure activities by individuals in a week:

1.5	2.4	3.6	2.6	1.6	2.4	2.0
3.5	2.5	1.8	2.4	2.5	3.5	4.0
2.6	1.6	2.2	1.8	3.8	2.5	1.5
2.8	1.8	4.5	1.9	1.9	3.1	1.6

The sample mean = 2.50 and the sample standard deviation = 0.8302.

The distribution can be written as $X \sim U(1.5, 4.5)$.

27) What type of distribution is this?

28) In this distribution, outcomes are equally likely. What does this mean?

29) What is the height of $f(x)$ for the continuous probability distribution?

30) What are the constraints for the values of x?

31) Graph $P(2 < x < 3)$.

32) What is $P(2 < x < 3)$?

33) What is $P(x < 3.5 | x < 4)$?

34) What is $P(x = 1.5)$?

35) What is the $90th$ percentile of square footage for homes?

36) Find the probability that a randomly selected individual spends more than 3 hours on leisure given that they spend more than 2 hours.

✎ **What is *m*, *μ*, and *σ*? And find the required probability.**

37) Suppose the time it takes to download a file, in seconds, is an exponential random variable with a decay parameter of $\frac{1}{20}$. If a file is currently downloading, find the probability that you will have to wait more than 10 seconds. Let *Y* be the download time, in seconds.

38) Consider the time a student spends on a homework problem, in minutes, to be an exponential random variable with a decay parameter of $\frac{1}{30}$. Find the probability that a student spends more than 15 minutes on a problem.

39) Assume the waiting time for a bus, in minutes, follows an exponential distribution with a decay parameter of $\frac{1}{10}$. Calculate the probability of waiting more than 20 minutes for the bus.

40) The lifespan of a certain type of battery, in hours, is an exponential random variable with a decay parameter of $\frac{1}{1000}$. What is the probability that the battery lasts more than 500 hours?

✎ **Answer the questions Based on the scenario.**

Consider a website where a new visitor is expected every 10 seconds on average, and the time between new visitor arrivals is exponentially distributed.

41) On average, how many seconds elapse between two successive new visitor arrivals?

42) How long on average does it take for five visitors to arrive after the site becomes active?

43) Find the probability that it takes less than 3 seconds for the next visitor to arrive after one has just arrived.

44) Find the probability that it takes more than 15 seconds for the next visitor to arrive.

45) Eighty percent of the visitors arrive within how many seconds of the previous visitor?

46) Is an exponential distribution reasonable for this situation?

✍ **Answer the questions Based on the scenario.**

Imagine a call center where a call is received on average every 5 minutes, and the time between calls is exponentially distributed.

47) On average, how many minutes elapse between two successive calls?

48) How long on average does it take for four calls to be received after the call center opens?

49) Find the probability that it takes less than 2 minutes for the next call to arrive after one has just been received.

50) Find the probability that it takes more than 10 minutes for the next call to arrive.

51) Fifty percent of the calls are received within how many minutes of the previous call?

52) Is an exponential distribution reasonable for this situation?

✍ **Use the following information to answer the next 10 questions.**

A certain electronic device operates before it needs recharging, and it follows an exponential distribution with a rate parameter $\lambda = 0.25$ (which corresponds to an average of 4 hours of operation)

53) What is m?

54) What is the probability density function (PDF)?

55) What is the cumulative distribution function (CDF)?

56) Draw the distribution.

57) Find $P(x < 4)$.

58) Find the $30th$ percentile.

59) Find the median.

60) Which is larger, the mean or the median?

✎ **Answer the questions.**

61) What does it mean if a test score is at the $75th$ percentile of a normal distribution of scores?

62) Calculate the $z-$score for a test score of 85, where the mean score is 75 and the standard deviation is 5.

63) If the heights of a group of students are normally distributed with a mean of $170\ cm$ and a standard deviation of $10\ cm$, what $z-$score corresponds to a height of $180\ cm$?

64) What percentage of data falls between $z-$scores of -1 and 1 in a standard normal distribution?

65) For a normal distribution with mean 100 and standard deviation 15, find the probability that a randomly selected value is less than 120.

66) In a standard normal distribution, what $z-$score separates the lowest 25% of data from the rest?

67) A set of data is normally distributed with a mean of 50 and a standard deviation of 5. Find the $z-$score for a data point of 40.

68) If a student's score is 1.5 standard deviations above the mean in a normally distributed class test, what is the $z-$score, and what does this tell us about their performance relative to the class?

69) If the probability of a train arriving on time is 0.123, what is the probability of it being late?

70) In a normal distribution of daily high temperatures, if the probability of the temperature being above a certain degree is 0.543, what is the probability of the temperature being at or below that degree?

✎ **Solve.**

71) A machine fills milk cartons with a mean of 500 ml and a standard deviation of 15 ml. Assuming the fill amounts are normally distributed, what is the probability that a randomly selected carton contains more than 520 ml of milk?

72) If the heights of a population are normally distributed with a mean of 68 inches and a standard deviation of 3 inches, what percentage of the population is shorter than 65 inches?

73) SAT scores are normally distributed with a mean of 1050 and a standard deviation of 200. A university offers scholarships to students scoring in the top 10%. What is the minimum score required for the scholarship?

74) A product's lifetime is normally distributed with a mean of 4 years and a standard deviation of 0.5 years. What is the probability that a product lasts more than 5 years?

Chapter 5: Answers

1) A PDF describes how the values of a continuous random variable are distributed. For any two numbers a and b with $a \leq b$, the probability that the variable lies in the interval $[a, b]$ is given by the integral of the PDF over that interval.

2) The area under the curve of a PDF between two points represents the probability of the random variable falling within that range. The total area under the entire PDF curve is always 1.

3) $P(X < 0.5) = \int_0^{0.5} 2x\, dx = [x^2]_0^{0.5} = 0.5^2 - 0^2 = 0.25$

4) Normalization refers to the requirement that the total area under a PDF must equal 1, representing the fact that the probability of the random variable taking on some value is certain.

5) $P(X > 4) = \int_4^6 \frac{1}{6-2} dx = \frac{1}{4} \times (6 - 4) = 0.5$

6) A PDF is used for continuous random variables, where probabilities are calculated over intervals. In contrast, a Probability Mass Function (PMF) is used for discrete random variables, where probabilities are associated with specific points.

7) The PDF of a normal distribution is bell-shaped and symmetric about the mean. It has its peak at the mean, and the probabilities taper off symmetrically on either side.

8) $Mean = \int_0^1 x \cdot f(x)\, dx = \int_0^1 x \cdot 3x^2\, dx = \int_0^1 3x^3\, dx = [0.75x^4]_0^1 = 0.75$

9) The graph of $g(y)$ is a horizontal line at $\frac{1}{6}$ from 0 to 6.

To find $P(1 < y < 5)$, calculate $(5 - 1) \times \frac{1}{6} = \frac{4}{6} = \frac{2}{3}$.

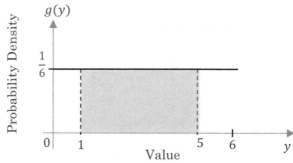

10) The graph of $h(z)$ is a horizontal line at $\frac{1}{10}$ from 0 to 10.

To find $P(3 < z < 9)$, calculate $(9 - 3) \times \frac{1}{10} = \frac{6}{10} = 0.6$.

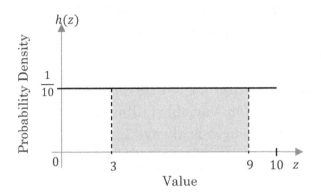

11) The graph of $i(t)$ is a horizontal line at $\frac{1}{12}$ from 0 to 12.

To find $P(4 < t < 8)$, calculate $(8 - 4) \times \frac{1}{12} = \frac{4}{12} = \frac{1}{3}$.

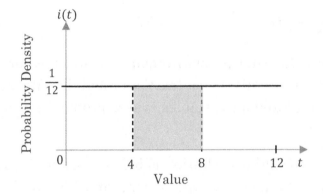

12) The graph of $j(w)$ is a horizontal line at $\frac{1}{15}$ from 0 to 15.

To find $P(5 < w < 10)$, calculate $(10 - 5) \times \frac{1}{15} = \frac{5}{15} = \frac{1}{3}$.

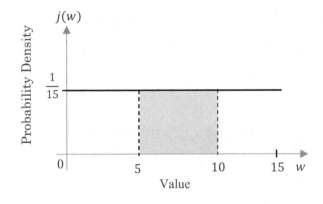

13) The PDF for a uniform distribution $U(20, 40)$ is:

$f(x) = \frac{1}{40-20} = \frac{1}{20}$ for $20 \leq x \leq 40$.

To find $P(25 < X < 35)$, calculate $(35 - 25) \times \frac{1}{20} = \frac{10}{20} = 0.5$.

The graph is a horizontal line at $\frac{1}{20}$ from 20 to 40 with the area between 25 and 35 shaded.

This graph represents a uniform distribution for a random variable X between 20 and 40. The shaded area between 25 and 35 illustrates the probability $P(25 < X < 35) = 0.5$.

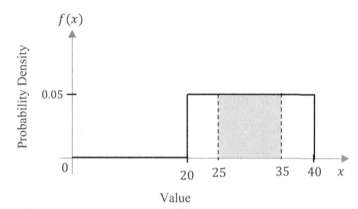

14) The PDF for an exponential distribution is $f(y) = 0.1\, e^{-0.1y}$ for $y \geq 0$.

To find $P(Y < 5)$, calculate $1 - e^{-0.1 \times 5} = 1 - e^{-0.5} \approx 0.3935$.

The graph will show a decreasing exponential curve starting from 0, with the area under the curve to the left of 5 shaded.

This graph depicts an exponential distribution for a random variable Y with a rate parameter $\lambda = 0.1$. The shaded area to the left of 5 represents the probability $P(Y < 5) \approx 0.3935$.

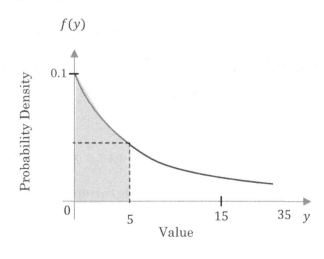

15) Let X be the grams of sugar used. X is uniformly distributed $U(50, 200)$. The probability density function $f(x) = \frac{1}{200-50} = \frac{1}{150}$ for $50 \leq x \leq 200$. To find $P(x < 180)$, calculate $(180 - 50) \times \frac{1}{150} = 0.867$. The probability is 0.867.

16) Mean, $\mu = 125$ grams, Standard Deviation $\sigma = 43.30$ grams.

17) A uniform distribution between $a = 50$ grams and $b = 200$ grams. Use the Percentile Formula for Uniform Distribution: $X_p = a + p(b - a)$
where p is the percentile in decimal form (e.g., 75% = 0.75).
$$X_{0.75} = 50 + 0.75(200 - 50) \rightarrow X_{0.75} = 50 + 112.5 \rightarrow X_{0.75} = 162.5$$
So, seventy-five percent of the time, the amount of sugar used is less than 162.5 grams.

18) Let D be the depth. D follows $U(5, 30)$. The PDF is $f(d) = \frac{1}{30-5} = \frac{1}{25}$. Calculate $P(D < 25)$ as $(25 - 5) \times \frac{1}{25} = 0.8$. The probability is 0.8.

19) Mean $\mu = 17.5$ meters, Standard Deviation $\sigma = 7.22$ meters.

20) Eighty percent of the time, the coral is found at a depth less than 25.0 meters.

21) Let T represent the time to complete the puzzle, with $T \sim U(1, 10)$. The PDF $f(t) = \frac{1}{10-1} = \frac{1}{9}$. To find $P(T < 8)$, calculate $(8 - 1) \times \frac{1}{9} = 0.778$. The probability is 0.778.

22) Mean $\mu = 5.5$ hours, Standard Deviation $\sigma = 2.60$ hours.

23) Sixty percent of the time, the puzzle is completed in less than 6.4 hours.

24) Let D be the migration distance. D is uniformly distributed $U(100, 1000)$. The PDF is $f(d) = \frac{1}{1000-100} = \frac{1}{900}$. Find $P(D < 900)$ as $(900 - 100) \times \frac{1}{900} = 0.889$. The probability is 0.889.

25) Mean $\mu = 550$ kilometers, Standard Deviation $\sigma = 259.81$ kilometers.

26) Eighty-five percent of the time, the migration distance is less than 865 kilometers.

27) This is a uniform distribution, as indicated by the notation $X \sim U(1.5, 4.5)$.

28) It means that any value between 1.5 hours and 4.5 hours is just as likely to occur as any other value in that range.

29) The height, or the probability density function (PDF), is $f(x) = \frac{1}{4.5-1.5} = \frac{1}{3}$.

30) The values of x must be between 1.5 and 4.5, inclusive.

31)

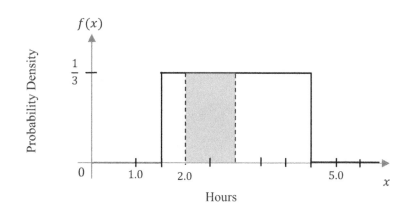

32) $P(2 < x < 3) = (3 - 2) \times \frac{1}{3} = \frac{1}{3}$

33) Since the distribution is uniform, $P(x < 3.5 | x < 4) = \frac{P(x<3.5 \text{ and } x<4)}{P(x<4)} = \frac{P(x<3.5)}{P(x<4)} = \frac{2}{2.5} = \frac{4}{5}$.

34) In a continuous distribution, the probability of any single point is zero, so $P(x = 1.5) = 0$.

35) The 90*th* percentile p is found by solving $\frac{p-1.5}{3} = 0.9$, giving $p = 0.9 \times 3 + 1.5 = 4.2$ (in 1,000 square feet).

36) $P(x > 3 | x > 2) = \frac{P(x>3)}{P(x>2)} = \frac{4.5-3}{4.5-2} = \frac{1.5}{2.5} = \frac{3}{5}$.

37) $m = \frac{1}{20}$, $\mu = 20$, $\sigma = 20$, $P(Y > 10) = e^{-\frac{10}{20}} = e^{-0.5} \approx 0.6065$

38) $m = \frac{1}{30}$, $\mu = 30$, $\sigma = 30$, $(X > 15) = e^{-\frac{15}{30}} = e^{-0.5} \approx 0.6065$

39) $m = \frac{1}{10}$, $\mu = 10$, $\sigma = 10$, $P(X > 20) = e^{-\frac{20}{10}} = e^{-2} \approx 0.1353$

40) $m = \frac{1}{1000}$, $\mu = 1000$, $\sigma = 1000$, $P(X > 500) = e^{-\frac{500}{1000}} = e^{-0.5} \approx 0.6065$

41) One visitor is expected every 10 seconds.

42) For five visitors, it would take $5 \times 10 = 50$ seconds on average.

43) $P(X < 3) = 1 - e^{-\frac{3}{10}} \approx 0.2592$. The graph would show an exponential curve with the area to the left of $x = 3$ shaded to represent this probability.

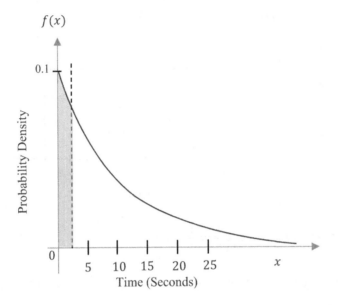

44) $P(X > 15) = 1 - P(X < 15) = e^{-\frac{15}{10}} \approx 0.2231$. The graph would show an exponential curve with the area to the right of $x = 15$ shaded.

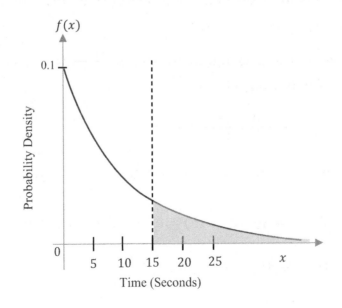

45) Solve $0.8 = 1 - e^{-\frac{t}{10}}$ for t, which gives $t \approx 16.1$ seconds.

46) Yes, as long as visitors arrive independently.

47) One call is expected every 5 minutes.

48) For four calls, it would take $4 \times 5 = 20$ minutes on average.

49) $P(X < 2) = 1 - e^{-\frac{2}{5}} \approx 0.3297$.
The graph would show an exponential curve with the area to the left of $x = 2$ shaded to represent this probability.

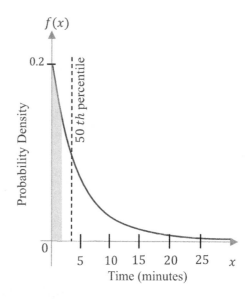

50) $P(X > 10) = 1 - P(X < 10) = e^{-\frac{10}{5}} \approx 0.1353$.
The graph would show an exponential curve with the area to the right of $x = 10$ shaded.

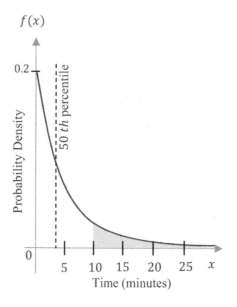

51) Solve $0.5 = 1 - e^{-\frac{t}{5}}$ for t, which gives $t \approx 3.4657$ minutes.

52) Yes, because calls are independent and random.

53) The rate parameter m (or λ) for the given exponential distribution $X \sim Exp(0.25)$ is 0.25.

54) The PDF $for\ X \sim Exp(0.25)$ is $f(x) = 0.25e^{-0.25x}$ for $x \geq 0$.

55) The CDF for $X \sim Exp(0.25)$ is $F(x) = 1 - e^{-0.25x}$ for $x \geq 0$.

56)

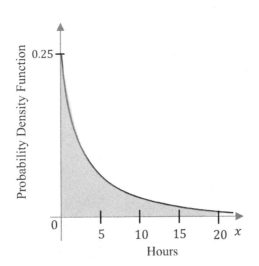 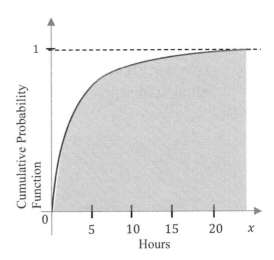

The left graph is the Probability Density Function (PDF), which shows the likelihood of the time between events at any given point. The shaded area under the curve from 0 to a specific point x represents the probability of an event happening before that time. The height of the curve starts at 0.25 when $x = 0$ and decreases as x increases, approaching zero.

The right graph is the Cumulative Distribution Function (CDF), which shows the cumulative probability of an event happening by a certain time x. The shaded area under the curve increases as x increases, approaching 1, which indicates certainty. The point where the CDF crosses a specific probability value (such as 0.7) corresponds to the percentile of interest.

57) $P(X < 4) = F(4) = 1 - e^{-0.25 \times 4} = 1 - e^{-1} \approx 0.6321$

58) For the 30th percentile p, set $F(p) = 0.3$. Solve $0.3 = 1 - e^{-0.25p}$ to get $p \approx 1.4266$ hours.

59) The median m is found by setting $F(m) = 0.5$. Solve $0.5 = 1 - e^{-0.25m}$ to get $m \approx 2.7726$ hours.

60) For any exponential distribution, the mean is always larger than the median. Here, the mean $\mu = \frac{1}{\lambda} = 4$ hours, which is larger than the median ≈ 2.7726 hours.

61) It means that the test score is higher than 75% of the scores in the distribution.

62) 2

63) 1

64) 68%

65) $z = \frac{120-100}{15} = \frac{20}{15} \approx 1.33$.

Using the z −table, $P(Z < 1.33) \approx 0.9082$, so there is about a 90.82% chance.

66) ≈ -0.675

67) -2

68) The z −score is 1.5. This tells us that the student scored better than the percentage of students that fall below a $z -$ score of 1.5 , which is approximately 93.32% of the class.

69) If the probability of on-time arrival is 0.123, the probability of it being late (the area to the right of the on-time arrival in a normal distribution) is $1 - 0.123 = 0.877$.

70) If the area to the right (temperatures above the degree) is 0.543, the area to the left (at or below the degree) is $1 - 0.543 = 0.457$.

71) Calculate the $z -$ score for $520\,ml$: $z = \frac{520-500}{15} \approx 1.33$. Using a standard normal distribution table, the probability of $z < 1.33$ is about 0.9082. Therefore, the probability of more than $520\,ml$ is $1 - 0.9082 = 0.0918$.

72) Calculate the z −score for 65 inches: $z = \frac{65-68}{3} = -1$

The probability of $z < -1$ is 0.1587, so 15.87% of the population is shorter than 65 inches.

73) Find the $z-$score that corresponds to the top 10%, which is the 90th percentile, $z \approx 1.28$. $Score = 1.28 \times 200 + 1050 \approx 1306$

So, the minimum score required for the scholarship is about 1306.

74) Calculate the $z-$score for 5 years: $z = \frac{5-4}{0.5} = 2$

The probability of $z < 2$ is 0.9772. Thus, the probability of a product lasting more than 5 years is $1 - 0.9772 = 0.0228$.

CHAPTER

6 Sampling Distributions

Topics that you'll learn in this chapter:

- ☑ Sampling Concepts
- ☑ Sampling Distributions of Sample Means and Proportions
- ☑ Central Limit Theorem for Sample Means
- ☑ Central Limit Theorem for Sums
- ☑ Sampling Distribution of Sample Variance

183

Sampling Concepts

- Sampling is a statistical process of selecting a subset of individuals from a population to estimate characteristics of the whole population.

- **Step-by-Step Guide: Implementing Sampling**

  - Define the Population: Clearly identify the population from which the sample is to be drawn.

  - Choose a Sampling Method: Depending on the research question, decide on the most appropriate sampling technique (e.g., random, stratified, systematic).

  - Determine the Sample Size: Decide on the size of the sample, which affects the accuracy of the results.

  - Execute the Sampling Process: Follow the chosen methodology to select the sample.

  - Analyze and Infer: Analyze the sample data and infer conclusions about the entire population.

Examples:

Example 1. A researcher wants to survey college students' opinions on a new campus policy. They decide to use stratified sampling by major to ensure all fields of study are represented. How should they proceed?

Solution: Divide the population of students into strata based on their major.

Randomly select a proportionate number of students from each stratum.

Conduct the survey within these selected groups.

Example 2. In a factory, a quality control manager wants to test every 10th item coming off the assembly line for defects, using systematic sampling. What steps should they take?

Solution: Start from a random point in the order of production.

Select every 10th item from that starting point for inspection.

Continue the process periodically to ensure consistent quality checks.

Sampling Distributions of Sample Means and Proportions

- When you take a sample and compute its mean, that mean is a point estimate of the population mean. If you repeat this process multiple times with different samples, the distribution of these sample means is the sampling distribution of the sample mean.

- **Step-by-Step Guide: Sampling Distribution of Sample Means**

  - Determine the population mean μ and standard deviation σ.

  - For each sample of size n, calculate the sample mean $\bar{x}$.

  - The mean of the sampling distribution of the sample mean is μ, and the standard deviation (standard error) is $\sigma_{\bar{x}} = \frac{\sigma}{\sqrt{n}}$.

- Similar to means, when you calculate the proportion of a certain outcome in a sample, it's an estimate of the population proportion. The distribution of these sample proportions is the sampling distribution of sample proportions.

- **Step-by-Step Guide: Sampling Distribution of Sample Proportions**

  - Identify the population proportion p.

  - For each sample, calculate the sample proportion $\hat{p}$.

  - The mean of the sampling distribution of the sample proportion is p, and the standard error is $\sqrt{\frac{p(1-p)}{n}}$.

Examples:

Example 1. Assume the average weight of a certain fruit in a large orchard is 150 grams with a standard deviation of 20 grams. What is the standard error of the mean for samples of size 30?

Solution: Standard Error $\sigma_{\bar{x}} = \frac{\sigma}{\sqrt{n}} = \frac{20}{\sqrt{30}} \approx 3.65$ grams.

Example 2. In a city, 40% of voters favor a particular policy. If a sample of 100 voters is taken, what is the standard error of the sample proportion?

Solution: Standard Error for Proportions $= \sqrt{\frac{p(1-p)}{n}} = \sqrt{\frac{0.4(0.6)}{100}} \approx 0.049$.

Central Limit Theorem for Sample Means

Key points and formulas include:

- **Central Limit Theorem:** It states that as the sample size n increases, the distribution of the sample means $\bar{X}$ approaches a normal distribution, regardless of X's original distribution. This is mathematically expressed as $\bar{X} \sim N(\mu_x, \frac{\sigma_x}{\sqrt{n}})$, where μ_x is the mean and σ_x is the standard deviation of X.

- $Z-$**Score for Sample Means:** Each sample mean $\bar{X}$ has a corresponding $z-$score different from the $z-$score of X. The formula to calculate the $z-$score of a sample mean is: $z = \frac{\bar{X} - \mu_x}{\frac{\sigma_x}{\sqrt{n}}}$

- **Standard Error:** The standard deviation of $\bar{X}$, known as the standard error of the mean, is given by: $\sigma_{\bar{x}} = \frac{\sigma}{\sqrt{n}}$

- **Calculating Probability:** To find the probability of $\bar{X}$ falling within a specific range, the 'normalcdf' function is used with the formula:
$$normalcdf(lower\ bound, upper\ bound, \mu_x, \frac{\sigma}{\sqrt{n}})$$

- **Determining Percentiles:** The 'invNorm' function is used to find percentiles for sample means. The formula is:
$$k = invNorm(percentile, \mu_x, \frac{\sigma}{\sqrt{n}})$$
Here, k represents the desired percentile.

- **Notice:** The probabilities and Percentiles in the solutions would be calculated using a normal distribution calculator or statistical software to obtain precise values.

Example:

Suppose the waiting time at a clinic is normally distributed with a mean of 30 minutes and a standard deviation of 8 minutes. For a sample of 50 patients, what is the probability that their average waiting time is more than 32 minutes?

Solution: The standard error is $\frac{\sigma}{\sqrt{n}} = \frac{8}{\sqrt{50}} \approx 1.13$ minutes.

Calculate the $Z-$score: $Z = \frac{32 - 30}{1.13} \approx 1.77$.

Using standard normal distribution tables, find the probability corresponding to $Z = 1.77$, which gives the probability that the average waiting time is more than 32 minutes.

Central Limit Theorem for Sums

- The CLT for Sums applies to a random variable X with any type of distribution, whether it is known or unknown.

- As the sample size n increases, the sum of these samples ΣX tends to be normally distributed.

- The resulting normal distribution is characterized by:
  - **Mean:** $n \times \mu_X$ (the original mean multiplied by the sample size).
  - **Standard Deviation:** $\sqrt{n} \times \sigma_X$ (the original standard deviation multiplied by the square root of the sample size).

- **Z −Score for Sums:** For any particular sum Σx, the z −score is calculated using $z = \frac{\Sigma x - n\mu_X}{\sqrt{n}\sigma_X}$.

- **Probabilities and Percentiles:**

  $normalcdf\,(lower\ value, upper\ value, n \times mean, \sqrt{n} \times standard\ deviation)$

  $invNorm\,(percentile, n \times mean, \sqrt{n} \times standard\ deviation)$

- **Notice:** Use a normal distribution calculator or statistical software to obtain precise values.

Example:

Suppose we have a factory production line, and the time it takes to assemble a product is normally distributed with a mean of 5 minutes and a standard deviation of 1 minute. A sample of 100 products is taken.
Find the probability that the total assembly time for the 100 products is more than 520 minutes.

Solution: Let Y represent the assembly time for one product. We have: $\Sigma Y \sim N(100 \times 5, \sqrt{100} \times 1)$.

The mean of the total assembly times $= n \times \mu_Y = 100 \times 5 = 500$ minutes.

The standard deviation of the total assembly times $= \sqrt{n} \times \sigma_Y = 10 \times 1 = 10$ minutes.

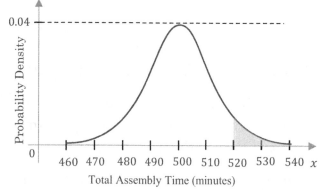

Total Assembly Time (minutes)

To find $P(\Sigma Y > 520)$, we calculate it using the normal distribution:

$normalcdf\,(520, 1E99, 500, 10) = 0.02275$ or 2.275%

Calculate Sampling Distribution of Sample Variance

- The Sampling Distribution of Sample Variance is a statistical concept that describes how the variance of a sample varies from sample to sample.

- Sample Variance: It is the measure of how spread out the values in a sample are around the mean. The formula for sample variance s^2 is:
$$s^2 = \frac{1}{n-1}\sum_{i=1}^{n}(x_i - \bar{x})^2$$
where n is the sample size, x_i are the individual sample points, and $\bar{x}$ is the sample mean.

- Why $n-1$: The $n-1$ in the denominator (instead of n) makes s^2 an unbiased estimator of the population variance.

- **Properties of the Sampling Distribution of Sample Variance**

  - Chi-Squared Distribution: For a normal population, the sampling distribution of sample variance follows a chi-squared distribution with $n-1$ degrees of freedom.

  - Expectation: The expected value of the sample variance is equal to the population variance.

  - Variance: The variance of the sampling distribution of the sample variance is $\frac{2\sigma^4}{n-1}$, where σ^2 is the population variance.

Examples:

Example 1. Assume the life span of a particular electronic component is normally distributed with a variance of 16 square years. What is the distribution of the sample variance for samples of size 10?

Solution: The sample variance s^2 follows a chi-squared distribution with $10 - 1 = 9$ degrees of freedom.
The expected value of s^2 is the population variance, which is 16 square years.

Example 2. From a normally distributed population with a variance of 25 square units, a researcher takes a sample of 20 units. What is the expectation and variance of the sample variance?

Solution: The expected value of the sample variance is the population variance, 25 square units.

The variance of the sampling distribution of the sample variance is $\frac{2\sigma^4}{n-1} = \frac{2\times25^2}{20-1} \approx$ 65.79 square units.

Chapter 6: Practices

✎ **Answer the questions.**

1) Why is random sampling important in statistics?

2) What is the difference between a sample and a population?

3) Define stratified sampling.

4) What is sampling error?

5) A teacher wants to understand the average time students spend on homework. She randomly selects 30 students from each grade level in her high school. What sampling method is this, and why is it beneficial?

6) A company wants to evaluate employee satisfaction. They randomly select 10% of their employees from each department and conduct interviews. What type of sampling is this, and how does it help?

7) A city council wants to gauge public opinion on a proposed park renovation. They choose to use stratified sampling based on neighborhoods. How should they carry out this survey?

8) A company intends to assess employee satisfaction across its various departments. They decide to implement stratified sampling by department. What steps should they follow?

9) A school district plans to evaluate parent attitudes towards new educational technologies. They opt for stratified sampling based on the grade levels of their children. What approach should they take?

10) A health research team is studying dietary habits in a metropolitan area. They decide to use stratified sampling by age groups. How should they proceed with their research?

✎ **Solve and answer the questions (Sampling distributions).**

11) If a high school survey finds that 120 out of 300 sampled students participate in extracurricular activities, how is the sample proportion calculated and what does it represent in terms of sampling distribution?

12) In a study to understand online learning preferences, 500 students are randomly surveyed, and 250 of them prefer online classes. What does the standard error of the sample proportion tell us in this context?

13) A math teacher is interested in estimating the average algebra test score of students in her class. She plans to take multiple random samples of 30 students each to calculate their average scores. Given that the entire class (the population) has an average score of 75 with a standard deviation of 10, what will be the mean and the standard error of the sampling distribution of these sample means?

14) A researcher wants to determine the average amount of time high school students spend on homework daily. She selects a sample of 50 students and calculates that they spend an average of 2 hours per day on homework. If the standard deviation of the time spent on homework in the student population is 30 minutes (0.5 hours), what are the mean and the standard error of the sampling distribution of the sample means when the study is repeated with different samples of 50 students each?

✎ **Answer the questions (Sampling distributions).**

15) A researcher is studying the average height of high school basketball players. She randomly selects 40 players and records their heights. How does this relate to the concept of the sampling distribution of the sample mean?

16) In a survey, a statistician wants to estimate the proportion of residents in a town who support a new policy. He randomly surveys 150 residents. What is important about the sampling distribution of the sample proportion in this scenario?

17) A biology teacher collects data on the number of plant species in various $1-$square-meter plots in a forest. She samples 50 plots. What does the central limit theorem imply for her data analysis?

18) A market researcher samples 200 people to determine the proportion who prefer a new soft drink flavor. How does the size of this sample affect the standard error of the sampling distribution of the proportion?

✎ **Answer the questions based on the scenarios (Use a normal distribution calculator or statistical software).**

A survey reported on July 10, 2020, that the average weekly hours spent on online gaming is 20 hours. Assume the standard deviation is 8 hours. Consider a sample of 64 gamers.

19) What are the mean and standard deviation for the sample mean hours spent on gaming?

20) What does the distribution look like?

21) Find the probability that the sample mean hours are more than 19 hours.

22) Find the 95th percentile for the sample mean hours (to one decimal place).

✎ **Solve (Use a normal distribution calculator or statistical software).**

23) The average amount of time it takes high school students to complete a standardized test is normally distributed with a mean of 1.5 hours and a standard deviation of 0.3 hours. A random sample of 40 students is taken. Find the probability that the sample mean time to complete the test is between 1.4 and 1.6 hours.

24) The time spent on daily homework by college students is normally distributed with a mean of 3 hours and a standard deviation of 1 hour. A sample of 30 students is selected randomly. What is the probability that the sample mean time spent on homework is between 2.8 and 3.2 hours?

25) The time it takes to assemble a certain toy is normally distributed with a mean of 30 minutes and a standard deviation of 5 minutes. A random sample of 50 toys is observed. Find the probability that the sample mean assembly time is between 28 and 32 minutes.

26) The amount of time high school students spend on homework each night is normally distributed with a mean of 2 hours and a standard deviation of 0.3 hours. A sample of 70 students is taken. Find the probability that the sample mean time spent is between 1.8 and 2.0 hours.

27) The time it takes for runners to complete a $10K$ race is normally distributed with a mean of 50 minutes and a standard deviation of 6 minutes. A sample of 80 runners is selected. What is the probability that the sample mean completion time is between 49 and 50 minutes?

28) The duration of a particular surgical procedure is normally distributed with a mean of 120 minutes and a standard deviation of 20 minutes. A sample of 25 surgeries is taken. What is the probability that the sample mean duration is between 115 and 125 minutes?

✍ **Answer the questions based on the scenarios (Use a normal distribution calculator or statistical software).**

In a study, the mean weight of a certain breed of dog is $50\,kg$ with a standard deviation of $5\,kg$. A sample of 25 dogs is taken.

29) What are the mean and standard deviation for the sample mean weight.

30) Describe the distribution.

31) Calculate the probability that the sample mean weight is more than $51\,kg$.

32) Determine the 75th percentile for the sample mean weight.

✍ **Answer the questions (Use a normal distribution calculator or statistical software).**

In a survey, the average number of books read by a person in a year is 12 books. Assume the standard deviation is 4 books. A group of 60 people is surveyed.

33) Calculate the mean and standard deviation for the total number of books read by the group. What is the distribution?

34) What is the probability that the total number of books read by the group is between 650 and 750 books?

35) Determine the 80th percentile for the total number of books read by the 60 people.

A study finds the average daily screen time for teenagers is 3 hours with a standard deviation of 1 hour. A sample of 40 teenagers is considered.

36) What are the mean and standard deviation for the total daily screen time for these teenagers? What is the distribution?

37) Find the probability that the total daily screen time is between 100 and 130 hours.

38) Find the 80th percentile for the total screen time for the sample of 40 teenagers.

Use the following information to answer the next 6 questions (Use a normal distribution calculator or statistical software).

In a metropolitan area, a study shows that on average, a commuter spends 20 minutes stuck in traffic. The standard deviation of this time is 3 minutes, and the sample size is 100 commuters.

39) Determine the median, the first quartile, and the third quartile for the sample mean time spent in traffic.

40) Calculate the median, the first quartile, and the third quartile for the total time spent by the sample of commuters in traffic.

41) Calculate the probability that on average, a commuter spends between 19.5 and 20.5 minutes in traffic.

42) Find the value that is two standard deviations above the sample mean traffic time.

43) Determine the Interquartile Range (IQR) for the total time spent in traffic by the sample of commuters.

44) Graph the data calculated in the previous questions.

Answer the questions.

45) What is the expected value of the sample variance for a population with a variance of σ^2 and a sample size of?

46) If the population variance is 16 and a sample of size 10 is taken, what is the expected sample variance?

47) How is the distribution of the sample variance S^2 for a normally distributed population related to the chi-square distribution?

48) A sample of size 25 is taken from a population with a standard deviation of 4. What is the expected value of the sample variance?

✎ Solve.

49) In a study of annual rainfall in a region, it is known that the variance of rainfall is 36 square inches. A meteorologist selects a sample of 30 years. What is the expected value and variance of the sample variance?

50) In a research on the daily energy consumption of households, the variance is found to be 20 square kWh. If a sample of 40 households is taken, what is the expected value and variance of the sample variance?

51) An economist analyzes the variance in monthly expenses of families, which is 50 square dollars. A sample of 15 families is taken. What are the expectation and variance of the sample variance?

52) Imagine that the height of a certain plant species is normally distributed with a variance of 9 square inches. What is the distribution of the sample variance for samples of size 15?

Chapter 6: Answers

1) Random sampling reduces bias and ensures that every individual in the population has an equal chance of being selected, making the sample more representative of the population.

2) A population includes all members of a specified group, while a sample consists of a part of the population selected for analysis.

3) Stratified sampling involves dividing the population into smaller groups, or strata, that share similar characteristics, and then randomly selecting samples from each stratum.

4) Sampling error is the difference between the results obtained from a sample and the actual characteristics of the entire population.

5) This is an example of stratified sampling. The teacher divides the population into strata (grade levels) and then randomly samples from each stratum. This ensures that each grade level is represented in the sample, providing a more accurate reflection of the entire population.

6) This is proportional stratified sampling. The company divides the employees into strata based on departments and then samples a proportion (10%) from each stratum. This method maintains the proportion of each department in the sample, ensuring that all departments are equally represented.

7) The council should first categorize the city's population into strata according to different neighborhoods. Then, they should randomly select a proportionate number of residents from each neighborhood and conduct the survey within these groups.

8) The company needs to divide its employee population into strata based on their department. Next, it should randomly select a representative number of employees from each department to participate in the satisfaction survey.

9) The school district should divide the parent population into strata, each representing a different grade level. They should then randomly select parents from each stratum and conduct the survey to gather their opinions on the new technologies.

10) The research team should first segment the metropolitan population into different strata based on age groups. They would then randomly select individuals from each age group and survey them about their dietary habits.

11) The sample proportion is calculated as: $\frac{120}{300} = 0.4 \ (or \ 40\%)$.

   This proportion represents an estimate of the true proportion of all high school students participating in extracurricular activities. In terms of sampling distribution, if this survey were repeated many times with different samples of 300 students each, the sample proportions would form a distribution. This distribution is centered around the true population proportion and its shape is approximately normal if the sample size is large enough.

12) The standard error of the sample proportion measures the variability of the proportion across different samples. In this scenario, it quantifies how much the proportion of students preferring online classes ($\frac{250}{500} = 0.5 \ or \ 50\%$) is expected to vary from one sample to another. A smaller standard error would indicate that if we were to conduct similar surveys repeatedly, the sample proportions would be more consistently close to the 50% mark, suggesting greater reliability of our sample estimate.

13) The mean of the sampling distribution of the sample means will be the same as the population mean, which is 75. The standard deviation of the sampling distribution of the sample means (Standard Error, SE): $SE = \frac{\sigma}{\sqrt{n}} = \frac{10}{\sqrt{30}} \approx 1.83$

14) The standard deviation of the sampling distribution of the sample means (Standard Error, SE): $SE = \frac{\sigma}{\sqrt{n}} = \frac{0.5}{\sqrt{50}} \approx 0.071$

   So, when the study is replicated with different samples of 50 students, the average time spent on homework will be around 2 hours with a standard error of approximately 0.071 hours. This standard error reflects the variability of the sample mean and indicates how much the average time spent on homework is expected to vary from one sample to another.

15) The average height calculated from the 40 players is a point estimate of the population mean. If the researcher were to repeat this sampling process many times, the means of these samples would form a sampling distribution. According to the central limit theorem, this distribution would be approximately normal if the sample size is large enough.

16) The proportion of residents in the sample who support the policy is an estimate of the true population proportion. The sampling distribution of this sample proportion will be approximately normal, assuming the sample size is sufficiently large, and the population is much larger than the sample (at least 10 times larger).

17) The central limit theorem implies that the distribution of the sample means (average number of species per plot) will tend toward a normal distribution as more plots are sampled, even if the original distribution of species per plot is not normal. This normality assumption allows for more reliable statistical inference from the data.

18) The standard error of the sampling distribution of the proportion decreases as the sample size increases. In this case, a sample size of 200 helps reduce the standard error compared to a smaller sample, leading to a more precise estimate of the population proportion.

19) $\mu_\chi = 20, \sigma_\chi = \frac{8}{\sqrt{64}} = 1$

20) The distribution is approximately normal (central limit theorem).

21) $P(X > 19) \approx normalcdf(19, E99, 20, 1) = 0.84.13$
Notice: The term `E99` is used to represent a very large number, practically approaching infinity. This is a common practice in statistical calculations, especially when using normal distribution functions like `normalcdf`.
In normal distribution calculations, when we want to find the probability of a value being greater than a certain number, we specify the upper limit as a very large number (like `E99`) to effectively cover all possible values greater than our point of interest. In this case, `E99` ensures that the calculation includes all values greater than 18 up to the very end of the right tail of the normal distribution.

22) $k = invNorm(0.95, 20, 1) \approx 21.6\ h$

23) $P(1.4 < X < 1.6) = normalcdf(1.4, 1.6, 1.5, \frac{0.3}{\sqrt{40}}) \approx 0.965$ or 96.5%.

24) $P(2.8 < X < 3.2) \approx normalcdf(2.8, 3.2, 3, \frac{1}{\sqrt{30}}) \approx 0.727$ or 72.7%.

25) $P(28 < X < 32) \approx normalcdf\left(28, 32, 30, \frac{5}{\sqrt{50}}\right) \approx 0.995$ or 99.5%.

26) $P(1.8 < X < 2.0) \approx normalcdf\left(1.8, 2.0, 2, \frac{0.3}{\sqrt{70}}\right) \approx 0.50$ or 50%.

27) $P(49 < X < 50) \approx normalcdf\left(49, 50, 50, \frac{6}{\sqrt{80}}\right) \approx 0.432$ or 43.2%.

28) $P(115 < X < 125) \approx normalcdf\left(115, 125, 120, \frac{20}{\sqrt{25}}\right) \approx 0.7887$ or 78.87%.

29) $\mu_\chi = 50, \sigma_\chi = \frac{5}{\sqrt{25}} = 1$

30) The distribution is approximately normal.

31) $P(X > 51) \approx normalcdf(51, E99, 50, 1) = 0.1587$

32) $k = invNorm\left(0.75, 50, \frac{5}{\sqrt{25}}\right) \approx 50.6kg$

33) The mean sum of books is $\mu_{\Sigma x} = 60 \times 12 = 720$ books, and the standard deviation for the sum is $\sigma_{\Sigma x} = \sqrt{60} \times 4 \approx 31.24$ books. The distribution is normal.

34) The probability that the sum is between 650 and 750 is calculated by:
$$normalcdf(650, 750, 720, 31.24) = 0.819$$

35) The 80th percentile is found by: $invNorm(0.80, 720, 31.24) = 746.29$

36) The mean total screen time is $\mu_{\Sigma x} = 40 \times 3 = 120$ hours, and the standard deviation for the total is $\sigma_{\Sigma x} = \sqrt{40} \times 1 \approx 6.32$ hours. The distribution is normal.

37) The probability for the total being between 100 and 130 hours is calculated by: $normalcdf(100, 130, 120, 6.32) = 94.24$

38) The 80th percentile is calculated by: $invNorm(0.80, 120, 6.32) = 125.32$

39) For the sample mean time spent in traffic:
Median (50th percentile) is equal to the population mean: 20 minutes.
First quartile (25th percentile): $invNorm(0.25, 20, 0.3) = 19.8$ (since $\frac{\sigma}{\sqrt{n}} = \frac{3}{\sqrt{100}} = 0.3$).
Third quartile (75th percentile): $invNorm(0.75, 20, 0.3) = 20.2$.

40) For the total time spent by commuters:
Median (50th percentile) is the sum of the means: $100 \times 20 = 2000$ minutes.
First quartile (25th percentile): $invNorm(0.25, 2000, 30) = 1979.77$ (since $\sqrt{n} \times \sigma = 10 \times 3 = 30$).
Third quartile (75th percentile): $invNorm(0.75, 2000, 30) = 2020.23$.

41) The probability that the average time is between 19.5 and 20.5 minutes:
$$normalcdf(19.5, 20.5, 20, 0.3) = 0.9044$$

42) The value that is two standard deviations above the sample mean is: $20 + 2 \times 0.3 = 20.6$ minutes.

43) Interquartile Range (IQR) for the total time spent in traffic by the sample of commuters: The IQR is approximately 0.405 minutes.

44)

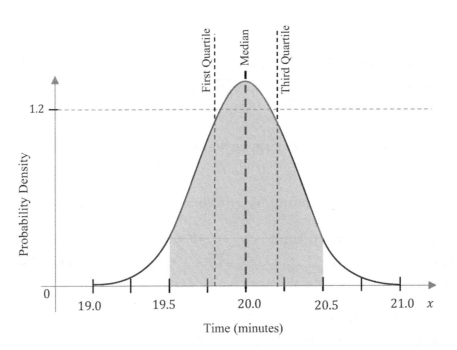

45) $E(S^2) = \sigma^2$ for large sample sizes.

46) $E(S^2) = \sigma^2 = 16$

47) For a normally distributed population, the distribution of S^2 follows a chi-square distribution with $n - 1$ degrees of freedom. $\frac{(n-1)S^2}{\sigma^2} \sim \chi^2_{n-1}$

48) $E(S^2) = \sigma^2 = 4^2 = 16$

49) Expected value of sample variance: 36 square inches.

Variance of sample variance: $\frac{2 \times 36^2}{30-1} = \frac{2592}{29} \approx 89.38$ square inches

50) Expected value of sample variance: 20 square kWh.

Variance of sample variance: $\frac{2 \times 20^2}{40-1} = \frac{800}{39} \approx 20.51$ square kWh.

51) Expected value of sample variance: 50 square dollars.

Variance of sample variance: $\frac{2 \times 50^2}{15-1} = \frac{5000}{14} \approx 357.14$ square dollars.

52) The sample variance s^2 follows a chi-squared distribution with $15 - 1 = 14$ degrees of freedom. The expected value of s^2 is the population variance, which is 9 square inches.

CHAPTER

7 Confidence Intervals

Topics that you'll learn in this chapter:

- ☑ Confidence Intervals for Population Mean
- ☑ Confidence Intervals for Population Proportion
- ☑ Confidence Intervals for Variance
- ☑ Determining Sample Size for Confidence Intervals

205

Confidence Intervals for Population Mean

- Confidence intervals are a range of values used to estimate the true value of a population parameter.
- **Creating Confidence Intervals for Population Mean**
  - Choose a Confidence Level: For example, 95%.
  - Calculate the Sample Mean $\bar{x}$: Find the mean of your sample data.
  - Find the Critical Value: This is a $z-$score (for normal distribution) or a $t-$score (for small sample sizes or unknown population standard deviation) corresponding to the chosen confidence level.
  - Compute the Margin of Error: Multiply the critical value by the standard error.
  - Construct the Interval: Add and subtract the margin of error from the sample mean.
- **Formula for Confidence Interval:**
  - For a population with known standard deviation and large sample size:
  $$\bar{x} \pm z \times \frac{\sigma}{\sqrt{n}}$$
  - For a population with unknown standard deviation or small sample size:
  $$\bar{x} \pm t \times \frac{s}{\sqrt{n}}$$

  where $\bar{x}$ is the sample mean, z or t is the critical value, σ or s is the standard deviation, and n is the sample size.

Example:

A sample of 30 students has an average test score of 78 with a standard deviation of 10. Construct a 95% confidence interval for the population mean test score.

Solution: Since the population standard deviation is known, use a $z-$score. For 95% confidence, $z \approx 1.96$.

The standard error is $\sigma_{\bar{x}} = \frac{\sigma}{\sqrt{n}} = \frac{10}{\sqrt{30}} \approx 1.83$.

Margin of Error: $1.96 \times 1.83 \approx 3.59$.

The confidence interval is 78 ± 3.59, or $[74.41, 81.59]$.

Confidence Intervals for Population Proportion

- Confidence intervals for population proportion are used to estimate the proportion of a population that has a certain characteristic, based on a sample.

- **Key Concepts**
  - Population Proportion (P): The proportion of the population that exhibits a particular attribute.
  - Sample Proportion ($\hat{p}$): The proportion in a sample that exhibits the attribute, calculated as $\hat{p} = \frac{x}{n}$, where x is the number of successes and n is the sample size.
  - Confidence Level: The probability that the interval contains the population proportion (commonly set at 95% or 99%).
  - Margin of Error: The amount of error allowed in the estimate of p.

- **Constructing Confidence Intervals for Population Proportion**
  - Calculate $\hat{p}$ from the sample data.
  - Choose a Confidence Level: such as 95% or 99%.
  - Calculate the Standard Error: For proportion, it is $\sqrt{\frac{\hat{p}(1-\hat{p})}{n}}$.
  - Find the Critical Value: Use a $z-$score for large sample sizes.
  - Compute the Margin of Error: Multiply the standard error by the critical value.
  - Construct the Interval: Add and subtract the margin of error from $\hat{p}$.

- Formula for Confidence Interval: $\hat{p} \pm z \times \sqrt{\frac{\hat{p}(1-\hat{p})}{n}}$

  where $\hat{p}$ is the sample proportion, z is the $z-$score corresponding to the desired confidence level, and n is the sample size.

Example:

In a survey of 200 people, 120 said they prefer online shopping. Construct a 95% confidence interval for the population proportion.

Solution: Sample proportion $\hat{p}$ is $\frac{120}{200} = 0.6$.

For a 95% confidence level, z value is approximately 1.96.

Standard error is $\sqrt{\frac{0.6(1-0.6)}{200}} \approx 0.034$.

Margin of Error: $1.96 \times 0.034 \approx 0.067$.

The confidence interval is 0.6 ± 0.067, or $[0.533, 0.667]$.

Confidence Intervals for Variance

- Confidence intervals for variance are statistical tools used to estimate the range within which the true variance of a population is expected to fall, based on a sample variance.

- **Key Concepts**
  - Population Variance (σ^2): The variance of the entire population.
  - Sample Variance (s^2): The variance calculated from a sample.
  - Chi-Squared Distribution: Used because the sample variance follows a chi-squared distribution if the population is normally distributed.
  - Degrees of Freedom: Equal to $n-1$, where n is the sample size.

- **Constructing Confidence Intervals for Variance**
  - Calculate Sample Variance (s^2): Obtain the sample variance from your sample data.
  - Choose a Confidence Level: Typically, 95% or 99%.
  - Determine the Chi-Squared Values:
    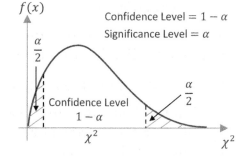
    - For the chosen confidence level, find $\chi^2_{\frac{\alpha}{2}}$ and $\chi^2_{1-\frac{\alpha}{2}}$ using the Chi-Square distribution table.
    - The degrees of freedom (df) is $n-1$, where n is the sample size.
  - Construct the Interval: Use the following formula to construct the confidence interval for variance: $\left(\frac{(n-1)s^2}{\chi^2_{1-\frac{\alpha}{2}}}, \frac{(n-1)s^2}{\chi^2_{\frac{\alpha}{2}}}\right)$.

    Here, n is the sample size, s^2 is the sample variance, and the χ^2 values correspond to the chosen confidence level and degrees of freedom.

Example:

A sample of 15 measurements has a variance of 20. Construct a 95% confidence interval for the population variance.

Solution: Degrees of freedom $df = n - 1 = 15 - 1 = 14$.

For a 95% confidence level, find $\chi^2_{0.025}$ and $\chi^2_{0.975}$ for 14 degrees of freedom from chi-squared tables. Suppose $\chi^2_{0.025} = 5.629$ and $\chi^2_{0.975} = 26.119$.

The confidence interval is $\frac{14 \times 20}{26.119} \approx 10.72$, $\frac{14 \times 20}{5.629} \approx 49.74$.

Determining Sample Size for Confidence Intervals

- In statistics, determining the appropriate sample size is crucial for constructing reliable confidence intervals. An adequately sized sample ensures that the interval is narrow enough to be useful while maintaining the desired confidence level.

- **Sample Size Formulas**

  - For Means: $n = \left(\frac{z \cdot \sigma}{E}\right)^2$, where n is the sample size, z is the $z - score$ corresponding to the desired confidence level, σ is the population standard deviation, and E is the margin of error.

  - For Proportions: $n = \frac{z^2 \cdot p \cdot (1-p)}{E^2}$, where p is the estimated proportion, and other symbols are as defined above.

- **Step-by-Step Guide: Determining Sample Size**

  - Define the Confidence Level: Decide on the confidence level.
  - Estimate the Population Variability: Use a pilot study or historical data to estimate σ or p.
  - Set the Margin of Error: Decide on the maximum acceptable error.
  - Calculate the Sample Size: Use the appropriate formula for means or proportions.

Examples:

Example 1. For a survey estimating a population mean, where the population standard deviation is estimated at 5, and the desired margin of error is 1 at a 95% confidence level, calculate the required sample size.

Solution: For a 95% confidence level, z is approximately 1.96.

$$n = \left(\frac{1.96 \times 5}{1}\right)^2 = 96.04$$

The required sample size is approximately 97 (rounded up).

Example 2. In a study to estimate a population proportion, if the estimated proportion is 0.5, the desired margin of error is 0.05 at a 99% confidence level, determine the sample size needed.

Solution: For a 99% confidence level, z is approximately 2.58.

$$n = \frac{2.58^2 \times 0.5 \times (1 - 0.5)}{0.05^2} = 665.64$$

The required sample size is approximately 666 (rounded up).

Chapter 7: Practices

✍ Calculate the confidence interval for the population mean.

1) A survey of 40 office workers finds that the average time spent on lunch break is 35 minutes with a standard deviation of 5 minutes. Construct a 95% confidence interval for the population mean lunch break duration.

2) A group of 50 gym members have an average weekly workout duration of 6 hours with a standard deviation of 1.2 hours. Construct a 95% confidence interval for the population mean workout duration.

3) In a study of 45 coffee shops, the average number of daily customers is found to be 110 with a standard deviation of 15. Construct a 95% confidence interval for the population mean number of daily customers.

4) A random sample of 35 patients at a clinic shows an average recovery time from a common cold of 8.5 days with a standard deviation of 2 days. Construct a 95% confidence interval for the population mean recovery time.

✍ Use the following information to answer the next five exercises.

The standard deviation of the heights of adult giraffes in a national park is known to be approximately 10 inches. We wish to construct a 95 percent confidence interval for the mean height of adult giraffes. We measure thirty adult giraffes. The sample mean is 190 inches, and the sample standard deviation is 8 inches.

5) Identify the following:

a. $\bar{x} =$ _____   b. $\sigma =$ _____   c. $n =$ _____

6) Define the random variables X and $\bar{X}$.

7) Which distribution should you use for this problem?

8) Construct a 95% Confidence Interval, and graph it.

9) Impact of Increasing Sample Size to 500?

✍ **Use the following information to answer the next eight exercises.**

Evaluate the average study time for undergraduate students at Autumn University during finals week. Assume the following information for a sample:
- Sample Mean ($\bar{x}$): 3.2 hours
- Sample Standard Deviation (s): 0.8 hours
- Sample Size (n): 40 students

10) How much area is in both tails (combined)? $\alpha =$ _____

11) How much area is in each tail? $\frac{\alpha}{2} =$ _____

12) Identify the following specifications:

  a. Lower limit   b. Upper limit   c. Error bound

13) The 95 percent confidence interval is _____.

14) Fill in the blanks on the graph with the areas, upper and lower limits of the confidence interval, and the sample mean.

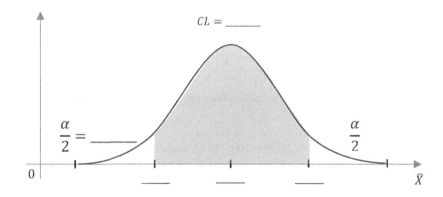

15) In one complete sentence, explain what the interval means.

16) Using the same mean, standard deviation, and level of confidence, suppose that n were 69 instead of 40. Would the error bound become larger or smaller? How do you know?

17) Using the same mean, standard deviation, and sample size, how would the error bound change if the confidence level were reduced to 90 percent? Why?

✎ **Use the following information to answer the question.**

In a study evaluating the battery life (in hours) of a new model of laptops, researchers have recorded the maximum battery life under normal usage conditions. The battery life of a laptop is a critical factor for consumers, especially for those who are frequently on the move. Each laptop model undergoes rigorous testing to ensure it meets industry standards. For a new line of laptops to be launched, the average battery life must meet or exceed a certain threshold. The table below shows the battery life recorded for a random selection of laptop models from a given manufacturer.

Table of Battery Life Records			
Laptop Model	Battery Life (Hours)	Laptop Model	Battery Life (Hours)
101	4.1	106	6.7
102	5.8	107	4.9
103	6.3	108	5.5
104	4.5	109	6.0
105	5.1	110	5.2

18) Find a 95 percent confidence interval for the true (population) mean of the battery lives for these laptops. Assume that the population standard deviation is $\sigma = 0.245$.

🖎 **Calculate the confidence interval for the population proportion**.

19) A classroom of 150 students was surveyed about their preference for morning or afternoon classes. 90 students expressed a preference for morning classes. Construct a 95% confidence interval for the proportion of students preferring morning classes.

20) During a local fair, 180 attendees were asked if they enjoyed the event. 162 attendees said they did. Construct a 95% confidence interval for the proportion of attendees who enjoyed the fair.

21) A group of 250 coffee drinkers was questioned on their preference for decaffeinated coffee. 75 said they prefer decaffeinated. Construct a 95% confidence interval for the proportion of decaffeinated coffee drinkers.

22) Out of 500 people in a town, 350 say they have a pet at home. Construct a 95% confidence interval for the proportion of people in the town who have pets.

🖎 **Use the following information to answer the next five exercises**.

A university cafeteria is evaluating the efficiency of its lunch service. It aims to reduce the time students spend in line before receiving their meal. A study group randomly surveyed 50 students. They found the average waiting time to be 20 minutes, with a sample standard deviation of 4 minutes.

23) Identify the following:
a. $\bar{x} = $ _____   b. $s_x = $ _____   c. $n = $ _____   d. $n - 1 = $ _____

24) Define the random variables X and $\bar{X}$ in words.

25) Which distribution should you use for this problem?

26) Construct a 95 percent confidence interval for the population mean waiting time. State the confidence interval, sketch the graph, and calculate the error bound.

27) Explain in complete sentences what the confidence interval means.

✎ **Use the following information to answer the next thirteen exercises.**

A local library holds a reading program where children are given a list of books to read over the summer. At the end of the program, a random sample of 30 children, consisting of 18 girls and 12 boys, is selected. We are interested in the true proportion of girls who participated in the reading program.

28) What is being counted?

29) In words, define the random variable X.

30) Calculate the following:

a. $x =$ _____   b. $n =$ _____   c. $\hat{p} =$ _____

31) State the estimated distribution of X. $X \sim$ _____.

32) How much area is in both tails combined?

33) How much area is in each tail?

34) Calculate the following:

a. lower limit   b. upper limit   c. error bound

35) The 92 percent confidence interval is _____.

36) Fill in the blanks on the graph with the areas, upper and lower limits of the confidence interval, and the sample proportion.

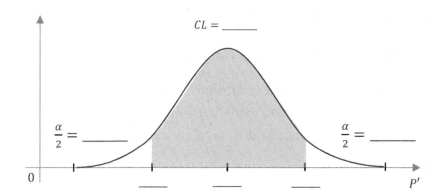

37) In one complete sentence, explain what the interval means.

38) Using the same p' and level of confidence, suppose that n were increased to 100. Would the error bound become larger or smaller? How do you know?

39) Using the same p' and $n = 30$, how would the error bound change if the confidence level were increased to 98 percent? Why?

40) If you decreased the allowable error bound, why would the minimum sample size increase (keeping the same level of confidence)?

✎ Calculate the confidence interval for the population variance.

41) A group of 21 engineers measured the tensile strength of a new metal alloy, resulting in a variance of 12 units squared. Construct a 95% confidence interval for the population variance of the metal's tensile strength.

42) In a quality control test, a batch of 10 manufactured widgets had a variance of 8.5 mm squared. Construct a 95% confidence interval for the population variance of widget sizes.

43) A psychologist studying stress levels assigns a stress score to 18 participants, resulting in a variance of 7.5 score units squared. Construct a 95% confidence interval for the population variance of stress scores.

44) A study on the battery life of a sample of 13 smartphones reveals a variance of 10 hours squared. Construct a 95% confidence interval for the population variance of the smartphones' battery life.

✎ Answer the questions.

45) What is a confidence interval for variance and why would it be used in statistics?

46) How does the size of the sample affect the confidence interval for variance?

47) Which distribution is used to construct a confidence interval for population variance and why?

48) What does a 95% confidence interval for variance tell you about the population variance?

49) Why are degrees of freedom (df) important when calculating the confidence interval for variance?

50) If you have a 99% confidence interval for variance that is very wide, what can you do to narrow it down?

✎ Answer the questions.

51) What does determining sample size for confidence intervals mean in statistics?

52) Why is the margin of error important when determining sample size for confidence intervals?

53) How does the desired level of confidence affect the sample size in a confidence interval?

54) What is the impact of population variability on the sample size for a confidence interval?

55) Can we always use the $z-$score when determining sample size for confidence intervals?

56) If the sample size calculation results in a fraction, should you round up or down?

✏️ Determine the Sample Size for Confidence Intervals.

57) A phone company wants to estimate the average monthly data usage among its customers. The estimated population standard deviation is $2GB$, and they want a margin of error of $0.5GB$ at a 90% confidence level. Calculate the required sample size.

58) A university is studying the average time students spend on homework each week. They estimate the standard deviation to be 3 hours, with a desired margin of error of 0.75 hours at a 99% confidence level. What is the required sample size?

59) A dietician is researching the average calorie intake of adults in a city. The standard deviation is believed to be 500 calories, and the margin of error should be 100 calories for a 95% confidence level. Determine the sample size needed.

60) A tech company is estimating the average lifespan of its hard drives with an estimated standard deviation of 6 months. They aim for a margin of error of 1 month with a 95% confidence level. Calculate the necessary sample size.

61) A marketing team wants to estimate the proportion of customers who prefer online advertisements over traditional billboards. They aim for a margin of error of 0.04 at a 95% confidence level. What sample size is needed if the estimated proportion is 0.6?

62) A health survey intends to find out the proportion of residents in a community practicing regular exercise. They want a margin of error of 0.03 at a 90% confidence level. What is the required sample size if they expect that around 70% of the residents exercise regularly?

63) A car manufacturer wants to estimate the proportion of potential customers interested in electric vehicles. They decide on a margin of error of 0.06 at a 95% confidence level. What sample size should they consider if they estimate that 40% of potential customers are interested?

64) A political analyst wants to predict the proportion of the population that supports a new policy initiative. They require a margin of error of 0.02 at a 99% confidence level. How large should the sample size be if it is believed that 50% of the population supports the initiative?

Chapter 7: Answers

1) 35 ± 1.55, or $[33.45, 36.55]$ 3) 110 ± 4.39, or $[105.61, 114.39]$

2) 6 ± 0.33, or $[5.67, 6.33]$ 4) 8.5 ± 0.67, or $[7.83, 9.17]$

5) a. $\bar{x}$ (sample mean) = 190 inches
   b. σ (population standard deviation) = 10 inches
   c. n (sample size) = 30

6) X represents the height of an adult giraffe in the population.
   $\bar{X}$ represents the mean height of the sample of 30 adult giraffes.

7) Use the t−distribution for this problem since we have a relatively small sample size and the population standard deviation is known.

8) The calculated 95% confidence interval for the mean height of adult giraffes, with a sample mean of 190 inches, sample standard deviation of 8 inches, and a sample size of 30, is approximately (187.01 inches, 192.99 inches). The margin of error for this confidence interval is ±2.99 inches.

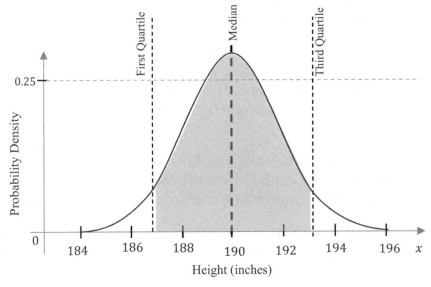

9) The confidence interval would become narrower if we weighed 500 adult giraffes instead of 30. This is because a larger sample size decreases the standard error, leading to a more precise estimate of the population mean and a smaller margin of error.

10) $\alpha = 0.05$ 12) a. ≈ 2.94 hours
                           b. ≈ 3.46 hours

11) $\frac{\alpha}{2} = 0.025$ c. ≈ 0.26 hours

13) approximately 2.94 to 3.46 hours.

14)

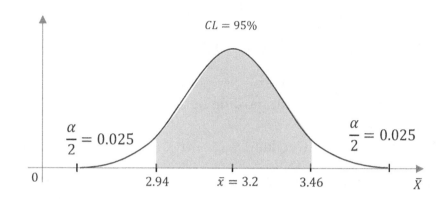

15) The 95% confidence interval means that we are 95% confident that the true average study time for all undergraduate students at Autumn University during finals week lies within this interval.

16) If the sample size were increased to 69 while maintaining the same mean, standard deviation, and level of confidence, the error bound would become smaller due to the increase in sample size, which decreases the standard error of the mean.

17) If the confidence level were reduced to 90 percent with the same mean, standard deviation, and sample size, the error bound would become smaller because the critical value associated with a 90% confidence level is smaller than that for a 95% confidence level, resulting in a narrower confidence interval.

18) First, we need to calculate the sample mean $\bar{x}$ from the given data.
$\bar{x} = \frac{1}{n}\sum_{i=1}^{n} x_i \rightarrow \bar{x} = \frac{4.1+5.8+6.3+4.5+5.1+6.7+4.9+5.5+6.0+5.2}{10} = \frac{54.1}{10} = 5.41\ h$
Then, we find the z −score that corresponds to a 95 percent confidence level (which is approximately 1.96).
Based on the data provided for the battery life of the laptop models and assuming a population standard deviation of 0.245 , the 95 percent confidence interval for the true mean battery life of these laptops is approximately (5.26 hours, 5.56 hours). This means we can be 95 percent confident that the average battery life of all laptops of this type will fall between these two values.
Confidence interval formula: $CI = \bar{x} \pm z \times \left(\frac{\sigma}{\sqrt{n}}\right)$
$CI = 5.41 + 1.96 \times \left(\frac{0.245}{\sqrt{10}}\right) = 5.56, CI = 5.41 - 1.96 \times \left(\frac{0.245}{\sqrt{10}}\right) = 5.26$

19) 0.6 ± 0.078, or approximately $[0.522, 0.678]$

20) 0.9 ± 0.043, or approximately $[0.857, 0.943]$

21) 0.3 ± 0.055, or approximately $[0.245, 0.355]$

22) 0.7 ± 0.041, or approximately $[0.659, 0.741]$

23) a. $\bar{x} = 20$ minutes (sample mean)
    b. $s_x = 4$ minutes (sample standard deviation)
    c. $n = 50$ (sample size)
    d. $n - 1 = 49$ (degrees of freedom)

24) X represents the individual waiting time for each student surveyed.
    $\bar{X}$ is the mean waiting time calculated from the sample of 50 students.

25) The $t-$distribution should be used because the sample size is 50 and we are estimating the population mean based on the sample mean and standard deviation.

26) To construct a 95% confidence interval, we first calculate the margin of error using the $t-$distribution. For a 95% confidence level, the $t-$critical value (t) can be found using the $t-$distribution table:
$$t \approx 2.009, \ df = 50 - 1 = 49$$
Margin of Error (Error Bound) $= t \times \frac{s_x}{\sqrt{n}} = 2.009 \times \frac{4}{\sqrt{50}} = 1.14 \ min$

Then, add and subtract this margin of error from the sample mean to find the confidence interval: $CI = \bar{x} \pm t \times \left(\frac{s}{\sqrt{n}} \right)$

$CI = 20 + 1.14 = 21.14, \ CI = 20 - 1.14 = 18.86$

The graph would show a normal distribution with the confidence interval highlighted. The error bound is the margin of error.

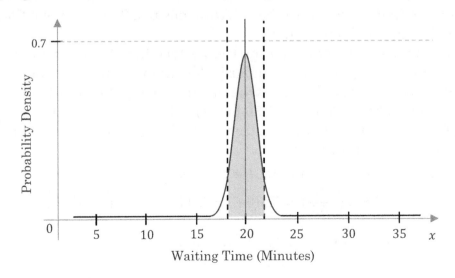

27) The confidence interval represents the range within which we expect the true mean waiting time for all students in the university cafeteria to lie, with 95% certainty. It means that if we were to take many samples and compute confidence intervals for each, about 95% of these intervals would contain the true mean waiting time.

28) The number of girls participating in the reading program.

29) X is the number of girls who participated in the reading program out of the random sample of 30 children.

30) a. $x = 18$ (number of girls).
    b. $n = 30$ (total number of children in the sample).
    c. $\hat{p} = \frac{x}{n} = \frac{18}{30} = 0.6$ (sample proportion of girls)

31) $X \sim binomial(n = 30, \hat{p} = 0.6)$
    Since n is large, we can approximate this distribution as normal for confidence interval calculations: $\hat{p} \sim N\left(p, \sqrt{\frac{\hat{p}(1-\hat{p})}{n}}\right)$

32) 8% $(100\% - 92\%)$ 33) 4% (8% divided by 2)

34) a. Lower limit: approximately 0.4435
    b. Upper limit: approximately 0.7565.
    c. Error bound: approximately 0.1565

35) approximately $[0.4435, 0.7565]$

36)

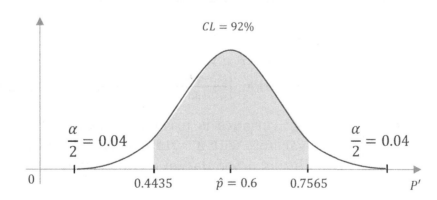

37) The 92% confidence interval suggests that there is a 92% probability that the true proportion of girls who participated in the reading program is between approximately 44.35% and 75.65%.

38) The error bound would become smaller. This is because the error bound for a proportion is given by $z_{\frac{\alpha}{2}}\sqrt{\frac{\hat{p}(1-\hat{p})}{n}}$. Increasing the sample size n reduces the value of $\sqrt{\frac{\hat{p}(1-\hat{p})}{n}}$, thus decreasing the error bound.

39) The error bound would become larger. This is because increasing the confidence level from 92% to 98% increases the critical value $z_{\frac{\alpha}{2}}$. A larger $z_{\frac{\alpha}{2}}$ results in a larger error bound since the error bound is directly proportional to the critical value.

40) Decreasing the allowable error bound would necessitate a larger sample size to achieve the same level of confidence because a smaller error bound implies a narrower interval, which requires more data to maintain the same statistical confidence.

41) Degrees of freedom: $df = n - 1 = 21 - 1 = 20$
Critical values: $\chi^2_{0.025,20} \approx 34.170$, and $\chi^2_{0.975,20} \approx 9.591$
Confidence Interval Calculation: $\left[\frac{(21-1)\times12}{34.17}, \frac{(21-1)\times12}{9.591}\right] \approx [7.02, 25.02]$

42) Degrees of freedom: $df = n - 1 = 10 - 1 = 9$
Critical values: $\chi^2_{0.025,9} \approx 19.023$, and $\chi^2_{0.975,9} \approx 2.700$
Confidence Interval Calculation: $\left[\frac{(10-1)\times8.5}{19.023}, \frac{(10-1)\times8.5}{2.700}\right] \approx [4.02, 28.33]$

43) Degrees of freedom: $df = n - 1 = 18 - 1 = 17$
Critical values: $\chi^2_{0.025,17} \approx 30.191$, and $\chi^2_{0.975,17} \approx 8.672$
Confidence Interval Calculation: $\left[\frac{(18-1)\times7.5}{30.191}, \frac{(18-1)\times7.5}{8.672}\right] \approx [4.22, 14.70]$

44) Degrees of freedom: $df = n - 1 = 13 - 1 = 12$
Critical values: $\chi^2_{0.025,13} \approx 23.337$, and $\chi^2_{0.975,13} \approx 4.404$
Confidence Interval Calculation: $\left[\frac{(13-1)\times10}{23.337}, \frac{(13-1)\times10}{4.404}\right] \approx [5.14, 27.26]$

45) A confidence interval for variance is a range of values that is likely to contain the population variance with a certain level of confidence. It is used to estimate the variability of a population characteristic based on sample data.

46) The size of the sample affects the width of the confidence interval for variance. Generally, larger samples lead to narrower confidence intervals, meaning the estimate is more precise.

47) The chi-squared distribution is used to construct a confidence interval for population variance because variance is always positive and the sampling distribution of the variance of a normally distributed variable follows a chi-squared distribution.

48) A 95% confidence interval for variance suggests that there is a 95% probability that the interval contains the true population variance. It provides a range of plausible values for the population variance based on the sample data.

49) Degrees of freedom (df) are important because they adjust the sample size to account for the fact that variance is calculated from sample data. They are used to determine the correct chi-squared distribution critical values when constructing the confidence interval.

50) To narrow down a wide 99% confidence interval for variance, you could increase the sample size, which decreases the standard error of the variance estimate, or you could choose a lower confidence level, such as 95%, which will produce a narrower interval albeit with less confidence.

51) Determining sample size for confidence intervals means calculating the number of observations needed in a sample to estimate a population parameter (like a mean or proportion) within a desired level of accuracy and confidence.

52) The margin of error defines the range above and below the sample estimate where the true population parameter is expected to lie; it helps determine the precision of the estimate, affecting how large the sample size needs to be.

53) A higher confidence level requires a larger sample size because it increases the $z-$score or $t-$score, which widens the confidence interval, demanding more data to ensure the same level of precision.

54) Greater population variability (standard deviation) increases the required sample size, as more data is needed to achieve a certain margin of error when the data is spread out more.

55) No, the $z-$score is used when the population standard deviation is known and the sample size is large. If the standard deviation is unknown and the sample is small, the $t-$score from the $t-$distribution is used instead.

56) You should always round up, even if the fraction is less than 0.5, to ensure that the sample size is sufficient to achieve the desired margin of error and confidence level.

57) $n = \left(\frac{z \cdot \sigma}{E}\right)^2 \rightarrow n = \left(\frac{1.645 \times 2}{0.5}\right)^2 = 43.29$

The required sample size is approximately 44 (rounded up).

58) $n = \left(\frac{z \cdot \sigma}{E}\right)^2 \rightarrow n = \left(\frac{2.576 \times 3}{0.75}\right)^2 = 106.17$

The required sample size is approximately 107 (rounded up).

59) $n = \left(\frac{z \cdot \sigma}{E}\right)^2 \rightarrow n = \left(\frac{1.96 \times 500}{100}\right)^2 = 96.04$

Required sample size is approximately 97 (rounded up).

60) $n = \left(\frac{z \cdot \sigma}{E}\right)^2 \rightarrow n = \left(\frac{1.96 \times 6}{1}\right)^2 = 138.29$

The required sample size is approximately 139 (rounded up).

61) $n = \frac{z^2 \cdot p \cdot (1-p)}{E^2} \rightarrow n = \left(\frac{1.96}{0.04}\right)^2 \times 0.6 \times (1-0.6) = 576.24$

Required sample size is approximately 577 (rounded up).

62) $n = \frac{z^2 \cdot p \cdot (1-p)}{E^2} \rightarrow n = \left(\frac{1.645}{0.03}\right)^2 \times 0.7 \times (1-0.7) = 631.4$

Required sample size is approximately 632 (rounded up).

63) $n = \frac{z^2 \cdot p \cdot (1-p)}{E^2} \rightarrow n = \left(\frac{1.96}{0.06}\right)^2 \times 0.4 \times (1-0.4) = 256.7$

Required sample size is approximately 257 (rounded up).

64) $n = \frac{z^2 \cdot p \cdot (1-p)}{E^2} \rightarrow n = \left(\frac{2.576}{0.02}\right)^2 \times 0.5 \times (1-0.5) = 4147.36.$

Required sample size is approximately 4148 (rounded up).

8 Hypothesis Testing

Topics that you'll learn in this chapter:

- ☑ Introduction to Null and Alternative Hypotheses
- ☑ Understanding Type I and Type II Errors
- ☑ One-Sample Hypothesis Tests
- ☑ Two-Sample Hypothesis Tests
- ☑ Comparing Two Population Proportions
- ☑ Comparing Two Population Means
- ☑ P-value Interpretation and Decision Making

Introduction to Null and Alternative Hypotheses

- In statistics, hypothesis testing is a method used to make decisions or inferences about a population parameter based on sample data.

- **Null Hypothesis (H_0):** The null hypothesis is a statement of no effect, no difference, or no change. It is the hypothesis that researchers aim to test against.

  - Status Quo: Represents the current accepted fact or the existing state of affairs.
  - Assumption: Initially assumed to be true until evidence suggests otherwise.

- **Alternative Hypothesis (H_1) or (H_a):** The alternative hypothesis is a statement that indicates a change, effect, or difference. It represents what the researcher aims to support or prove.

  - Contrasts with (H_0): It is directly opposite to the null hypothesis.
  - Research Focus: The hypothesis that the study is designed to investigate.

- **Types of Hypotheses**

  - Two-Tailed Test: ($H_0: \mu = \mu_0$) vs. ($H_a: \mu \neq \mu_0$). Tests for any difference from the null value.
  - One-Tailed Test: Either ($H_0: \mu \leq \mu_0$) vs. ($H_a: \mu > \mu_0$) (testing for an increase) or ($H_0: \mu \geq \mu_0$) vs. ($H_a: \mu < \mu_0$) (testing for a decrease).

Examples:

Example 1. A pharmaceutical company claims that its new drug lowers blood pressure more effectively than the current standard. Formulate the null and alternative hypotheses for testing this claim.

Solution: H_0: The new drug is no more effective than the current standard (no change).
H_a: The new drug is more effective than the current standard (positive change).

Example 2. A researcher believes that the average GPA of students in a particular program is higher than the national average of 3.0. State the null and alternative hypotheses.

Solution: H_0: The average GPA of students in the program is 3.0 or lower (status quo).
H_a: The average GPA of students in the program is higher than 3.0.

Understanding Type I and Type II Errors

- In the context of hypothesis testing in statistics, two types of errors can occur when making a decision about a population based on sample data: Type I and Type II errors.

- **Type I Error (False Positive):** A Type I error occurs when the null hypothesis (H_0) is true but is incorrectly rejected.

- Significance Level (α): The probability of committing a Type I error is denoted by α, the significance level of the test (commonly set at 0.05 or 5%).

- **Type II Error (False Negative):** A Type II error happens when the null hypothesis is false but is incorrectly failed to be rejected.

- Beta (β): The probability of committing a Type II error is denoted by β. The power of the test, which is $1 - \beta$, represents the probability of correctly rejecting a false null hypothesis.

- **Balancing Type I and Type II Errors**

- Trade-off: Lowering the probability of one type of error generally increases the probability of the other.

Examples:

Example 1. A new screening test for a disease is being evaluated. What are Type I and Type II errors?

Solution: A Type I error in this context would be a false positive, indicating a patient has the disease when they do not. A Type II error would be a false negative, failing to identify the disease in a patient who actually has it.

Example 2. In a legal trial, what will be the types I and II error?

Solution: In a legal trial, a Type I error corresponds to convicting an innocent person (falsely rejecting the null hypothesis of innocence), while a Type II error relates to acquitting a guilty person (failing to reject the null hypothesis when it is false).

One-Sample Hypothesis Tests

- One-sample hypothesis tests are statistical procedures used to determine whether there is enough evidence in a sample of data to infer that a certain condition is true for the entire population.

- These tests compare the sample mean or proportion to a known population mean or proportion.

- **Key Steps in One-Sample Hypothesis Testing**

  - State the Hypotheses: Null Hypothesis (H_0), Alternative Hypothesis (H_a).

  - Select the Appropriate Test: For means, use a $t-$test if the population standard deviation is unknown; otherwise, use a $z-$test. For proportions, use a $z-$test.

  - Determine the Significance Level (α): Commonly set at 0.05 or 5%.

  - Calculate the Test Statistic: for means is $t = \frac{\bar{x}-\mu_0}{\frac{s}{\sqrt{n}}}$ or $z = \frac{\bar{x}-\mu_0}{\frac{\sigma}{\sqrt{n}}}$ and for proportions is $z = \frac{\hat{p}-p_0}{\sqrt{\frac{p_0(1-p_0)}{n}}}$

  - Make a Decision: Reject H_0 if the test statistic is in the critical region or $p-$value $< \alpha$. Fail to reject H_0 otherwise.

Example:

A company claims that its employees have an average IQ of 110. A sample of 30 employees has an average IQ of 108 with a standard deviation of 15. Test the company's claim at a 5% significance level.

Solution: $H_0: \mu = 110$ and $H_a: \mu \neq 110$. Since the population standard deviation is unknown, use a one-sample $t-$test. Test statistic: $t = \frac{108-110}{\frac{15}{\sqrt{30}}} \approx -0.73$.

Degrees of freedom for a one-sample $t-$test is $n-1$, which is $30-1 = 29$.

Use statistical tables or software to find the $p-$value: 0.471

Since this $p-$value is greater than the significance level of 0.05, we fail to reject the null hypothesis. Therefore, based on this sample, there is no statistically significant evidence to refute the company's claim that the average IQ of its employees is 110.

Two-Sample Hypothesis Tests

- **Types of Two-Sample Tests**

  - Two-Sample t −Test: Compares the means of two independent groups. It can be divided into Equal variance (pooled) t −test and unequal variance (Welch's) t −test.
  - Two-Sample z −Test for Proportions: Compares the proportions between two groups.

- **Steps in Two-Sample Hypothesis Testing**

  - Formulate the Hypotheses: Null Hypothesis, Alternative Hypothesis
  - Choose the Appropriate Test: Based on the type of data (means or proportions) and whether the variances of the two populations are assumed to be equal.
  - Determine the Significance Level (α): Commonly 0.05.
  - Calculate the Test Statistic: For means, use the appropriate t − test formula and for proportions: Use the z −test formula.
  - Make a Decision: Reject H_0 if the test statistic falls in the critical region or if p −value $< \alpha$. Fail to reject H_0 otherwise.

Example:

Two different teaching methods are tested to determine if there is a difference in their effectiveness. The test scores from two independent samples of students are as follows: Group A ($n = 30$, mean= 78, $SD = 10$) and Group B ($n = 35$, mean = 82, $SD = 12$). Test at a 5% significance level.

Solution: $H_0: \mu_A = \mu_B$ and $H_a: \mu_A \neq \mu_B$.
Use Welch's t −test due to different sample sizes and variances. Calculate the test statistic:

$$t = \frac{\bar{x}_1 - \bar{x}_2}{\sqrt{\frac{s_1^2}{n_1} + \frac{s_2^2}{n_2}}} = \frac{78 - 82}{\sqrt{\frac{10^2}{30} + \frac{12^2}{35}}} \approx -1.47$$

Since the sample sizes and standard deviations are different, we use the Welch-Satterthwaite equation to approximate the degrees of freedom.

$$df = \frac{\left(\frac{s_1^2}{n_1} + \frac{s_2^2}{n_2}\right)^2}{\frac{1}{n_1-1}\left(\frac{s_1^2}{n_1}\right)^2 + \frac{1}{n_2-1}\left(\frac{s_2^2}{n_2}\right)^2} = \frac{\left(\frac{10^2}{30} + \frac{12^2}{35}\right)^2}{\frac{1}{30-1}\left(\frac{10^2}{30}\right)^2 + \frac{1}{35-1}\left(\frac{12^2}{35}\right)^2} \approx 62.96$$

Use statistical tables or software to find the p −value: 0.147
Since this p −value is greater than the significance level of 0.05, we fail to reject the null hypothesis. Therefore, there is no statistically significant difference in the effectiveness of the two teaching methods as measured by the test scores of Group A and Group B at the 5% significance level.

Comparing Two Population Proportions

- Comparing two population proportions or means is a common statistical procedure used to determine if there are significant differences between two groups.

  ▪ Objective: To test if the proportions of a certain characteristic in two populations are different.

  ▪ Test Statistic: The z −test is typically used, with the formula:

$$z = \frac{\hat{p}_1 - \hat{p}_2}{\sqrt{p(1-p)\left(\frac{1}{n_1}+\frac{1}{n_2}\right)}}$$

  where $\hat{p}_1$ and $\hat{p}_2$ are the sample proportions, n_1 and n_2 are the sample sizes, and p is the pooled sample proportion.

  ▪ Pooled Sample Proportion:

$$p = \frac{x_1 + x_2}{n_1 + n_2}$$

  where x_1 and x_2 are the number of successes in each sample.

Example:

A survey shows that 120 out of 200 men and 130 out of 250 women prefer a certain brand. Test if there is a significant difference in preference between men and women.

Solution: The results of the two-proportion z − test for comparing brand preferences between men and women are:

Men: $\hat{p}_1 = \frac{120}{200}$, $n_1 = 200$

Women: $\hat{p}_2 = \frac{130}{250}$, $n_2 = 250$

$$p = \frac{x_1 + x_2}{n_1 + n_2} \rightarrow p = \frac{120 + 130}{200 + 250} \rightarrow p = 0.56$$

Use a two-proportion z −test to compare $\hat{p}_1$ and $\hat{p}_2$ Test Statistic:

$$z = \frac{\hat{p}_1 - \hat{p}_2}{\sqrt{p(1-p)\left(\frac{1}{n_1}+\frac{1}{n_2}\right)}} \rightarrow z = \frac{0.6 - 0.52}{\sqrt{0.56(0.44)\left(\frac{1}{200}+\frac{1}{250}\right)}} \rightarrow z \approx 1.699$$

P −value = 0.089

Finally, the p −value is 0.89, if a significance level of 0.05 is considered.

The p −value is greater than your significance level, then the difference is not statistically significant.

Comparing Two Population Means

- Comparing two population proportions or means is a common statistical procedure used to determine if there are significant differences between two groups.

  - Objective: To determine if there is a significant difference between the means of two populations.

  - Tests Used:

    Independent Samples $t-$Test: When the samples are independent and either the population variances are known and equal, or unknown but assumed equal.

    Welch's $t-$Test: When the variances are not assumed to be equal.

  - Test Statistic:

    For equal variances: $t = \frac{\bar{x}_1 - \bar{x}_2}{s_p\sqrt{\frac{1}{n_1}+\frac{1}{n_2}}}$. For unequal variances: $t = \frac{\bar{x}_1 - \bar{x}_2}{\sqrt{\frac{s_1^2}{n_1}+\frac{s_2^2}{n_2}}}$

    where $\bar{x}_1$ and $\bar{x}_2$ are the sample means, s_1^2 and s_2^2 are the sample variances, and s_p is the pooled standard deviation.

Example:

Two groups of students, one taught with method A and the other with method B, take the same test. Group A ($n = 25$, mean $= 78$, $SD = 10$) and Group B ($n = 25$, mean $= 82$, $SD = 12$). Test if there is a significant difference in means.

Solution: we can use an independent two-sample $t-$test.
H_0: There is no difference in the means of the two groups. (i.e., $\mu_1 = \mu_2$)
H_a: There is a difference in the means of the two groups. (i.e., $\mu_1 \neq \mu_2$)
The formula for the $t-$statistic in an independent two-sample $t-$test is:
$$t = \frac{\bar{x}_1 - \bar{x}_2}{\sqrt{\frac{s_1^2}{n_1}+\frac{s_2^2}{n_2}}} = \frac{78-82}{\sqrt{\frac{10^2}{25}+\frac{12^2}{25}}} = -1.2$$

Since the sample sizes are equal, the degrees of freedom is: $df = (n_1 + n_2 - 2) = 25 + 25 - 2 = 48$

The $p-$value for this test is approximately 0.2360. Since this $p-$value is greater than the typical significance level of 0.05, we do not reject the null hypothesis. Therefore, there is no statistically significant difference in the test scores between Group A and Group B, as taught by different methods.

P –value Interpretation and Decision Making

- **Understanding P –values:** The p –value is the probability of obtaining test results at least as extreme as the observed results, under the assumption that the null hypothesis is correct.

  - Lower P –value: Indicates stronger evidence against the null hypothesis.
  - Threshold (α): A predefined level of significance (commonly 0.05 or 5%) used to decide whether to reject the null hypothesis.

- **Interpreting P –values:**

  - P –value $< \alpha$: The results are statistically significant. This means there is sufficient evidence to reject the null hypothesis in favor of the alternative hypothesis.
  - P –value $\geq \alpha$: The results are not statistically significant. This means there is insufficient evidence to reject the null hypothesis.

- **Making Decisions Based on P –values**

  - Set the Significance Level: Before conducting the test, decide on the α level (e.g., 0.05).

  - Calculate the P –value: Perform the hypothesis test to find the p –value.

  - Compare P –value and Alpha:
    If p –value $< \alpha$, reject H_0.
    If p –value $\geq \alpha$, fail to reject H_0.

  - Contextual Interpretation: Consider the results in the context of the research question. A statistically significant result may not always be practically significant.

Examples:

Example 1. In a study, the p –value is calculated to be 0.03. If the significance level is set at 0.05, what decision should be made?

Solution: Since $0.03 < 0.05$, the result is statistically significant.
The null hypothesis should be rejected in favor of the alternative hypothesis.

Example 2. A clinical trial reports a p –value of 0.07. If the significance level is 0.05, how should the results be interpreted?

Solution: Since $0.07 \geq 0.05$, the result is not statistically significant. There is insufficient evidence to reject the null hypothesis.

Chapter 8: Practices

✎ **Fill in the correct symbol $(=, \neq, \geq, <, \leq, >)$ for the null and alternative hypotheses.**

We're investigating if the average amount of daily screen time for teenagers is different from 3 hours.

1) $H_0: \mu$ ____ 3 hours

2) $H_a: \mu$ ____ 3 hours

We aim to determine if the average number of cups of coffee consumed by office workers is less than 3 cups per day. How should the hypotheses be stated?

3) $H_0: \mu$ ____ 3 cups

4) $H_a: \mu$ ____ 3 cups

We are researching to see if the average number of books read by adults in a year is different from 5 books.

5) $H_0: \mu$ ____ 5

6) $H_a: \mu$ ____ 5

We want to test if the average time spent on homework by high school students is less than 2 hours per day. What are the null and alternative hypotheses?

7) $H_0: \mu$ ____ 2 hours

8) $H_a: \mu$ ____ 2 hours

A study on dietary habits mentions that 15% of the population in a certain region are vegetarians. Test if the percentage of vegetarians in a specific city within that region is more than 15%. What are the null and alternative hypotheses?

9) $H_0: p$ ____ 0.15

10) $H_a: p$ ____ 0.15

According to a report, 40% of smartphone users utilize health tracking apps. Test if the percentage of users in a specific age group (18 − 25 years) using these apps is greater than 40%. What are the hypotheses?

11) $H_0: p$ _____ 0.40

12) $H_a: p$ _____ 0.40

Our study aims to determine if the average height of adult males in a specific country is different from $175\ cm$.

13) $H_0: \mu$ _____ $175\ cm$

14) $H_a: \mu$ _____ $175\ cm$

It's stated that 10% of high school students participate in musical extracurricular activities. Test if the percentage in a specific high school is higher than 10%. How should the hypotheses be stated?

15) $H_0: p$ _____ 0.10

16) $H_a: p$ _____ 0.10

✍ Explain Type I and Type II errors for each.

17) Suppose the null hypothesis, H_0, is: The new vaccine is effective against a specific virus. State the Type I and Type II errors.

18) Suppose the null hypothesis, H_0, is: The water in a lake is not polluted. State the Type I and Type II errors.

19) Suppose the null hypothesis, H_0, is: The new software update does not contain critical bugs. State the Type I and Type II errors.

20) Suppose the null hypothesis, H_0, is: A new teaching method has no effect on student learning outcomes. State the Type I and Type II errors.

✎ Determine both Type I and Type II errors for the following scenario. Which type of error has the greater consequence.

21) Suppose the null hypothesis, H_0, is: The school's computer lab equipment is functioning correctly on the day of an important exam. Which type of error has the greater consequence, Type I or Type II?

22) Suppose the null hypothesis, H_0, is: The fire alarm system in an office building is operational. Which type of error has the greater consequence?

23) A new smartphone model claims a battery life of at least 24 hours. Describe both the Type I and Type II errors in context. Which error is more serio?

24) A study claims that a new educational program increases student test scores by at least 20%. Describe the Type I and Type II errors. Which error is more serious?

25) Suppose the null hypothesis, H_0, is: The new diet plan has no effect on weight loss. Which type of error has the greater consequence?

26) A new safety protocol in a factory claims to reduce accidents by at least 50%. Describe the Type I and Type II errors. Which error is more serious?

27) Suppose the null hypothesis, H_0, is: The bridge's structural integrity is sound. Which type of error has the greater consequence?

28) A certain brand of air purifier claims to eliminate 99% of airborne bacteria. Describe the Type I and Type II errors. Which is more serious?

✍ **Based on the provided hypotheses, answer the questions and generate a p −value graph.**

29) $H_0: \mu = 10$, $H_a: \mu < 10$

Assume the p −value is 0.0935. What type of test is this?

30) $H_0: \mu \leq 1$, $H_a: \mu > 1$

Assume the p −value is 0.1243. What type of test is this?

31) $H_0: p = 0.5$ $H_a: p \neq 0.5$

Assume the p −value is 0.2564. What type of test is this?

✍ **Based on the provided scenarios, calculate the p −value. Draw a graph that shows the p −value.**

32) A normal distribution has a standard deviation of 2. We want to test the claim that the mean is less than 8. A sample of 25 is taken with a sample mean of 7.4.

$H_0: \mu \geq 8$
$H_a: \mu < 8$

33) A normal distribution has a standard deviation of 5. The claim is that the mean is not equal to 50. A sample of 16 is taken with a sample mean of 53.

$H_0: \mu = 50$
$H_a: \mu \neq 50$

34) A normal distribution has a standard deviation of 3. We test the claim that the mean is greater than 20. A sample of 9 is taken with a sample mean of 21.5.

$H_0: \mu \leq 20$
$H_a: \mu > 20$

35) A normal distribution has a standard deviation of 4. The claim is that the mean is less than10. A sample of 49 is taken with a sample mean of 8.5.

$H_0: \mu \geq 10$
$H_a: \mu < 10$

Determine whether there is sufficient evidence for each scenario?

36) A restaurant claims that, on average, their food delivery time is 30 minutes. To test this claim, a random sample of 25 deliveries was taken, and it was found that the average delivery time for this sample is 32 minutes, with a standard deviation of 5 minutes. The restaurant's claim is being tested at a 1% significance level. Is there enough evidence to conclude that the restaurant's average delivery time is different from 30 minutes?

37) A smartphone manufacturer asserts that, on average, the battery life of their smartphones is 20 hours. To investigate this assertion, a random sample of 50 smartphones was selected. The sample revealed an average battery life of 18 hours, with a standard deviation of 3 hours. The significance level for testing the manufacturer's claim is set at 2.5%. Is there sufficient evidence to conclude that the average battery life of the smartphones is significantly different from the claimed 20 hours?

38) A fitness club asserts that, on average, their members lose 5 pounds in the first month of membership. To investigate this assertion, a random sample of 20 club members was selected. The sample revealed an average weight loss of 4 pounds, with a standard deviation of 2 pounds. The significance level for testing the club's claim is set at 10%. Is there enough evidence to conclude that the average weight loss of the club members is different from the claimed 5 pounds?

39) A car manufacturer maintains that, on average, their cars achieve a fuel efficiency of 30 miles per gallon (*mpg*). A random sample of 35 cars was taken, and it was found that the average fuel efficiency for this sample is 32 *mpg*, with a standard deviation of 4 *mpg*. The manufacturer's claim is being tested at a 3% significance level. Is there sufficient evidence to conclude that the average fuel efficiency of the cars is different from the claimed 30 *mpg*?

40) A teacher asserts that her students' average homework completion time is less than 30 minutes. To investigate this assertion, a random sample of 20 students was selected, revealing an average completion time of 28 minutes, with a standard deviation of 5 minutes. The significance level for testing the teacher's claim is set at 10%. Can it be concluded that the average homework completion time is less than 30 minutes?

✍ Answer the questions based on the scenarios.

41) Is there a significant difference in battery life between two different smartphone brands, Brand *A* and Brand *B*?

Brand *A* has a sample size of 25 with an average battery life of 18 hours and a standard deviation of 3 hours, while Brand *B* has a sample size of 30 with an average battery life of 20 hours and a standard deviation of 4 hours. Test the difference at a 5% significance level.

42) Are there varying effects on weight loss between two different workout routines, Group *X* and Group *Y*?

Group *X* consists of 40 individuals with an average weight loss of $5\,kg$ and a standard deviation of $1\,kg$, while Group *Y* comprises 35 individuals with an average weight loss of $6\,kg$ and a standard deviation of $1.5\,kg$. Test the difference at a 5% significance level.

43) Does the choice of advertising strategy significantly impact product sales?

Strategy *A*, with 50 data points, yielded an average sales figure of $5000 and a standard deviation of $800, while Strategy *B*, with 45 data points, resulted in an average sales figure of $5500 and a standard deviation of $900. Test the difference at a 5% significance level.

44) Is there a significant difference in exam scores between two study methods, Method *X* and Method *Y*?

Method *X* was followed by 28 individuals with an average score of 85 and a standard deviation of 9, while Method *Y* was followed by 32 individuals with an average score of 88 and a standard deviation of 10. Test the difference at a 5% significance level.

45) Two different types of fertilizer are tested to see if there is a significant difference in their effects on plant growth. The heights of two sets of plants are measured: Group A ($n = 20$, $mean = 25\ cm$, $SD = 4\ cm$) and Group B ($n = 25$, $mean = 28\ cm$, $SD = 5\ cm$). Test the difference at a 5% significance level.
Is there a significant difference in the effects of the two types of fertilizer on plant growth?

46) Two different teaching methods are evaluated to see if there is a significant difference in their effectiveness. The test scores for Group M ($n = 22$, $mean = 78$, $SD = 10$) and Group N ($n = 28$, $mean = 82$, $SD = 12$) are assessed. Test the difference at a 5% significance level.
Is there a significant difference in the effectiveness of the two teaching methods?

Determine whether there is a significant difference between the two groups examined in the scenarios.

47) In a study, 45 out of 80 high school students and 75 out of 120 college students reported enjoying online classes. Test if there is a significant difference in the enjoyment of online classes between high school and college students.

48) A health survey found that 300 out of 500 adults aged $30 - 40$ and 350 out of 600 adults aged $41 - 50$ engage in regular exercise. Test if there is a significant difference in exercise habits between the two age groups.

49) A survey was conducted to determine the difference in smartphone usage between teenagers and adults. 150 out of 200 teenagers reported using their smartphones for more than 3 hours a day, while 120 out of 180 adults reported the same. Is there a significant difference in smartphone usage between the two groups?

50) In a market study, 210 out of 300 customers preferred Brand X, and 230 out of 350 customers preferred Brand Y. Is there a significant difference in preference for these brands?

🖎 Determine whether there is a significant difference between the two groups examined in the scenarios.

51) A teacher wants to compare the effectiveness of two teaching methods. Method *A* was used for a class of 30 students who achieved an average test score of 75 with a standard deviation of 10. Method *B* was used for a class of 35 students who achieved an average score of 80 with a standard deviation of 9. Is there a significant difference in the test scores between the two methods?

52) An experiment was conducted to see if a new fertilizer affects plant growth. The control group (20 plants) had an average growth of 15 *cm* with a standard deviation of 2 *cm*, while the treated group (25 plants) had an average growth of 18 *cm* with a standard deviation of 2.5 *cm*. Is the difference in growth significant?

53) A study aims to determine if there is a difference in the average duration of exercise between men and women. 50 men reported an average of 40 minutes with a standard deviation of 15 minutes, and 60 women reported an average of 35 minutes with a standard deviation of 10 minutes. Is there a significant difference?

54) Researchers are comparing sleep duration in two different age groups. Group A (40 participants) averages 7 hours of sleep with a standard deviation of 1 hour, while Group B (35 participants) averages 6.5 hours with a standard deviation of 1.2 hours. Is the difference significant?

✎ Comparing Study Methods.

In a research study to compare the effectiveness of two different study methods on students' exam scores, Method 1 was applied to a group of 50 students, and Method 2 was applied to another group of 45 students. The exam scores were analyzed, and the p −values were calculated.

55) If the p −value obtained for comparing the effectiveness of Method 1 and Method 2 is 0.03, what should be concluded regarding the null hypothesis?

56) If another test comparing a different aspect of the study methods yields a p −value of 0.08, what should be concluded?

✎ Interpret the results and state a conclusion in simple, nontechnical terms.

57) A study was conducted to see if a new teaching method increases the pass rate in a mathematics exam. The pass rate under traditional teaching methods is 70%. The hypothesis test results are:

$H_0: p = 0.70, H_a: p > 0.70, \alpha = 0.05, p$ −value = 0.04

58) A dietary supplement company claims their product reduces the average body weight. The known average weight loss without supplements is $2kg$. The hypothesis test results are:

$H_0: \mu = 2kg, H_a: \mu < 2kg, \alpha = 0.05, p$ −value = 0.03

59) A technology firm claims that their new software reduces the average time to complete a certain task from 5 hours. The hypothesis test results are:

$H_0: \mu = 5$ hours, $Ha: \mu < 5$ hours, $\alpha = 0.10, p$ −value = 0.15

60) A car manufacturer claims that their new model is more fuel efficient than the previous average of 30 miles per gallon (mpg). The hypothesis test results are:

$H_0: \mu = 30\ mpg, Ha: \mu > 30\ mpg, \alpha = 0.01, p$ −value = 0.008

Chapter 8: Answers

1) H_0: $\mu = 3$ hours (The null hypothesis assumes the mean is 3 hours).

2) H_a: $\mu \neq 3$ hours (The alternative hypothesis suggests a different mean from 3 hours).

3) H_0: $\mu \geq 3$ cups (The null hypothesis claims the mean is 3 cups or more).

4) H_a: $\mu < 3$ cups (The alternative hypothesis asserts the mean is less than 3 cups).

5) H_0: $\mu = 5$ books (The null hypothesis posits the mean is 5 books).

6) H_a: $\mu \neq 5$ books (The alternative hypothesis proposes a different mean from 5 books).

7) H_0: $\mu \geq 2$ hours (The null hypothesis assumes the mean time is at least 2 hours).

8) H_a: $\mu < 2$ hours (The alternative hypothesis suggests the mean time is less than 2 hours).

9) H_0 : $p \leq 0.15$ (The null hypothesis assumes that the proportion of vegetarians is at most 15%).

10) H_a: $p > 0.15$ (The alternative hypothesis suggests the proportion is more than 15%).

11) H_0: $p \leq 0.40$ (The null hypothesis posits the proportion of users in this age group is at most 40%).

12) H_a: $p > 0.40$ (The alternative hypothesis proposes the proportion is greater than 40%).

13) H_0: $\mu = 175\ cm$ (The null hypothesis claims the mean is $175\ cm$).

14) H_a: $\mu \neq 175\ cm$ (The alternative hypothesis asserts a different mean from $175\ cm$).

15) H_0: $p \leq 0.10$ (The null hypothesis states the proportion is at most 10%).

16) H_a: $p > 0.10$ (The alternative hypothesis contends the proportion is more than 10%).

17) Type I error: Concluding the vaccine is not effective when, in fact, it is effective. This mistake involves rejecting a true null hypothesis.
Type II error: Concluding the vaccine is effective when it's not. This error occurs by accepting a false null hypothesis.
α = Probability of thinking the vaccine is not effective when it is.
β = Probability of thinking the vaccine is effective when it's not.

18) Type I error: Concluding the water is polluted when it's actually clean, leading to unnecessary actions or panic.
Type II error: Assuming the water is clean when it's actually polluted, which might result in health hazards.
α = Probability of wrongly thinking the water is polluted.
β = Probability of wrongly assuming the water is clean.

19) Type I error: Believing the update has critical bugs when it doesn't, possibly causing delay in implementation.
Type II error: Assuming the update is bug-free when it has critical bugs, leading to potential software failures.
α = Probability of incorrectly identifying critical bugs.
β = Probability of failing to identify existing critical bugs.

20) Type I error: Concluding the teaching method affects learning outcomes when it doesn't, which might lead to unnecessary changes in curriculum.
Type II error: Assuming the teaching method has no effect when it actually does, possibly missing out on improved teaching techniques.
α = Probability of wrongly attributing effects to the method.
β = Probability of not recognizing the actual effects of the method.

21) Type I error: Believing the equipment is malfunctioning when it's actually fine, leading to unnecessary exam rescheduling.
Type II error: Assuming the equipment is fine when it's actually malfunctioning, possibly disrupting the exam.
The error with the greater consequence is Type II, as it directly impacts the exam process.

22) Type I error: Assuming the system is nonfunctional when it works, possibly leading to unnecessary maintenance.
Type II error: Believing the system works when it doesn't, risking safety during a fire.
The error with the greater consequence is Type II, due to the potential safety risks.

23) Type I: A consumer believes the battery life is less than 24 hours when it actually lasts at least 24 hours.

Type II: A consumer believes the battery lasts at least 24 hours when it actually lasts less than that.

The more serious error is Type II, as it can lead to consumer dissatisfaction and potential issues with the phone running out of battery unexpectedly.

24) Type I: Believing the program increases scores by less than 20% when it does increase them by at least 20%.

Type II: Thinking the program increases scores by at least 20% when it actually increases them by less.

The more serious error is Type II, as it can lead to the unnecessary adoption of an ineffective educational program.

25) Type I error: Concluding the diet affects weight loss when it doesn't, potentially misleading consumers.

Type II error: Believing the diet has no effect when it actually does, possibly missing a beneficial health intervention.

The error with the greater consequence depends on context; Type I could mislead many, while Type II could miss a health benefit.

26) Type I: Believing the protocol reduces accidents by less than 50% when it actually does by at least 50%.

Type II: Assuming the protocol reduces accidents by at least 50% when it actually reduces them by less.

The more serious error is Type II, as it can lead to overconfidence in the safety protocol and potentially more accidents if the protocol is not as effective as believed.

27) Type I error: Believing the bridge is unsafe when it's sound, possibly leading to unnecessary closures.

Type II error: Assuming the bridge is safe when it's structurally compromised, risking accidents.

The error with the greater consequence is Type II, due to the potential danger to public safety.

28) Type I: Assuming the purifier eliminates less than 99% of bacteria when it actually does.

Type II: Believing the purifier eliminates 99% of bacteria when it actually eliminates less.

The more serious error is Type II, especially in healthcare settings, as it can lead to a false sense of security regarding air cleanliness.

29) This is a left-tailed test, as the alternative hypothesis is less than the null hypothesis value. The $p-$value indicates the probability of observing a sample mean less than or equal to the observed mean, assuming the null hypothesis is true.

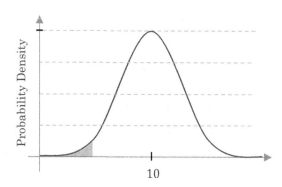

30) This is a right-tailed test, as the alternative hypothesis is greater than the null hypothesis value. The $p-$value represents the probability of observing a sample mean greater than or equal to the observed mean under the null hypothesis.

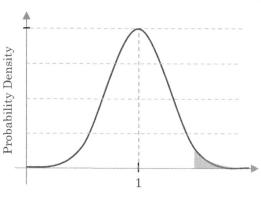

31) This is a two-tailed test, where the alternative hypothesis suggests that the population parameter is not equal to the null hypothesis value. The $p-$ value is the probability of observing a sample proportion at least as extreme as the observed sample proportion, in either direction, assuming the null hypothesis is true.

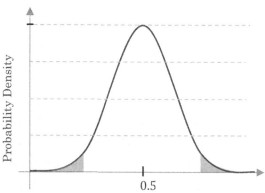

32) Null Hypothesis (H_0): $\mu \geq 8$.
Alternative Hypothesis (H_a): $\mu < 8$.
This setup indicates we are conducting a one-tailed hypothesis test (left-tailed). To find the $p-$value, we use the formula for the $z-$score:
$$z = \frac{\bar{x} - \mu}{\frac{\sigma}{\sqrt{n}}} \rightarrow z = \frac{7.4 - 8}{\frac{2}{\sqrt{25}}} \rightarrow z = \frac{-0.6}{0.4} \rightarrow z = -1.5$$
Use the negative $Z-$score table to find the $P-$value. And the $p-$value calculated is approximately 0.0668.

To graph this, I will:
- Sketch a normal distribution curve.
- Mark the mean at 8.
- Highlight the area to the left of the critical value that corresponds to a $p-$value of 0.0668.

This graphical representation shows that, based on your sample data, there is sufficient evidence to reject the null hypothesis in favor of the alternative hypothesis (H_a): $\mu < 8$, with the calculated $p-$value of 0.0668.

Notice: To accurately create the graph, calculate the probability density ($y-$values) for each $x-$value using the normal distribution equation.

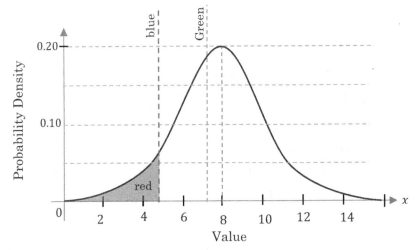

- The curve is centered around the hypothesized mean ($\mu = 8$).
- The critical region, shown in red, represents the area where the calculated $p-$value of approximately 0.0668 lies. This is the region to the left of the critical value.
- The green dashed line marks the sample mean (7.4), which lies within the critical region.
- The blue dashed line indicates the critical value corresponding to the calculated $p-$value.

33) Null Hypothesis (H_0): $\mu = 50$.

Alternative Hypothesis (H_a): $\mu \neq 50$.

This setup indicates we are conducting a two-tailed hypothesis test.

Compute the $z-$score: $z = \frac{\bar{x}-\mu}{\frac{\sigma}{\sqrt{n}}} \rightarrow z = \frac{53-50}{\frac{5}{\sqrt{16}}} \rightarrow z = \frac{3}{1.25} \rightarrow z = 2.4$

Use the $Z-$score table for two tailed test to find the $P-$value. And the

p −value calculated is approximately 0.0164.

To graph this, I will:

- Sketch a normal distribution curve centered at $\mu = 50$.
- Highlight the areas in both tails of the distribution corresponding to the p −value of 0.0164.
- This involves finding the critical values that encapsulate the central region containing $1 - 0.0164 = 0.9836$ of the probability.

This graphical representation shows that, based on your sample data, there is significant evidence to reject the null hypothesis (H_0): $\mu = 50$ in favor of the alternative hypothesis (H_a): $\mu \neq 50$, given the p −value of 0.0164.

Notice: To accurately create the graph, calculate the probability density (y −values) for each x −value using the normal distribution equation.

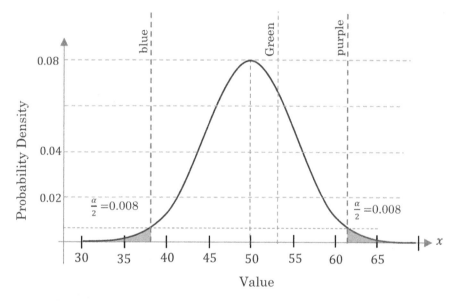

- The normal distribution curve is centered around the population mean ($\mu = 50$).
- The critical regions, shown in red, represent the areas where the p −value is 0.0164 in a two-tailed test. These regions are located in both tails of the distribution.
- The green dashed line marks the sample mean (53), which is used to determine if the sample falls within the critical regions.
- The blue and purple dashed lines indicate the left and right critical values, respectively. These values delineate the boundaries of the central region containing 98.36% of the probability ($1 - 0.0164$).

34) Null Hypothesis (H_0): $\mu \leq 20$.

Alternative Hypothesis (H_a): $\mu > 20$.

This setup indicates we are conducting a one-tailed hypothesis test (Right-tailed).

To find the $p-$value, we use the formula for the $z-$score:

$$z = \frac{\bar{x} - \mu}{\frac{\sigma}{\sqrt{n}}} \rightarrow z = \frac{21.5 - 20}{\frac{3}{\sqrt{9}}} \rightarrow z = \frac{1.5}{1} \rightarrow z = 1.5$$

A $p-$value of 0.0668 indicates that there is a 6.68% chance of observing such a result due to random sampling variability if the null hypothesis is true.

This graphical representation shows that, with a $p-$value of 0.0668, there is marginal evidence to reject the null hypothesis (H_0: $\mu \leq 20$) in favor of the alternative hypothesis (H_a: $\mu > 20$). However, the $p-$value is close to the common significance level of 0.05, suggesting that while there is some evidence against the null hypothesis, it may not be strong enough to conclusively support the alternative hypothesis in more stringent testing scenarios.

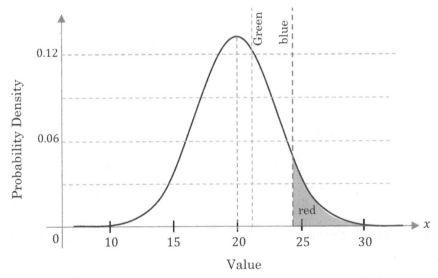

- The curve is centered around the hypothesized mean ($\mu = 20$).
- The critical region, shown in red, represents the area where the calculated $p-$value of approximately 0.0668 lies. This region is located in the right tail of the distribution.
- The green dashed line marks the sample mean (21.5), indicating where your sample mean falls in relation to the distribution.
- The blue dashed line indicates the critical value corresponding to the calculated $p-$value.

35) Null Hypothesis (H_0): $\mu \geq 10$.

Alternative Hypothesis (H_a): $\mu < 10$.

This setup indicates we are conducting a one-tailed hypothesis test (Left-tailed).

To find the p −value, we use the formula for the z −score:

$$z = \frac{\bar{x} - \mu}{\frac{\sigma}{\sqrt{n}}} \rightarrow z = \frac{8.5 - 10}{\frac{4}{\sqrt{49}}} \rightarrow z = \frac{-1.5}{\frac{4}{7}} \rightarrow z = -2.625$$

Use the negative z −score table to find the p −value. And the p −value calculated is approximately 0.0043.

This graphical representation shows that, with a p −value of approximately 0.0043, there is strong evidence to reject the null hypothesis (H_0: $\mu \geq 10$) in favor of the alternative hypothesis (H_a: $\mu < 10$). The sample mean of 8.5 is significantly lower than the hypothesized population mean of 10.

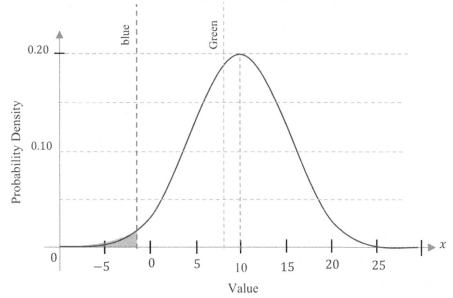

- The curve is centered around the hypothesized mean ($\mu = 10$).
- The critical region, shown in red, represents the area where the calculated p −value of approximately 0.0043 lies. This region is located in the left tail of the distribution.
- The green dashed line marks the sample mean (8.5).
- The blue dashed line indicates the critical value corresponding to the calculated p −value.

36) Null Hypothesis (H_0): The average delivery time of the restaurant (μ) is 30 minutes.

Alternative Hypothesis (H_a): The average delivery time of the restaurant (μ) is not equal to 30 minutes.

Significance Level (α): 1%

Sample Size (n): 25

Sample Mean ($\bar{x}$): 32 minutes

Standard Deviation (σ): 5 minutes

Calculate the test statistic (z −score) using the formula:

$$z = \frac{\bar{x} - \mu}{\frac{\sigma}{\sqrt{n}}} \to z = \frac{32 - 30}{\frac{5}{\sqrt{25}}} \to z = \frac{2}{1} = 2$$

Using a standard normal distribution table or calculator, the critical values for a two-tailed test at a 1% significance level are approximately −2.576 and 2.576.

Compare the test statistic (z) to the critical values: Since 2 is less than 2.576 in absolute value, it falls outside the critical region.

Since the test statistic falls outside the critical region, we fail to reject the null hypothesis (H_0).

At a 1% significance level, there is not enough evidence to conclude that the average delivery time of the restaurant is different from 30 minutes. The sample mean of 32 minutes is within the confidence interval based on the critical values.

37) Null Hypothesis (H_0): The average battery life of the smartphones (μ) is 20 hours.

Alternative Hypothesis (H_a): The average battery life of the smartphones (μ) is not equal to 20 hours.

Significance Level (α): 2.5%

Sample Size (n): 50

Sample Mean ($\bar{x}$): 18 hours

Standard Deviation (σ): 3 hours

Calculate the test statistic (z −score): $z = \frac{\bar{x} - \mu}{\frac{\sigma}{\sqrt{n}}} \to z = \frac{18 - 20}{\frac{3}{\sqrt{50}}} \to z = -4.7$

Using a standard normal distribution table or calculator, the critical values for a two-tailed test at a 2.5% significance level are approximately −1.96 and 1.96.

Compare the test statistic (z) to the critical values: Since −4.71 is less than

−1.96 in absolute value, it falls in the critical region.

Since the test statistic falls in the critical region, we reject the null hypothesis (H_0).

At a 2.5% significance level, there is enough evidence to conclude that the average battery life of the smartphones is significantly different from the claimed 20 hours, as the sample mean of 18 hours falls outside the confidence interval based on the critical values.

38) Null Hypothesis (H_0): The average weight loss of the club's members (μ) is 5 pounds.

Alternative Hypothesis (H_a): The average weight loss of the club's members (μ) is not equal to 5 pounds.

Significance Level (α): 10%

Sample Size (n): 20

Sample Mean ($\bar{x}$): 4 pounds

Standard Deviation (S): 2 pounds

Calculate the test statistic (t −score): $t = \frac{\bar{x}-\mu}{\frac{s}{\sqrt{n}}} \rightarrow t = \frac{4-5}{\frac{2}{\sqrt{20}}} \approx -2.24$

Using the t −distribution table or calculator, the critical values for a two-tailed test at a 10% significance level with degrees of freedom (df) of 19 (20 − 1) are approximately −1.729 and 1.729.

If the absolute value of the calculated t −value is greater than the critical t −value, we reject the null hypothesis.

Since $|t| = 2.24$ is greater than 1.729, we reject the null hypothesis at the 10% significance level. There is sufficient evidence to conclude that the average weight loss of the club members is different from the claimed 5 pounds.

39) Null Hypothesis (H_0): The average fuel efficiency of the cars (μ) is 30 mpg.

Alternative Hypothesis (H_a): The average fuel efficiency of the cars (μ) is not equal to 30 mpg.

Significance Level (α): 3%

Sample Size (n): 35

Sample Mean ($\bar{x}$): 32 mpg

Standard Deviation (S): 4 mpg

Calculate the test statistic (t −score): $t = \frac{\bar{x}-\mu}{\frac{s}{\sqrt{n}}} \rightarrow t = \frac{32-30}{\frac{4}{\sqrt{35}}} \approx 2.96$

Degrees of freedom $df = n - 1 = 35 - 1 = 34$. For a two-tailed test at $\alpha =$

0.03 with $df = 34$, we look up the critical t−value in the t−distribution table. The critical t−values for $\frac{\alpha}{2} = 0.015$ are approximately ± 2.449.

If the absolute value of the calculated t−value is greater than the critical t−value, we reject the null hypothesis.

Since $|t| = 2.96$ is greater than 2.449, we reject the null hypothesis at the 3% significance level. There is sufficient evidence to conclude that the average fuel efficiency of the cars is different from the claimed 30 mpg.

40) Null Hypothesis (H_0): The average homework completion time of the students (μ) is greater than or equal to 30 minutes.
Alternative Hypothesis (H_a): The average homework completion time of the students (μ) is less than 30 minutes.
Significance Level (α): 10%
Sample Size (n): 20
Sample Mean $(\bar{x})$: 28 minutes
Standard Deviation (σ): 5 minutes
Calculate the test statistic (t−score): $t = \frac{\bar{x}-\mu}{\frac{s}{\sqrt{n}}} \rightarrow t = \frac{28-30}{\frac{5}{\sqrt{20}}} \approx -2.83$

Degrees of freedom $df = n - 1 = 20 - 1 = 19$. For a one-tailed test at $\alpha = 0.10$ with $df = 19$, we look up the critical t−value in the t−distribution table. The critical t−value for $\alpha = 0.10$ is approximately -1.33.

If the calculated t−value is less than the critical t−value, we reject the null hypothesis.

Since $t = -1.79$ is less than -1.33, we reject the null hypothesis at the 10% significance level. There is sufficient evidence to conclude that the average homework completion time is less than 30 minutes.

41) Battery Life between Brand A and Brand B:
t−statistic: $t = \frac{18-20}{\sqrt{\frac{3^2}{25}+\frac{4^2}{30}}} \approx -2.116$

Degrees of Freedom: $df = \frac{\left(\frac{s_1^2}{n_1}+\frac{s_2^2}{n_2}\right)^2}{\frac{1}{n_1-1}\left(\frac{s_1^2}{n_1}\right)^2+\frac{1}{n_2-1}\left(\frac{s_2^2}{n_2}\right)^2} = \frac{\left(\frac{3^2}{25}+\frac{4^2}{30}\right)^2}{\frac{1}{25-1}\left(\frac{3^2}{25}\right)^2+\frac{1}{30-1}\left(\frac{4^2}{30}\right)^2} \approx 52.47$

For $\alpha = 0.05$ (two-tailed) and $df \approx 53$, the critical t−value is approximately ± 2.006. Since $|t| = 2.116$ is greater than 2.006, we reject the null hypothesis. There is sufficient evidence to conclude that there is a significant difference in battery life between Brand A and Brand B.

42) Weight Loss between Group X and Group Y:

t−statistic: −3.347

Degrees of Freedom: 57.95

For $\alpha = 0.05$ (two-tailed) and $df \approx 63$, the critical t−value is approximately ±2.000.

Since $|t| = 3.348$ is greater than 2.000, we reject the null hypothesis. There is sufficient evidence to conclude that there is a significant difference in weight loss between Group X and Group Y.

43) Sales Impact of Advertising Strategies A and B:

t−statistic: −2.85

Degrees of Freedom: $88.60 \approx 89$

For $\alpha = 0.05$ (two-tailed) and $df \approx 89$, the critical t−value is approximately ±1.987.

Since $|t| = 2.85$ is greater than 1.987, we reject the null hypothesis. There is sufficient evidence to conclude that the choice of advertising strategy significantly impacts product sales.

44) Exam Scores between Study Method X and Method Y:

t−statistic: −1.223

Degrees of Freedom: $57.95 \approx 58$

For $\alpha = 0.05$ (two-tailed) and $df \approx 58$, the critical t−value is approximately ±2.002.

Since $|t| = 1.223$ is less than 2.002, we fail to reject the null hypothesis. There is not sufficient evidence to conclude that there is a significant difference in exam scores between Method X and Method Y.

45) Effect of Fertilizer Types on Plant Growth (Group A vs. Group B):

t−statistic: −2.24

Degrees of Freedom: $42.98 \approx 43.00$

For $\alpha = 0.05$ (two-tailed) and $df \approx 43$, the critical t−value is approximately ±2.016.

Since $|t| = 2.24$ is greater than 2.016, we reject the null hypothesis. There is sufficient evidence to conclude that there is a significant difference in plant growth between the two fertilizers.

46) Effectiveness of Different Teaching Methods (Group *M* vs. Group *N*):

t−statistic: −1.285

Degrees of Freedom: $47.77 \approx 48$

For $\alpha = 0.05$ (two-tailed) and $df \approx 48$, the critical t−value is approximately ± 2.011.

Since $|t| = 1.286$ is less than 2.011, we fail to reject the null hypothesis. There is not sufficient evidence to conclude that there is a significant difference in the effectiveness of the two teaching methods.

47) High school students: $\hat{p}_1 = \frac{45}{80}$, $n_1 = 80$. College students: $\hat{p}_2 = \frac{75}{120}$, $n_2 = 120$.

$$\hat{p} = \frac{45+75}{80+120} = \frac{120}{200} = 0.6$$

Test Statistic: $z = \dfrac{\hat{p}_1 - \hat{p}_2}{\sqrt{\hat{p}(1-\hat{p})\left(\frac{1}{n_1}+\frac{1}{n_2}\right)}} \rightarrow z = \dfrac{0.5625 - 0.625}{\sqrt{0.6(0.4)\left(\frac{1}{80}+\frac{1}{120}\right)}} \rightarrow z \approx -0.885$

For $\alpha = 0.05$ (two-tailed), the critical z−value is ± 1.96.

Since $|z| = 0.885$ is less than 1.96, we fail to reject the null hypothesis. There is not sufficient evidence to conclude a significant difference in the enjoyment of online classes between high school and college students.

48) Adults $30 - 40$: $\hat{p}_1 = \frac{300}{500}$, $n_1 = 500$. Adults $41 - 50$: $\hat{p}_2 = \frac{350}{600}$, $n_2 = 600$.

$$\hat{p} = \frac{300+350}{500+600} \approx 0.59$$

Test Statistic: $z = \dfrac{\hat{p}_1 - \hat{p}_2}{\sqrt{\hat{p}(1-\hat{p})\left(\frac{1}{n_1}+\frac{1}{n_2}\right)}} \rightarrow z = \dfrac{0.6 - 0.583}{\sqrt{0.59(0.41)\left(\frac{1}{500}+\frac{1}{600}\right)}} \rightarrow z \approx 0.57$

For $\alpha = 0.05$ (two-tailed), the critical z−value is ± 1.96.

Since $|z| = 0.57$ is less than 1.96, we fail to reject the null hypothesis. There is not sufficient evidence to conclude a significant difference in exercise habits between the two age groups.

49) Teenagers: $\hat{p}_1 = \frac{150}{200}$, $n_1 = 200$. Adults: $\hat{p}_2 = \frac{120}{180}$, $n_2 = 120$.

$$\hat{p} = \frac{150+120}{200+180} \approx 0.71$$

Test Statistic: $z = \dfrac{\hat{p}_1 - \hat{p}_2}{\sqrt{\hat{p}(1-\hat{p})\left(\frac{1}{n_1}+\frac{1}{n_2}\right)}} \rightarrow z = \dfrac{0.75 - 0.667}{\sqrt{0.71(0.29)\left(\frac{1}{200}+\frac{1}{180}\right)}} \rightarrow z \approx 1.78$

For $\alpha = 0.05$ (two-tailed), the critical z−value is ± 1.96.

Since $|z| = 1.78$ is less than 1.96, we fail to reject the null hypothesis. There is not sufficient evidence to conclude a significant difference in smartphone usage between teenagers and adults.

50) Brand X: $\hat{p}_1 = \frac{210}{300}$, $n_1 = 300$. Brand Y: $\hat{p}_2 = \frac{230}{350}$, $n_2 = 350$.

$$\hat{p} = \frac{210+230}{300+350} \approx 0.677$$

Test Statistic: $z = \frac{\hat{p}_1 - \hat{p}_2}{\sqrt{\hat{p}(1-\hat{p})\left(\frac{1}{n_1}+\frac{1}{n_2}\right)}} \rightarrow z = \frac{0.7-0.657}{\sqrt{0.677(0.323)\left(\frac{1}{300}+\frac{1}{350}\right)}} \rightarrow z \approx 1.169$

For $\alpha = 0.05$ (two-tailed), the critical $z-$value is ± 1.96.

Since $|z| = 1.17$ is less than 1.96, we fail to reject the null hypothesis. There is not sufficient evidence to conclude a significant difference in brand preference between Brand X and Brand Y.

51) Method A: $\bar{x}_1 = 75$, $s_1 = 10$, $n_1 = 30$. Method B: $\bar{x}_2 = 80$, $s_2 = 9$, $n_2 = 35$

Use a two-sample $t-$test: $t = \frac{\bar{x}_1 - \bar{x}_2}{\sqrt{\frac{s_1^2}{n_1}+\frac{s_2^2}{n_2}}} = \frac{75-80}{\sqrt{\frac{10^2}{30}+\frac{9^2}{35}}} = -2.104$

Degrees of Freedom: $df = \dfrac{\left(\frac{s_1^2}{n_1}+\frac{s_2^2}{n_2}\right)^2}{\frac{1}{n_1-1}\left(\frac{s_1^2}{n_1}\right)^2 + \frac{1}{n_2-1}\left(\frac{s_2^2}{n_2}\right)^2} = \dfrac{(3.33+2.314)^2}{\frac{3.33^2}{29}+\frac{2.314^2}{34}} \approx 59.005 \approx 60$

For $\alpha = 0.05$ (two-tailed) and $df \approx 60$, the critical $t-$value is ± 2.000.

Since $|t| = 2.13$ is greater than 2.000, we reject the null hypothesis. There is sufficient evidence to conclude a significant difference in test scores between the two teaching methods.

52) Control: $\bar{x}_1 = 15$, $s_1 = 2$, $n_1 = 20$. Treated: $\bar{x}_2 = 18$, $s_2 = 2.5$, $n_2 = 25$

Perform a two-sample $t-$test: $t = \frac{\bar{x}_1 - \bar{x}_2}{\sqrt{\frac{s_1^2}{n_1}+\frac{s_2^2}{n_2}}} = \frac{15-18}{\sqrt{\frac{2^2}{20}+\frac{2.5^2}{25}}} = -4.47$

Degrees of Freedom: $df = \dfrac{\left(\frac{s_1^2}{n_1}+\frac{s_2^2}{n_2}\right)^2}{\frac{1}{n_1-1}\left(\frac{s_1^2}{n_1}\right)^2 + \frac{1}{n_2-1}\left(\frac{s_2^2}{n_2}\right)^2} = \dfrac{(0.2+0.25)^2}{\frac{0.2^2}{19}+\frac{0.25^2}{24}} \approx 42.99 \approx 43$

For $\alpha = 0.05$ (two-tailed) and $df \approx 43$, the critical $t-$value is ± 2.016.

Since $|t| = 4.47$ is greater than 2.016, we reject the null hypothesis. There is sufficient evidence to conclude a significant difference in plant growth between the control and treated groups.

53) Men: $\bar{x}_1 = 40$, $s_1 = 15$, $n_1 = 50$. Women: $\bar{x}_2 = 35$, $s_2 = 10$, $n_2 = 60$.

Use a two-sample $t-$test: $t = \dfrac{\bar{x}_1 - \bar{x}_2}{\sqrt{\dfrac{s_1^2}{n_1} + \dfrac{s_2^2}{n_2}}} = \dfrac{40-35}{\sqrt{\dfrac{15^2}{50} + \dfrac{10^2}{60}}} = 2.013$

Degrees of Freedom: $df = \dfrac{\left(\dfrac{s_1^2}{n_1} + \dfrac{s_2^2}{n_2}\right)^2}{\dfrac{1}{n_1-1}\left(\dfrac{s_1^2}{n_1}\right)^2 + \dfrac{1}{n_2-1}\left(\dfrac{s_2^2}{n_2}\right)^2} = \dfrac{(4.5+1.667)^2}{\dfrac{4.5^2}{49} + \dfrac{1.667^2}{59}} \approx 82.61 \approx 83$

For $\alpha = 0.05$ (two-tailed) and $df \approx 83$, the critical $t-$value is ± 1.990.
Since $|t| = 2.013$ is greater than 1.990, we reject the null hypothesis. There is sufficient evidence to conclude a significant difference in the average duration of exercise between men and women.

54) Group A: $\bar{x}_1 = 7$, $s_1 = 1$, $n_1 = 40$. Group B: $\bar{x}_2 = 6.5$, $s_2 = 1.2$, $n_2 = 35$

Conduct a two-sample $t-$test: $t = \dfrac{\bar{x}_1 - \bar{x}_2}{\sqrt{\dfrac{s_1^2}{n_1} + \dfrac{s_2^2}{n_2}}} = \dfrac{7-6.5}{\sqrt{\dfrac{1^2}{40} + \dfrac{1.2^2}{35}}} = 1.945$

Degrees of Freedom: $df = \dfrac{\left(\dfrac{s_1^2}{n_1} + \dfrac{s_2^2}{n_2}\right)^2}{\dfrac{1}{n_1-1}\left(\dfrac{s_1^2}{n_1}\right)^2 + \dfrac{1}{n_2-1}\left(\dfrac{s_2^2}{n_2}\right)^2} = \dfrac{(0.025+0.04114)^2}{\dfrac{0.025^2}{39} + \dfrac{0.04114^2}{34}} \approx 66.48 \approx 67$

For $\alpha = 0.05$ (two-tailed) and $df \approx 70$, the critical $t-$value is ± 2.00.
Since $|t| = 1.945$ is less than 2.00, we fail to reject the null hypothesis. There is not sufficient evidence to conclude a significant difference in sleep duration between the two age groups.

55) Since the $p-$value (0.03) is less than the significance level $(\alpha = 0.05)$, we reject the null hypothesis. There is sufficient evidence to conclude that there is a significant difference in the effectiveness of Method 1 and Method 2.

56) Since the $p-$value (0.08) is greater than the significance level $(\alpha = 0.05)$, we fail to reject the null hypothesis. There is not sufficient evidence to conclude that there is a significant difference in the aspect of the study methods being tested in this particular comparison.

57) Since the $p-$value (0.04) is less than the significance level (0.05), we reject the null hypothesis. This means there is enough evidence to suggest that the new teaching method increases the pass rate in the mathematics exam. Simple Interpretation: The new teaching method appears to help more students pass the mathematics exam compared to the traditional method.

58) Since the p −value (0.03) is less than the significance level (0.05), we reject the null hypothesis. This means there is enough evidence to suggest that the dietary supplement reduces the average body weight by more than the known average of 2 kg.

Simple Interpretation: The dietary supplement seems to help people lose more weight than they would without it.

59) Since the p −value (0.15) is greater than the significance level (0.10), we fail to reject the null hypothesis. This means there is not enough evidence to suggest that the new software reduces the average time to complete the task.

Simple Interpretation: There is not enough evidence to show that the new software makes completing the task any faster than the previous time of 5 hours.

60) Since the p −value (0.008) is less than the significance level (0.01), we reject the null hypothesis. This means there is enough evidence to suggest that the new car model is more fuel efficient than the previous average of 30 mpg.

Simple Interpretation: The new car model seems to be more fuel efficient, using less fuel per mile, compared to the older models.

CHAPTER

9

The Chi-Square Distribution

Topics that you'll learn in this chapter:

- ☑ Chi-Square Distribution
- ☑ Goodness-of-Fit Test
- ☑ Tests of Independence and Homogeneity
- ☑ Tests of Homogeneity
- ☑ Test of a Single Variance

Chi-Square Distribution

- The Chi-Square distribution is a family of distributions that take only positive values and are skewed to the right, particularly prominent in categorical data analysis.

- The shape of the Chi-Square distribution depends on the degrees of freedom (df). As the df increases, the distribution becomes more symmetric.

- Degrees of Freedom is a critical parameter of the Chi-Square distribution, usually denoted as df. It is associated with the number of independent observations in a dataset.

- Chi-Square values are always positive or zero, as they are based on squared quantities.

- The Chi-Square statistic (χ^2) is calculated using the formula: $\chi^2 = \sum \frac{(O_i - E_i)^2}{E_i}$

  where O_i is the observed frequency, and E_i is the expected frequency under the null hypothesis.

- For the chi-square (χ^2) distribution, the population mean is $\mu = df$ (degrees of freedom), and the population standard deviation is $\sigma = \sqrt{2(df)}$

Example:

Suppose you want to test whether a die is fair. You roll it 60 times, and the numbers 1 through 6 appear 10, 10, 5, 10, 15, and 10 times, respectively. Test at the 5% significance level.

Solution: To test whether the die is fair, a chi-square goodness-of-fit test can be used. Here's a brief solution:

Observed Frequencies: 1, 2, 4 and 6 appeared 10 times each; 3 appeared 5 times; 5 appeared 15 times.

Expected Frequencies: If the die is fair, each number should appear $\frac{60}{6} = 10$ times.

And calculate $\chi^2 = \sum \frac{(O_i - E_i)^2}{E_i}$, where O_i and E_i are the observed and expected frequencies, respectively. and $df = 5$ (which is 6 sides -1).

Critical Value: For 5 degrees of freedom at the 5% significance level, it's approximately 11.07 (Look up the chi-square distribution table).

Conclusion: If the chi-square statistic is greater than 11.07, reject the null hypothesis (die is not fair). For your data, the chi-square statistic calculation is:

$$\chi^2 = \frac{(10-10)^2}{10} + \frac{(10-10)^2}{10} + \frac{(5-10)^2}{10} + \frac{(10-10)^2}{10} + \frac{(15-10)^2}{10} + \frac{(10-10)^2}{10} = 5$$

Since 5 is less than 11.07, we do not reject the null hypothesis at the 5% significance level. Therefore, there is not enough evidence to conclude that the die is unfair.

Goodness-of-Fit Test

- The Goodness-of-Fit test is a statistical hypothesis test used to determine how well a set of observed values fits a particular theoretical distribution.

- **Steps in Conducting a Goodness-of-Fit Test**
  - Define Hypotheses:
    H_0: The data follows the specified distribution.
    H_a: The data does not follow the specified distribution.
  - Calculate Expected Frequencies: Based on the theoretical distribution.
  - Compute the Chi-Square Statistic: $\chi^2 = \sum \frac{(O_i - E_i)^2}{E_i}$, where O_i is the observed frequency and E_i is the expected frequency for each category.
  - Determine Degrees of Freedom Usually:
    $df = number\ of\ categories - 1 - number\ of\ parameters\ estimated$.
    Number of Parameters Estimated: This refers to the parameters of the theoretical distribution that are estimated from the data.
  - Compare with Critical Value: Refer to the Chi-Square distribution table to find the critical value for the given degrees of freedom and significance level.
  - Make a Decision: Reject H_0 if the computed χ^2 is greater than the critical value.

Example:

A researcher wants to test if the observed frequencies of four categories (30, 40, 50, 80) fit an expected uniform distribution. Total observations are 200.

Solution: To test if the observed frequencies fit an expected uniform distribution, you can use a chi-square goodness-of-fit test. Here's the solution:
Observed frequencies is 30, 40, 50, 80, and expected frequencies is $\frac{200}{4} = 50$.

And calculate $\chi^2 = \sum \frac{(O_i - E_i)^2}{E_i}$, where O_i and E_i are the observed and expected frequencies, respectively. And $df = 3$ (which is number of categories -1).
Critical Value: Look up the critical value for 3 degrees of freedom at the 5% significance level, which is approximately 7.815.
Conclusion: If the chi-square statistic is greater than 7.815, reject the null hypothesis (the distribution is not uniform).

$$\chi^2 = \frac{(30-50)^2}{50} + \frac{(40-50)^2}{50} + \frac{(50-50)^2}{50} + \frac{(80-50)^2}{50} = 28$$

Since the chi-square statistic (28) is greater than the critical value (7.815), we reject the null hypothesis. Therefore, the observed frequencies do not fit a uniform distribution.

Tests of Independence

- Test of Independence, often conducted using the Chi-Square statistic, help determine whether variables in a contingency table are related.

- **Test of Independence**
  - Objective: To assess whether two categorical variables are independent of each other.
  - Chi-Square Statistic: $\chi^2 = \sum \frac{(O_{ij}-E_{ij})^2}{E_{ij}}$, where O_{ij} is the observed frequency and E_{ij} is the expected frequency in each cell of the contingency table.
  - Expected Frequencies: $E_{ij} = \frac{Total\ of\ Row\ i \times Total\ of\ Column\ j}{Grand\ Total}$
  - Calculation: If the calculated χ^2 value is greater than the critical value from the Chi-Square distribution, reject the null hypothesis of independence.
  - The degrees of freedom: For a chi-square test of independence, the df is:
    $$df = (number\ of\ rows - 1) \times (number\ of\ columns - 1)$$

Example:

A market research company conducts a survey to investigate if there is an association between age group and preference for a type of product. The survey results are as follows:
Objective: To test at the 5% significance level whether age group and product preference are independent.

Age Group	Product A	Product B	Total
Under 30	30	70	100
30 − 60	60	40	100
Over 60	10	90	100
Total	100	200	300

Solution: Under the null hypothesis (Age group and product preference are independent), the expected frequency for each cell is calculated by multiplying the row total and column total and then dividing by the grand total.
For Under 30: Product $A = \frac{100 \times 100}{300} = 33.33$, Product $B = \frac{100 \times 200}{300} = 66.67$
For 30 − 60: Product $A = 33.33$, Product $B = 66.67$
For Over 60: Product $A = 33.33$, Product $B = 66.67$
Use the formula: $\chi^2 = \sum \frac{(O_{ij}-E_{ij})^2}{E_{ij}} = \frac{(30-33.33)^2}{33.33} + \frac{(70-66.67)^2}{66.67} + \frac{(60-33.33)^2}{33.33} + \frac{(40-66.67)^2}{66.67} +$
$\frac{(10-33.33)^2}{33.33} + \frac{(90-66.67)^2}{66.67} = 57.0$
And $df = (r-1)(c-1) = (3-1)(2-1) = 2$
The critical value for 2 degrees of freedom at the 5% level is approximately 5.991. Since the chi-square statistic (57.0) is much greater than the critical value (5.991), we reject the null hypothesis (H_0). This suggests that there is a significant association between age group and product preference, indicating that these variables are not independent.

Tests of Homogeneity

- Tests of Homogeneity, often conducted using the Chi-Square statistic, help determine whether different populations have the same distribution of characteristics.

- **Test of Homogeneity**
  - Objective: To determine if different populations or groups have identical distributions of a categorical variable.
  - Procedure: Similar to the test of independence, using a contingency table.
  - Chi-Square Calculation: Same formula as the test of independence.
  - Interpretation: A significant result suggests that the distributions of the categorical variable are not the same across the populations or groups.
- For both tests, the degrees of freedom (df) are calculated as:
$$df = (number\ of\ rows - 1) \times (number\ of\ columns - 1)$$

Example:

Two schools, School A and School B, are testing the effectiveness of a new teaching method. The schools want to see if the distribution of grades among students is similar in both schools. After implementing

Grade	School A	School B	Total
A	30	40	70
B	50	30	80
C	20	30	50
Total	100	100	200

the new method for a semester, they collect the following data:
Objective: To test at the 5% significance level whether the distribution of grades is homogeneous across the two schools.

Solution: Under the null hypothesis (The distribution of grades is homogeneous across the two schools), the expected frequency for each cell is calculated by multiplying the row total and column total and then dividing by the grand total.
For Grade A: School $A = \frac{70 \times 100}{200} = 35$, School $B = \frac{70 \times 100}{200} = 35$
For Grade B: School $A = \frac{80 \times 100}{200} = 40$, School $B = \frac{80 \times 100}{200} = 40$
For Grade C: School $A = \frac{50 \times 100}{200} = 25$, School $B = \frac{50 \times 100}{200} = 25$
Use the formula: $\chi^2 = \sum \frac{(O_{ij} - E_{ij})^2}{E_{ij}} = \frac{(30-35)^2}{35} + \frac{(40-35)^2}{35} + \frac{(50-40)^2}{40} + \frac{(30-40)^2}{40} +$
$\frac{(20-25)^2}{25} + \frac{(30-25)^2}{25} = 8.43$
And $df = (r-1)(c-1) = (3-1)(2-1) = 2$
The critical value for 2 degrees of freedom at the 5% level is approximately 5.991. Since the chi-square statistic (8.43) is greater than 5.991, we reject the null hypothesis (H_0), suggesting the distribution of grades is not homogeneous across the two schools.

Test of a Single Variance

- A test of a single variance is a statistical method used to determine whether the population variance of a data set is equal to a specified value.

- The test is applicable when the population is normally distributed. And it's used when the focus is on the spread or consistency of the data, such as in quality control scenarios.

- Null Hypothesis (H_0): The population variance σ^2 is equal to a specified value σ_0^2.

- Alternative Hypothesis (H_a): The population variance σ^2 is not equal to σ_0^2 (two-tailed), greater than σ_0^2 (right-tailed), or less than σ_0^2 (left-tailed).

- The test statistic for a single variance Chi-Square test is calculated as:

$$\chi^2 = \frac{(n-1)s^2}{\sigma_0^2}$$

where n is the sample size, s^2 is the sample variance, and σ_0^2 is the hypothesized population variance.

- The degrees of freedom for the test is $n - 1$, where n is the sample size.

Example:

A researcher believes that the variance in heights of a certain plant species is not 15. A sample of 25 plants show a variance of 18 . Conduct a two-tailed test at the 5% level.

Solution: H_0: $\sigma^2 = 15$ and H_a: $\sigma^2 \neq 15$.
The test statistic for a variance test is calculated using the formula:

$$\chi^2 = \frac{(n-1) \times s^2}{\sigma_0^2} = \frac{(25-1) \times 18}{15} = \frac{432}{15} = 28.8$$

In a two-tailed test, the 5% significance level is split into two tails of the distribution: 2.5% in the lower tail and 2.5% in the upper tail. Refer to a chi-square distribution table for the critical values at the 2.5 th and 97.5 th percentiles for 24 degrees of freedom.
The critical value at the 2.5th percentiles is approximately 39.36, and at the 97.5th percentiles is approximately 12.40.
the Chi-Square Statistic (28.8) Falls Within the Range of the Critical Values.

Conclusion: Based on the chi-square test conducted with a sample of 25 plants, where the sample variance was found to be 18, and testing at a 5% significance level, we do not have sufficient evidence to reject the null hypothesis. Therefore, we cannot conclude with confidence that the variance in the heights of the plant species is different from 15.

Chapter 9: Practices

✎ Explain each question.

1) What is the chi-square distribution primarily used for in statistics?

2) How is the shape of the chi-square distribution affected by the degrees of freedom?

3) Can the chi-square distribution take negative values?

4) What is the purpose of a Goodness-of-Fit test in statistics?

5) When performing a Goodness-of-Fit test, what does the null hypothesis typically state?

6) What type of data is appropriate for a Chi-Square Goodness-of-Fit test?

✎ Answer the questions.

7) A teacher wants to test if there is a significant difference in the preferred learning style (visual, auditory, kinesthetic) among her students. She collects data from 60 students.
   What statistical test should the teacher use to analyze this data?

8) In a genetics study, a biologist observes 100 fruit flies, 56 with red eyes and 44 with white eyes. The expected ratio of red to white-eyed fruit flies is $1:1$.
   How can the biologist determine if the observed ratio significantly deviates from the expected ratio?

9) A researcher is studying the relationship between two categorical variables: type of car (sedan, SUV, hatchback) and customer satisfaction (satisfied, neutral, dissatisfied). Data is collected from 300 car owners.
   What should the researcher calculate to understand the association between car type and customer satisfaction?

10) In a survey, 150 participants were asked about their preference for three brands of soap. The observed frequencies are recorded, and the expected frequencies are based on the hypothesis that there is no preference among the brands.
    What is the null hypothesis in this Chi-Square Goodness-of-Fit test?

✍ **Solve.**

11) A researcher wants to know which day of the week teenagers are most active on social media. It is assumed that activity is the same throughout the weekdays.

Day of the Week	Monday	Tuesday	Wednesday	Thursday	Friday
Frequency	15	12	9	9	15

Is there a significant difference in the days teenagers are most active on social media during the weekdays? Test at a 5 percent significance level.

12) A gym wants to know which day each week their members are most likely to work out. The gym management believes that the workouts are evenly distributed throughout the week. Suppose a random sample of 63 gym members were asked on which day of the week they had their longest workout session. The results were distributed as follows:

Days	Number of members
Sunday	9
Monday	12
Tuesday	8
Wednesday	11
Thursday	7
Friday	8
Saturday	8

From the population of gym members, do the days for the longest workout sessions occur with equal frequencies during a week? What type of hypothesis test should be used?

13) Teachers want to know which night each week their students are doing most of their homework. They assume that homework is done uniformly every night from Monday to Sunday. Suppose a random sample of 56 students were asked on which night of the week they did the most homework. The results are distributed as follows:

Night of the Week	Frequency
Sunday	20
Monday	2
Tuesday	3
Wednesday	10
Thursday	2
Friday	6
Saturday	13

At the 1 percent significance level. Does the actual data on which night students do most of their homework differ significantly from the teachers' assumption that homework is done equally every night.

✎ Determine the appropriate test to be used in the next questions.

14) A botanist is analyzing the growth patterns of a new species of plant. She expects that the plants will grow a certain number of centimeters each month. After several months of growth, she measures the actual height of each plant to see if they match her expected growth pattern.

15) A political scientist wants to understand voting behavior in a small town. He hypothesizes that each age group will contribute a certain percentage to the total vote. After the election, he gathers data on the actual percentage that each age group contributed to the total votes.

16) A music producer predicts that sales of different music genres will be distributed in a certain way over the quarter. At the end of the quarter, the producer looks at the actual sales data to test the accuracy of her predictions.

17) A tech company is interested in the relationship between the type of computer (desktop, laptop, tablet) and programming efficiency. A random sample of 500 programmers is taken across these device groups.
What is the appropriate test for analyzing the relationship between the type of computer and programming efficiency?

18) The CEO of a startup is interested in the relationship between marketing budget categories (low, medium, high) and revenue growth percentages. A random sample of 100 startups is taken for the study.
What is the appropriate test for analyzing the relationship between marketing budget categories and revenue growth?

19) A student counselor is interested in the relationship between the number of hours students study and their exam scores. They collect a random sample of 50 students, recording their study hours and exam scores.
What is the appropriate test for analyzing the relationship between study hours and exam scores?

🖎 **Use the following information to answer the next nine questions.**

A fitness coach has predicted the distribution of attendance for his classes based on the sales channels. The actual and expected attendance is noted, and a goodness-of-fit test is performed.

Sales channels	Number of Cases
Online	500
In-Store	300
Partner Retailers	120
Direct Sales	80
Total	1000

Sales channels	Number of Cases	Number Expected (round to two decimal places)
Online	50.0%	500
In-Store	30.0%	
Partner Retailers	10.0%	
Direct Sales	10.0%	
Total	100%	

20) Expected Number of Cases per Sales Channel:

21) Null Hypothesis (H_0):

22) Alternative Hypothesis (H_a):

23) Test Type:

24) Degrees of Freedom (df):

25) Chi-Square Test Statistic:

26) P −Value:

27) Graph the chi-square distribution:

28) Decision:

29) Reason for the Decision:

30) Conclusion:

🔖 **Use the following information to answer the next questions.**

A fitness coach predicts the proportion of attendance for his classes during the week. The expected proportions and the actual attendance for a class of 20 are provided.

Grade	Proportion
A	0.25
B	0.30
C	0.35
D	0.10

Grade	Frequency
A	7
B	7
C	5
D	1

31) Degrees of Freedom (df):

32) Null and Alternative Hypotheses:

33) Chi-Square Test Statistic:

34) P−Value:

35) Conclusion at the 5 Percent Significance Level:

🔖 **Use the following information to answer the questions.**

A hotel chain is interested in the relationship between the length of stay and the type of room booked. A random sample of 200 guests is taken. The results are displayed in a table. The hotel wants to know if a guest's choice in room type is independent of the length of their stay.

Length of Stay	Standard Room	Deluxe Room	Suite	Total
1 − 3 nights	30	25	15	70
4 − 7 nights	40	35	25	100
8 + nights	10	15	5	30
Total	80	75	45	200

36) State the hypotheses:

37) Degrees of Freedom (df):

38) Expected Passengers for 4 − 7 nights in Deluxe Room:

39) Expected Passengers for 8 + nights in Suite:

40) Test Statistic:

41) P−Value:

42) Conclusion at the 5 Percent Level of Significance:

✎ **Solve.**

43) A high school wants to know if there's an association between gender and preference for a specific course (Science, Math, Literature).

Gender	Science	Math	Literature	Total
Male	30	20	10	60
Female	20	30	10	60
Total	50	50	20	120

44) Does the survey data indicate an association between age group (Under 30 and 30 and over) and preference for coffee shops (Shop *A* and Shop *B*)?

Age Group	Shop *A*	Shop *B*	Total
Under 30	40	20	60
30 and over	30	10	40
Total	70	30	100

45) Does the provided data table suggest an association between occupation (Professional, Student) and preference for specific smartphone brands (Brand *X*, Brand *Y*)?

Occupation	Brand *X*	Brand *Y*	Total
Professional	50	30	80
Student	40	40	80
Total	90	70	160

46) Does the preference for a movie genre (Action, Drama) depend on the region (Urban, Rural)?

Region	Action	Drama	Total
Urban	60	40	100
Rural	30	20	50
Total	90	60	150

🖎 **Solve.**

47) A study is conducted to see if smartphone brand preference (Brand *A*, Brand *B*) is the same in two different cities.

City	Brand A	Brand B	Total
City 1	80	120	200
City 2	70	130	200
Total	150	250	400

Is there a difference in smartphone brand preference (Brand *A*, Brand *B*) between City 1 and City 2?

48) To find if the preference for a favorite sport (Football, Basketball) is homogeneous among students in three different schools.

School	Football	Basketball	Total
School *A*	60	40	100
School *B*	50	50	100
School *C*	70	70	100
Total	180	120	300

Do students in Schools *A*, *B*, and *C* have different preferences for sports (Football, Basketball)?

49) Investigating if reading habits (Fiction, Non-Fiction) differ across different age groups (Under 20, 20 − 40, Over 40).

Are the reading habits (Fiction, Non-Fiction) different across the age groups (Under 20, 20 − 40, Over 40)?

Age Group	Fiction	Non-Fiction	Total
Under 20	100	50	150
20 − 40	120	80	200
Over 40	80	120	200
Total	300	250	550

50) Assessing whether job satisfaction (Satisfied, Unsatisfied) is consistent across different industries (Tech, Healthcare, Education).
Is job satisfaction (Satisfied, Unsatisfied) consistent across different industries (Tech, Healthcare, Education)?

Industry	Satisfied	Unsatisfied	Total
Tech	200	100	300
Healthcare	150	150	300
Education	180	120	300
Total	530	370	900

✎ Answer the questions based on the scenarios.

The standard deviation of daily screen time for teenagers is 1.5 hours. A researcher claims that this standard deviation is greater than 1.5 hours.

51) What type of test should be used?

52) State the null and alternative hypotheses.

53) Is this a right-tailed, left-tailed, or two-tailed test?

The standard deviation of weekly exercise hours for adults in a community is 2.2 hours. A health survey of 40 adults finds a standard deviation of 2.5 hours. It is believed that the standard deviation in the community might be different from 2.2 hours.

54) What type of test should be used?

55) State the null and alternative hypotheses.

56) $df = $ _____

The average time spent reading books per week varies among college students. The standard deviation of reading time is known to be 2.3 hours. A random sample of 25 college students shows a standard deviation of reading time of 2.6 hours. A librarian suspects that the variance in reading times is different from the known value.

57) What type of test should be used?

58) What is the test statistic?

59) What is the p−value?

60) What can you conclude at the 5 percent significance level?

✍ Determine if a single variance significantly differs from a hypothesized value.

61) Determine if the variance of the heights of high school basketball

players is different from 15 square inches.

Heights (in inches): $72, 74, 73, 75, 70$

62) Test if the variance of a set of test scores is more than 10.

Scores: $85, 90, 75, 80, 95$

63) Verify if the daily production variance of 18 is not equal to the industry

standard of 20.

Daily Production: $17, 19, 18, 20, 22$

64) Determine if the variance in sleep hours of students is less than 2

hours.

Sleep Hours: $6, 7, 8, 5, 9$

Chapter 9: Answers

1) The chi-square distribution is primarily used for testing hypotheses on categorical data.

2) The shape of the chi-square distribution becomes more symmetric and approaches a normal distribution as the degrees of freedom increase.

3) No, the chi-square distribution is always non-negative, as it is based on squared values.

4) The Goodness-of-Fit test is used to determine if sample data fits a distribution from a population with a specific distribution. Essentially, it tests how well the observed data matches the expected data.

5) The null hypothesis for a Goodness-of-Fit test typically states that there is no significant difference between the observed frequencies and the expected frequencies.

6) The Chi-Square Goodness-of-Fit test is appropriate for categorical data where observations can be classified into discrete categories.

7) The teacher should use the Chi-Square Test for Independence to analyze the data.

8) The biologist can use the Chi-Square Goodness-of-Fit test to determine if the observed ratio significantly deviates from the expected $1:1$ ratio.

9) The researcher should calculate the Chi-Square statistic to understand the association between car type and customer satisfaction.

10) The null hypothesis is that there is no difference in preference for the three soap brands among the participants.

11) The expected frequency is ($\frac{60}{5} = 12$). A Chi-Square statistic of 3.0 is quite small. Typically, the critical value for 4 degrees of freedom at a 0.05 significance level is much larger (around 9.49).
There is no significant difference in the days teenagers are most active on social media during the weekdays based on this data and analysis.

12) To determine if there is a significant difference in the days gym members are most active, a Chi-Square test for goodness of fit can be used.

The total number of observations (gym members) is 63.

The expected frequency for the longest workout sessions, assuming they are evenly distributed throughout the week, is ($\frac{63}{7} = 9$) members per day.

The calculated Chi-Square statistic for the new data is approximately ($\chi^2 \approx 2.23$).

This Chi-Square statistic would be compared against a critical value from a Chi-Square distribution table with 6 degrees of freedom (since there are 7 days -1) at a chosen significance level (commonly 0.05). Given the low value of the Chi-Square statistic, it is likely that there would be no significant difference.

13) To answer this, we would perform a Chi-Square Goodness-of-Fit test with the null hypothesis that homework is done uniformly from Monday to Sunday. We'd expect each night to have an average frequency of $\frac{56}{7} = 8$ since there are 7 days in the week.

The calculated Chi-Square statistic is ($\chi^2 = 34.25$). The expected frequency for each night, under the assumption of uniform distribution, is 8 students per night. There are 6 degrees of freedom since we have 7 categories (days of the week).

To determine if this Chi-Square statistic indicates a significant difference at the 1 percent significance level, we compare it to the critical value from the Chi-Square distribution table for 6 degrees of freedom. Typically, the critical value at the 1 percent significance level for 6 degrees of freedom is around 16.81.

Since our calculated Chi-Square statistic (34.25) is much higher than the critical value, we can conclude that the actual data on which night students do most of their homework differ significantly from the teachers' assumption that homework is done equally every night.

14) The appropriate test would be a t −test for a single sample if the expected growth is a single value, or a Chi-Square goodness of fit test if there are multiple categories of expected growth measurements.

15) The appropriate test would be a Chi-Square goodness of fit test to see if the actual percentages significantly differ from the expected percentages.

16) The appropriate test would be a Chi-Square goodness of fit test to compare the observed sales distribution with the expected distribution.

17) The appropriate test would be a Chi-Square Test for Independence to determine if there is a significant association between the two categorical variables: type of computer and programming efficiency.

18) One-Way ANOVA: The CEO is examining the relationship between a categorical independent variable (marketing budget categories: low, medium, high) and a continuous dependent variable (revenue growth percentages). One-Way ANOVA is suitable for comparing the means of the continuous variable across multiple categories of the independent variable to see if there are statistically significant differences.

19) Pearson's correlation coefficient: The student counselor is interested in the relationship between two continuous variables (study hours and exam scores). Pearson's correlation coefficient measures the strength and direction of the linear relationship between these two variables. If the relationship needs to be modeled, linear regression analysis can also be applied.

20) Online: 500
In-Store: 300
Partner Retailers: 100
Direct Sales: 100

21) The occurrence of product sales follows the distribution of sales channels in the region.

22) The occurrence of product sales does not follow the distribution of sales channels in the region.

23) This is a right-tailed test since the chi-square distribution is not symmetrical and the test statistic is always positive.

24) The degrees of freedom are 3 (number of categories minus one).

25) The chi-square test statistic is 8.0.

26) The $p-$value is approximately 0.046.

27) The graph depicts the chi-square distribution with the test statistic marked and the p −value region shaded.

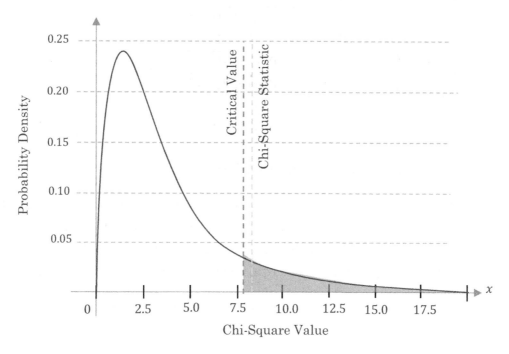

28) Reject the null hypothesis, because the p −value is less than the significance level of 0.05.

29) The p −value is less than the alpha level ($\alpha = 0.05$), indicating that there is a statistically significant difference between the observed and expected sales.

30) It appears that the pattern of product sales in the region does not correspond to the distribution of sales channels. This conclusion is drawn from the chi-square test indicating a significant difference between the observed frequencies and the expected frequencies based on the regional sales channel distribution.

31) There are 4 categories (A, B, C, D), so the degrees of freedom are $4 - 1 = 3$.

32) Null Hypothesis (H_0): The actual class attendance fits the fitness coach's predicted distribution.
Alternative Hypothesis (H_a): The actual class attendance does not fit the fitness coach's predicted distribution.

33) The chi-square test statistic is approximately 2.038.

Grade	Observed (O_i)	Expected (E_i)
A	7	$0.25 \times 20 = 5$
B	7	$0.30 \times 20 = 6$
C	5	$0.35 \times 20 = 7$
D	1	$0.10 \times 20 = 2$

$$\chi^2 = \frac{(7-5)^2}{5} + \frac{(7-6)^2}{6} + \frac{(5-7)^2}{7} + \frac{(1-2)^2}{2} = 2.038$$

34) The $p-$value is approximately 0.565.

35) With a $p-$value of approximately 0.565, which is higher than the significance level of 0.05, we fail to reject the null hypothesis. This means there is no significant difference between the observed attendance and the predicted proportions according to the fitness coach's expectations.

36) H_0: The choice of room type is independent of the length of stay.
H_a: The choice of room type is dependent on the length of stay.

37) $df = (Number\ of\ rows\ -1) \times (Number\ of\ columns\ -1)$

$$= (3-1) \times (3-1) = 2 \times 2 = 4.$$

38) To calculate the expected frequency: $\frac{(Total\ for\ 4-7\ nights \times Total\ for\ Deluxe\ Room)}{Grand\ Total}$

$$Expected = \frac{100 \times 75}{200} = \frac{7500}{200} = 37.5$$

39) To calculate the expected frequency: $\frac{Total\ for\ 8+\ nights \times Total\ for\ Suite}{Grand\ Total}$

$$Expected = \frac{30 \times 45}{200} = \frac{1350}{200} = 6.75$$

40) The chi-square test statistic is approximately 2.72.

41) The $p-$value is approximately 0.605.

42) Since the $p-$value (0.605) is greater than the significance level (0.05), we fail to reject the null hypothesis.
Conclusion: There is not enough evidence to suggest that a guest's choice in room type is dependent on the length of their stay at the 5 percent level of significance.

43) Chi-Square Test Statistic: ($\chi^2 = 4.0$).

P −Value: Approximately 0.135

Degrees of Freedom: ($df = 2$)

Expected Frequencies:

For Science: 25 (both Male and Female)

For Literature: 10 (both Male and Female)

Interpretation:

Since the p −value is approximately 0.135, which is greater than the conventional alpha level of 0.05, we do not have sufficient evidence to reject the null hypothesis.

This suggests that, based on the sample data, there is no significant association between gender and course preference in this high school. The preference for Science, Math, and Literature courses appears to be independent of gender.

44) Chi-Square Test Statistic: (χ^2) is approximately 0.793.

P −Value: Approximately 0.504.

Degrees of Freedom: ($df = 1$).

Expected Frequencies:

For Shop A (Under 30): 42

For Shop B (Under 30): 18

For Shop A (30 and over): 28

For Shop B (30 and over): 12

Interpretation:

With a p −value of approximately 0.504, which is greater than the typical alpha level of 0.05, we do not have sufficient evidence to reject the null hypothesis.

This indicates that, based on the sample data, there is no significant association between age group and coffee shop preference in this survey. The preference for Shop A or Shop B seems to be independent of whether customers are under or over 30 years of age.

45) Chi-Square Test Statistic: (χ^2) is approximately 2.54.

   P −Value: Approximately 0.151.

   Degrees of Freedom: ($df = 1$).

   Expected Frequencies:

   For Brand X (Professionals): 45

   For Brand Y (Professionals): 35

   For Brand X (Students): 45

   For Brand Y (Students): 35

   Interpretation:

   With a p −value of approximately 0.151, which is greater than the conventional alpha level of 0.05, we do not have sufficient evidence to reject the null hypothesis.

   This suggests that, based on this sample data, there is no significant association between occupation (professional or student) and smartphone brand preference (Brand X or Brand Y). The preference for smartphone brands appears to be independent of occupation.

46) Chi-Square Test Statistic: (χ^2) is 0.0.

   P −Value: 1.0.

   Degrees of Freedom: ($df = 1$).

   Expected Frequencies:

   For Action (Urban): 60

   For Drama (Urban): 40

   For Action (Rural): 30

   For Drama (Rural): 20

   Interpretation:

   The p −value of 1.0, which is significantly greater than the typical alpha level of 0.05, indicates that we do not have sufficient evidence to reject This suggests that, based on this sample data, there is no significant association between the region (Urban or Rural) and movie genre preference (Action or Drama). The preference for movie genres appears to be independent of the region.

47) Chi-Square Test Statistic: (χ^2) is approximately 1.0666.

$P-$Value: Approximately 0.353.

Degrees of Freedom: ($df = 1$).

Expected Frequencies:

For City 1: Brand A: 75, Brand B: 125

For City 2: Brand A: 75, Brand B: 125

Interpretation:

With a $p-$value of approximately 0.353, which is greater than the conventional alpha level of 0.05, we do not have sufficient evidence to reject the null hypothesis.

This suggests that, based on this sample data, there is no significant difference in smartphone brand preference (Brand A or Brand B) between the two cities. The preference for smartphone brands appears to be homogeneous across these cities.

48) Chi-Square Test Statistic: (χ^2) is approximately 28.33.

$P-$Value: Approximately 0.0155.

Degrees of Freedom: ($df = 2$) (calculated as $(3 - 1) \times (2 - 1) = 2$).

Expected Frequencies:

For Football: 60 (in each school: School A, B, C)

For Basketball: 40 (in each school: School A, B, C)

Interpretation:

The $p-$value of approximately 0.0155, which is less than the conventional alpha level of 0.05, suggests that we have sufficient evidence to reject the null hypothesis.

This indicates that, based on this sample data, there is a significant difference in sports preference (Football or Basketball) among the students of the three schools. The preference for these sports is not homogeneous across the schools.

49) Chi-Square Test Statistic: (χ^2) is approximately 28.36.

$P-$Value: Approximately (6.96×10^{-7}).

Degrees of Freedom: ($df = 2$) (calculated as $(3 - 1) \times (2 - 1) = 2$).

Expected Frequencies: $E_{ij} = \dfrac{Row\ Total_i \times Column\ Total_j}{Grand\ Total}$

For Fiction: Under 20: 81.82   For Non-Fiction: Under 20: 68.18

$20 - 40$: 109.09 $20 - 40$: 90.91

Over 40: 109.09   Over 40: 90.91

The extremely low p−value (much less than the conventional alpha level of 0.05) suggests that we have sufficient evidence to reject the null hypothesis. This indicates that, based on this sample data, there is a significant difference in reading habits (Fiction or Non-Fiction) among different age groups. The preference for these types of books is not homogeneous across the age groups.

50) Chi-Square Test Statistic: (χ^2) is approximately 17.44.
   P−Value: Approximately (0.000163).
   Degrees of Freedom: ($df = 2$) (calculated as $(3 - 1) \times (2 - 1) = 2$).
   Expected Frequencies: $E_{ij} = \frac{Row\ Total_i \times Column\ Total_j}{Grand\ Total}$

   For Satisfied: Tech: 176.67   For Unsatisfied: Tech: 123.33
   Healthcare: 176.67   Healthcare: 123.33
   Education: 176.67   Education: 123.33

   The p−value of approximately 0.000163, significantly lower than the conventional alpha level of 0.05, suggests that we have sufficient evidence to reject the null hypothesis.
   This indicates that, based on this sample data, there is a significant difference in job satisfaction (Satisfied or Unsatisfied) across the different industries. Job satisfaction appears not to be consistent across Tech, Healthcare, and Education industries.

51) A chi-square test for variance should be used.

52) H_0: $\sigma^2 \leq 1.5^2$ (The standard deviation is less than or equal to 1.5 hours).
   H_a: $\sigma^2 > 1.5^2$ (The standard deviation is greater than 1.5 hours).

53) This is a right-tailed test.

54) A chi-square test for variance should be used.

55) H_0: $\sigma^2 = 2.2^2$ (The standard deviation is 2.2 hours).
   H_a: $\sigma^2 \neq 2.2^2$ (The standard deviation is not 2.2 hours).

56) $df = 40 - 1 = 39$

57) The appropriate test for this scenario is a chi-square test for variance.

58) The calculated test statistic is approximately 30.67.

59) The p −value for this test is approximately 0.827.

60) Since the p −value (0.327) is greater than the significance level of 0.05, we do not have enough evidence to reject the null hypothesis.
This implies that at the 5 percent significance level, we cannot conclude that the variance in reading times among college students is significantly different from the known value of 2.3 hours square.

61) Hypothesis:
$H_0: \sigma^2 = 15$, $H_a: \sigma^2 \neq 15$
Sample variance (s^2):
Calculate the mean: 72.8
Find variance: $s^2 \approx 3.7$
Test statistic (chi-square): $\chi^2 = \frac{(n-1)s^2}{\sigma^2} = \frac{4 \times 3.7}{15} \approx 0.99$
Critical value (from chi-square distribution table for $df = n - 1 = 4$):
For a two-tailed test at the 0.05 significance level, the critical values are 0.484 and 11.143.
Decision: Since 0.99 is within the range (0.484, 11.143), we fail to reject H_0.

62) Hypothesis:
$H_0: \sigma^2 \leq 10$, $H_a: \sigma^2 > 10$
Sample variance (s^2):
Calculate the mean: 85
Find variance: $s^2 = 62.5$
Test statistic (chi-square): $\chi^2 = 25$
Critical value for a one-tailed test with $df = 4$ at the 0.05 level is 9.488.
Decision: the test statistic exceeds 9.488, so reject H_0.

63) Hypothesis:
$H_0: \sigma^2 = 20$, $H_a: \sigma^2 \neq 20$
Sample variance (s^2):
Calculate the mean: 19.2
Find variance: $s^2 = 3.7$
Test statistic (chi-square): $\chi^2 = 0.74$
For a two-tailed test at the 0.05 significance level with degrees of freedom ($df = 4$), the critical values from the chi-square distribution table are approximately 0.484 and 11.143.
Decision: since 0.74 is within the range (0.484, 11.143), we fail to reject the null hypothesis.

64) Hypothesis

$H_0: \sigma^2 \geq 2$, $H_a: \sigma^2 < 2$

Sample variance (s^2):

Calculate the mean: 7

Find variance: $s^2 = 2.5$

For a one-tailed test at the 0.05 significance level with degrees of freedom ($df = 4$), the critical value from the chi-square distribution table is approximately 0.484 ($\chi^2_{0.05,4} \approx 0.484$).

Decision: In this case, since 5 is greater than 0.484, we do not reject the null hypothesis.

10 Correlation and Linear Regression

Topics that you'll learn in this chapter:

- ☑ Understanding Linear Equations
- ☑ The Regression Equation
- ☑ Scatter Plots
- ☑ Calculate and Interpret Correlation Coefficients
- ☑ Scatterplots and Correlation Coefficients
- ☑ Correlation and Causation
- ☑ Prediction Using Regression
- ☑ Identifying and Managing Outliers
- ☑ Simple Linear Regression Analysis
- ☑ Coefficient of Determination (R −squared)
- ☑ Residual Analysis
- ☑ Multiple Linear Regression

285

Understanding Linear Equations

- Linear equations are foundational in statistics and mathematics, forming the basis for understanding relationships between variables. They are represented in the form $y = mx + c$, where y and x are variables, m is the slope of the line, and c is the y −intercept.

- Slope (m): This indicates the steepness of the line. A positive slope means an upward trend, while a negative slope indicates a downward trend.

- Y − intercept (c): This is the point where the line crosses the y − axis, indicating the value of y when x is 0.

- Variables: x is the independent variable, and y is the dependent variable.

Examples:

Example 1. Solve and graph the equation $y = 2x + 3$.

Solution: Identify Slope and Intercept: Slope is: $m = 2$, Y −intercept is $c = 3$.

Create a Table:

If $x = 0$, $y = 2(0) + 3 = 3$.
If $x = 1$, $y = 2(1) + 3 = 5$.
If $x = -1$, $y = 2(-1) + 3 = 1$.

x	y
−1	1
0	3
1	5

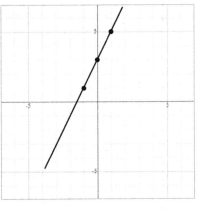

Graph the Equation: Plot (0,3), (1,5), (−1,1) and draw a line.

Interpretation: The line shows a positive linear relationship between x and y.

Example 2. Find the x −intercept of the equation $y = -4x + 8$.

Solution: X −intercept: The x −intercept occurs when $y = 0$.

Solve for x: Set y to 0 and solve: $0 = -4x + 8$

Rearrange to get $4x = 8$.

Divide both sides by 4 to find $x = 2$.

Answer: The x −intercept is at $x = 2$.

The Regression Equation

- In statistics, a regression equation is used to describe the relationship between one or more independent variables and a dependent variable.

- A simple linear regression equation is typically expressed as:

$$y = \beta_0 + \beta_1 x + \epsilon$$

where:
- y is the dependent variable.
- x is the independent variable.
- β_0 is the y −intercept (constant term).
- β_1 is the slope of the regression line.
- ϵ represents the error term.

Examples:

Example 1. In a study on marketing spend and sales, you are given that the estimated regression equation is $y = 50 + 20x$. Interpret the equation and predict sales for a marketing spend of $100.

Solution: Interpretation: The y − intercept ($\beta_0 = 50$) suggests that when marketing spend is $0, sales are at $50. The slope ($\beta_1 = 20$) indicates that for every $1 increase in marketing spend, sales increase by $20.

Prediction: For $x = 100$, $y = 50 + 20(100) = 2050$. So, with a marketing spend of $100, sales are predicted to be $2050.

Example 2. A regression analysis on temperature ($°C$) and ice cream sales $ gives the equation $y = 30 + 15x$. What does this mean, and what are the predicted sales at $20°C$?

Solution: Interpretation: The y −intercept ($\beta_0 = 30$) indicates the base sales ($) when temperature is $0°C$. The slope ($\beta_1 = 15$) shows that for each degree increase in temperature, sales increase by $15.

Prediction: At $20°C$, $y = 30 + 15(20) = 330$. Therefore, sales are predicted to be $330.

Scatter Plots

A scatter plot is a diagram with points to represent the relationship between two variables.

On a scatter plot, you can use a trend line to make predictions.

A scatter plot shows a positive trend if y tends to increase as x increases.

A scatter plot shows a negative trend if y tends to decrease as x increases.

An outlier is an extreme point in a data set that is separated from all other points.

Example:

The following table shows the number of people in a family and the amount of money they spend on movie tickets.

Number of people	1	2	3	4	5	6	7
Money	13	14	17	15	28	18	16

a) Make a scatter plot to represent the data.

b) Does this scatter plot show a positive trend, a negative trend, or no trend?

c) Find the outlier on the scatter plot.

Solution:

a) Write the ordered pairs. Number of people goes on the $x-$axis, so put the number of people first. The amount of money goes on the $y-$axis, so put the amount of money second. (1,13), (2,14), (3,17), (4,15), (5,28), (6,18), (7,16).

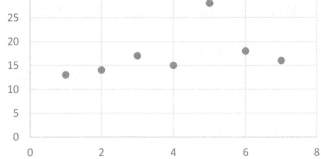

Now, graph the ordered pairs.

b) y tends to increase as x increases. So, this scatter plot shows a positive trend.

c) (5,28) is the outlier because this point is separated from all other points in the data set.

Calculate and Interpret Correlation Coefficients

- The correlation coefficient which is represented with sign r determines how close the points of a data set are to being linear. In other words, it evaluates the linear correlation's strength in the data set. The correlation coefficient is used for a set of n data points, (x_i, y_i) where $1 \le i \le n$. Whenever the correlation coefficient is closer to 1 or -1, the linear correlation of the data can be stronger. The correlation coefficient is 1 if the points of the data set are on a line with a positive slope. The correlation coefficient is -1 if the data set's points are on a line with a negative slope.
- The formula for the correlation coefficient is as follows $r = \frac{1}{n-1} \cdot \sum_{i=1}^{n} \frac{(x_i - \bar{x})(y_i - \bar{y})}{s_x s_y}$. In this formula, $\bar{x}$ is the $x-$values' mean, $\bar{y}$ is the $y-$values' mean, s_x is the $x-$values' sample standard deviation, s_y is the $y-$values' sample standard deviation, and n is the data points' number.
- If the data points have a positive trend or an increasing trend, the correlation coefficient is positive. If the data points have a negative trend or decreasing trend, the correlation coefficient is negative.

Example:

Find the correlation coefficient of the following data and then interpret the answer. Round your answer to the nearest thousandth.

Arthur plans to improve his studies. In order to achieve this goal, he has written down the number of pages read daily and the hours of daily reading in the table below. He records the hours of daily reading, x, and the number of pages reads daily, y.

Hours of daily reading	The number of pages read daily
3	60
4	75
6	82
7	90
8	105

Solution: Each row in the above table shows a data point (x_i, y_i). x_i is the number of hours Arthur reads per day and y_i is the number of pages Arthur reads per day. You can simply use your calculator to find the above data set's correlation coefficient: $r = 0.968971 \approx 0.969$. The correlation coefficient is positive. So, the data points have a positive trend or increasing trend. The correlation coefficient is so close to 1, so the data set has a strong linear correlation.

Scatterplots and Correlation Coefficients

- A scatterplot is a graphical representation of the relationship between two variables.

    - Notice: Look for patterns in the points. A linear pattern suggests a linear relationship, while a non-linear pattern indicates a more complex relationship.

- The correlation coefficient, often denoted as r, measures the strength and direction of a linear relationship between two variables. It ranges from -1 to 1, where:
    - $r = 1$ indicates a perfect positive linear relationship.
    - $r = -1$ indicates a perfect negative linear relationship.
    - $r = 0$ suggests no linear relationship.

- The formula for Pearson's correlation coefficient is:
$$r = \frac{n(\sum XY) - (\sum X)(\sum Y)}{\sqrt{(n \sum X^2 - (\sum X)^2)(n \sum Y^2 - (\sum Y)^2)}}$$

Example:

Create a scatterplot for the following data and estimate the correlation coefficient:

$X: 1, 2, 3, 4, 5$

$Y: 2, 4, 6, 8, 10$

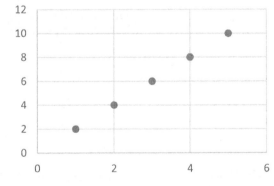

Solution: Scatterplot: Plot the points $(1,2), (2,4), (3,6), (4,8), (5,10)$.

The points lie in a straight line, suggesting a strong linear relationship.

Correlation Coefficient:

$$r = \frac{n(\sum XY) - (\sum X)(\sum Y)}{\sqrt{(n \sum X^2 - (\sum X)^2)(n \sum Y^2 - (\sum Y)^2)}} \rightarrow$$

$$r = \frac{5(1\times2 + 2\times4 + 3\times6 + 4\times8 + 5\times10) - (15)(30)}{\sqrt{(5(1^2 + 2^2 + 3^2 + 4^2 + 5^2) - 15^2)(5(2^2 + 4^2 + 6^2 + 8^2 + 10^2) - 30^2)}} = \frac{100}{\sqrt{10000}} = 1$$

By calculation, r would be 1, indicating a perfect positive linear relationship.

Correlation and Causation

- Correlation explains a connection between variables. When a variable changes the other variable also changes. In other words, a correlation is a statistical indicator of the association between variables. These variables have covariation and change together. But remember this covariation isn't certain because of a direct or indirect causal connection.

- Causation shows you when one variable changes, it causes changes in the other variable. In fact, you can see a cause-and-effect relationship between variables. The 2 variables are associated together and there is also a causal connection between them.

- Keep in mind a correlation doesn't signify causation, but causation always signifies correlation. There are 2 situations when a correlation isn't causation:

  • The third variable problem happens when a confounded variable affects two other variables and makes them seem causally linked when they are not.

  • The directionality problem happens when 2 variables have a correlation connection and might really have a causal link, but it isn't possible to determine which variable is the reason for changing in the other.

Examples:

Example 1. Determine whether the following relationship reflects both correlation and causation or not.

For book readers, having more free time is associated with reading more books.

Solution: This relationship reflects both correlation and causation because when a variable changes the other variable also changes. On the other hand, when one variable changes, it causes changes in the other variable. Naturally, for book readers, having more free time will lead to reading more books.

Example 2. Determine whether the following relationship reflects both correlation and causation or not.

Comedy shows on TV are associated with reading more about comedians.

Solution: This relationship doesn't reflect both correlation and causation because reading about comedians doesn't cause people to watch comedy shows on TV. Another factor should be used to explain the correlation, like being interested in comedy and comedians.

Prediction Using Regression

- Linear Regression: Focuses on predicting a dependent variable based on the value of an independent variable. $y = \beta_0 + \beta_1 x$, where β_0 is the $y-$intercept, β_1 is the slope, x is the independent variable, and y is the dependent variable.

- Multiple Regression: Involves more than one independent variable and is expressed as $y = \beta_0 + \beta_1 x_1 + \beta_2 x_2 + \ldots + \beta_n x_n$.

- **Step-by-Step Guide to Making Predictions**

  - Data Collection: Gather data on the variables involved.

  - Model Selection: Choose either linear or multiple regression based on the number of independent variables.

  - Estimate Coefficients: Use statistical methods to estimate the values of β_0, $\beta_1, \beta_2, \ldots, \beta_n$.

  - Model Evaluation: Assess the model's accuracy using measures like $R-$squared.

  - Make Predictions: Input values for the independent variable(s) into the regression equation to get predictions for the dependent variable.

Examples:

Example 1. Given a regression equation for house prices based on size (sq. ft) and age (years) $y = 1000 + 150x_1 - 2000x_2$, predict the price of a house that is $2000 \, sq.ft$ and 10 years old.

Solution: Input Values: Size $x_1 = 2000 \, sq.ft$, Age $x_2 = 10$ years.

Prediction: Use the equation (Multiple Regression):

$$y = 1000 + 150(2000) - 2000(10) = 281,000$$

The predicted house price is \$281,000.

Example 2. If the regression equation for predicting weight (kg) based on height (cm) is $y = 0.45x + 50$, predict the weight for a person who is $170 \, cm$ tall.

Solution: Input Value: Height $x = 170 \, cm$.

Prediction: Plug in the value into the equation: $y = 0.45(170) + 50 = 126.5$

So, the predicted weight is $126.5 \, kg$.

Identifying and Managing Outliers

- An outlier is a data point that is significantly different from the other data points in a dataset. It can be unusually high or low. Outliers can skew statistical analyses and lead to incorrect conclusions.

- Graphical Methods: The most common method is using box plots. A data point is considered an outlier if it lies outside the interquartile range (IQR).
  The IQR is calculated as: $IQR = Q_3 - Q_1$
  where Q_1 is the first quartile and Q_3 is the third quartile.

- $Z-$Score Method: A $Z-$score measures how many standard deviations a data point is from the mean. A data point with a $Z-$score greater than 3 or less than -3 is typically considered an outlier. $Z-$score is calculated as: $Z = \frac{X-\mu}{\sigma}$
  where X is the data point, μ is the mean, and σ is the standard deviation.

- **Managing Outliers**

  - Exclusion: If the outlier is due to an error, it can be excluded from the data set.
  - Transformation: Applying a transformation (like logarithmic or square root) can reduce the impact of outliers.
  - Imputation: Replace the outlier with an average value from the dataset.

Example:

Determine if there are any outliers in the dataset: $23, 22, 21, 45, 24, 22, 26$ using the IQR method.

Solution: Arrange the data in ascending order: $21, 22, 22, 23, 24, 26, 45$

Find the first quartile (Q_1) and the third quartile (Q_3):

First Quartile (Q_1): The median of the first half of the data (including the median if there is an odd number of data points) is 22.

Third Quartile (Q_3): The median of the second half of the data is 26.

Calculate the IQR: $IQR = Q_3 - Q_1 = 26 - 22 = 4$

Determine the Lower and Upper Bounds:

Lower Bound: $Q_1 - 1.5 \times IQR = 22 - 1.5 \times 4 = 17.5$

Upper Bound: $Q_3 + 1.5 \times IQR = 26 + 1.5 \times 4 = 29.5$

Any data point outside the range of 17.5 to 29.5 is considered an outlier. In this dataset, the value 45 is outside this range, making it an outlier.

Therefore, the dataset $\{23, 22, 21, 45, 24, 22, 26\}$ has one outlier, which is 45.

Simple Linear Regression Analysis

- ## Analysis Steps in Simple Linear Regression

  - Data Collection: Gather a dataset where both the dependent and independent variables are continuous.

  - Data Visualization: Use scatter plots to visualize the relationship between X and Y.

  - Estimating Coefficients: The slope (β_1) and intercept (β_0) are calculated using statistical formulas based on minimizing the sum of the squared differences between the observed and predicted values.

  - Model Fitting: Using the least squares method, fit the best line that minimizes the discrepancies between observed and predicted values.

  - Model Assessment: Evaluate the model's performance using metrics like $R-$squared, which quantifies the proportion of variance in the dependent variable that's predictable from the independent variable.

Example:

Analyze the relationship between hours studied (X) and exam score (Y) using the dataset: Hours Studied $= \{2, 3, 5, 7, 9\}$ and Exam Score $= \{75, 78, 80, 85, 90\}$.

Solution: First, we can create a scatter plot to visually inspect the relationship between hours studied and exam score. Calculate the Regression Line: $Y = a + bX$ where Y is the exam score, X is the hours studied, a is the $y-$intercept, and b is the slope of the line. Compute Slope (b) and Intercept (a) (where N is the number of observations):

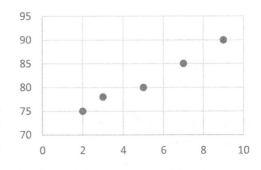

$$b = \frac{N(\sum XY) - (\sum X)(\sum Y)}{N(\sum X^2) - (\sum X)^2} = \frac{5(2 \times 75 + 3 \times 78 + 5 \times 80 + 7 \times 85 + 9 \times 90) - (2 + 3 + 5 + 7 + 9)(75 + 78 + 80 + 85 + 90)}{5(2^2 + 3^2 + 5^2 + 7^2 + 9^2) - (2 + 3 + 5 + 7 + 9)^2} = \frac{337}{164} = 2.05$$

$$a = \frac{\sum Y - b(\sum X)}{N} = \frac{(75 + 78 + 80 + 85 + 90) - 2.05(2 + 3 + 5 + 7 + 9)}{5} = 70.94$$

$$Y = a + bX = 70.94 + 2.05X$$

In this linear model, with the increase in the number of study hour, it is expected that the exam score will also increase.

Example Prediction: If a student studies for 6 hours, the predicted exam score, according to our linear regression model, would be approximately 83.24. ($Y = 70.94 + 2.05 \times 6 \rightarrow Y = 83.24$)

Coefficient of Determination (R –squared)

- The Coefficient of Determination, commonly known as R –squared (R^2), is a statistical measure in regression analysis that represents the proportion of variance for a dependent variable that's explained by an independent variable or variables in a regression model.

- Value Range: R –squared values range from 0 to 1. A higher R –squared value indicates a better fit between the regression model and the observed data.

  - An R^2 of 0 means the model explains none of the variability of the response data around its mean.
  - An R^2 of 1 means the model explains all the variability of the response data around its mean.

- The formula for R –squared is: $R^2 = 1 - \frac{SS_{res}}{SS_{tot}}$

  Where:

  SS_{res} is the sum of squares of residuals, calculated as $\sum(y_i - \hat{y}_i)^2$.

  SS_{tot} is the total sum of squares, calculated as $\sum(y_i - \bar{y})^2$.

  y_i is the observed value, $\hat{y}_i$ is the predicted value, and $\bar{y}$ is the mean of observed values.

Example:

Calculate the R –squared for a linear model where the observed values are $\{3, 4, 5, 6, 7\}$ and the predicted values are $\{2.8, 3.9, 5.1, 6.2, 7.1\}$

Solution: To calculate the R –squared (R^2) for the given linear model with observed values $\{3, 4, 5, 6, 7\}$ and predicted values $\{2.8, 3.9, 5.1, 6.2, 7.1\}$, we follow these steps:

Calculate the Mean of Observed Values:

The mean of the observed values $\bar{y}$ is calculated to be $\frac{3+4+5+6+7}{5} = 5$.

Calculate the Sum of Squares of Residuals (SS_{res}):

$$SS_{res} = (3 - 2.8)^2 + (4 - 3.9)^2 + (5 - 5.1)^2 + (6 - 6.2)^2 + (7 - 7.1)^2 = 0.11$$

Calculate the Total Sum of Squares (SS_{tot}):

$$SS_{tot} = (3 - 5)^2 + (4 - 5)^2 + (5 - 5)^2 + (6 - 5)^2 + (7 - 5)^2 = 10$$

Calculate R –squared (R^2):

$$R^2 = 1 - \frac{SS_{res}}{SS_{tot}} = 1 - \frac{0.11}{10} = 0.989$$

Therefore, the R –squared value for the given linear model is 0.989. This high value indicates that the model explains a significant proportion of the variance in the observed data.

Residual Analysis

- Understanding Residuals: A residual is calculated as the difference between an observed value and its predicted value from the regression model. Mathematically, if y_i is the observed value and $\hat{y}_i$ is the predicted value for the i −th observation, the residual e_i is given by:

$$e_i = y_i - \hat{y}_i$$

- Plotting Residuals: To perform residual analysis, plot the residuals against the predicted values or another variable to look for patterns. Ideally, the residuals should appear random and not show any discernible pattern.

- Identifying Outliers: Look for outliers in the residual plot. Outliers are points with a large residual value and can unduly influence the regression model.

Examples:

Example 1. Suppose you have a simple linear regression model where y represents sales and x represents advertising budget. The regression equation is $y = 2x + 5$.

Observed values: $y = [15, 20, 25]$

Predicted values based on $x = [5, 7, 9]$: $\hat{y} = [15, 19, 23]$

Calculate the residuals and comment on them.

Solution: Residuals: $e_1 = 15 - 15 = 0$

$$e_2 = 20 - 19 = 1$$

$$e_3 = 25 - 23 = 2$$

The residuals are relatively small, indicating a good fit of the model to the data.

Example 2. For a dataset, the regression model predicts $\hat{y} = 3x + 4$.

The observed values are $y = [10, 14, 18]$ for $x = [2, 3, 4]$.

Calculate the residuals and analyze if there's a pattern.

Solution: Residuals: $e_1 = 10 - (3 \times 2 + 4) = 10 - 10 = 0$

$$e_2 = 14 - (3 \times 3 + 4) = 14 - 13 = 1$$

$$e_3 = 18 - (3 \times 4 + 4) = 18 - 16 = 2$$

There seems to be a slight increasing trend in the residuals, suggesting the model might not be capturing some aspect of the data trend.

Multiple Linear Regression

- Understanding the Model: In MLR, the relationship between the dependent variable y and independent variables $x_1, x_2, \ldots, x_n$ is modeled as:

$$y = \beta_0 + \beta_1 x_1 + \beta_2 x_2 + \cdots + \beta_n x_n + \epsilon$$

- Here, β_0 is the intercept, $\beta_1, \beta_2, \ldots, \beta_n$ are the coefficients of the independent variables, and ϵ is the error term.

- Assumptions: MLR assumes:

  - Linearity: The relationship between the dependent and independent variables is linear.
  - Independence: Observations are independent of each other.
  - Normality: The residuals are normally distributed.

- Model Fitting: Use statistical software to fit the MLR model to your data. This involves finding the coefficients $\beta_0, \beta_1, \ldots, \beta_n$ that minimize the sum of squared residuals.

Example:

Suppose we are working with a real estate company, and they want to predict the price of houses based on various features. We have a dataset with the following columns:

Task: We need to create a multiple linear regression model to predict the house price based on the size, number of bedrooms, and age of the house.

Size (sq ft)	Bedrooms	Age (Years)	Price (USD)
2104	3	45	399900
1600	3	30	329900
2400	3	32	369000
1416	2	40	232000
3000	4	15	539900

Solution: The multiple linear regression model can be represented as:

$$Price = \beta_0 + \beta_1 \times Size + \beta_2 \times Bedrooms + \beta_3 \times Age$$

where $\beta_0, \beta_1, \beta_2$ and β_3 are the parameters our model needs to learn.
And split the data into features (X) and target variable (Y). X would be a matrix containing columns for Size, Bedrooms, and Age. Y would be a vector containing the house prices.

Use a statistical software or a programming language like Python or R to fit the multiple linear regression model to your data. This typically involves finding values of β that minimize the error between the predicted prices and the actual prices in the dataset.

This model would help the real estate company to estimate house prices based on multiple features, aiding them in setting competitive and realistic prices for their properties.

Chapter 10: Practices

✎ Is the following an example of a linear equation? Why or why not?

1) Does the graph representing the relationship between the total distance traveled y in miles and the time x in hours for a car moving at varying speeds represent a linear equation?

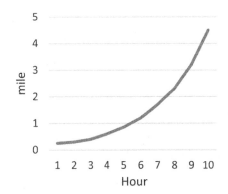

2) Does the graph that shows the total amount of money saved y over time in months x when saving a fixed amount each month represent a linear equation?

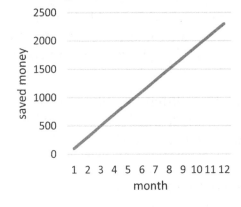

3) Is the graph displaying the total cost y of buying x pounds of apples at a constant price per pound a linear equation?

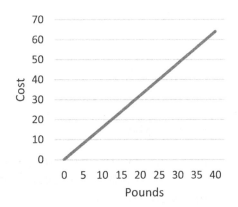

4) Does the graph that plots the total savings y over time x with a regular monthly deposit and compounded interest represent a linear equation?

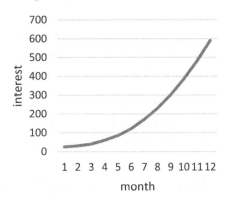

According to the scenarios: What are the independent and dependent variables? What is the y–intercept, and what is the slope? Interpret them using complete sentences.

5) Oliver runs a small gardening service. He charges a flat rate of $40 for a visit plus $20 for each hour of work. A linear equation that expresses the total amount Oliver earns for each gardening job is $y = 40 + 20x$.

6) Mia offers piano lessons. She charges a registration fee of $30 plus $25 for each hour of lesson. A linear equation that describes the total income Mia earns per student is $y = 30 + 25x$.

7) Leo manages a small printing service. He has a setup fee of $50 for each order plus $10 for every poster printed. The linear equation for the total cost to a customer is $y = 50 + 10x$.

8) Julia runs a home-cleaning business. She charges a base fee of $35 for each cleaning session plus $18 for every hour she cleans. The linear equation representing Julia's earnings per session is $y = 35 + 18x$.

Find the equation based on the scenarios.

9) Bella's Bakery makes custom cakes. The price for services is $20 per cake plus a $15 one-time setup fee. The total cost to a customer depends on the number of cakes ordered.

10) Carlos' Car Wash charges $12 for each car wash plus a $5 environmental fee per visit. The total cost to a customer depends on the number of cars washed in a visit.

11) Diana's Doggy Daycare charges $18 per day for each dog plus a $20 one-time registration fee. The total cost to a customer depends on the number of days a dog is cared for.

12) Ethan's Tutoring Center charges $25 per hour for tutoring plus a $10 materials fee per session. The total cost to a student depends on the number of hours of tutoring received.

Interpret and predict.

13) In a study on the effect of study hours on exam scores, the estimated regression equation is $y = 60 + 5x$. Interpret the equation and predict the exam score for a student who studies 10 hours.

14) In an analysis of temperature impact on electricity usage, the regression equation is $y = 150 + 30x$. Interpret this equation and predict the electricity usage when the temperature is 20 degrees above a reference temperature.

15) In a study on the impact of advertising duration on product awareness, the regression equation is $y = 10 + 2x$. Interpret the equation and predict the product awareness score for 25 hours of advertising.

16) In research on the relationship between hours of operation and revenue for a store, the regression equation is $y = 200 + 40x$. Interpret the equation and predict the revenue for a store open for 12 hours a day.

17) A regression analysis on weekly hours spent on online advertising (x) and website traffic (visitors) gives the equation $y = 200 + 50x$. What does this tell us, and what is the predicted traffic for 10 hours of advertising?

18) A regression analysis on the number of years of experience (x) and the salary of employees (\$) yields the equation $y = 40,000 + 2,000x$. What does this equation represent, and what is the expected salary for an employee with 5 years of experience?

19) A study on the amount of fertilizer used (kg) and the yield of crops (tons) provides the regression equation $y = 3 + 0.5x$. What is the interpretation, and what is the predicted yield for 20 kg of fertilizer used?

20) An analysis on the amount of money spent on books (\$) and the number of books sold gives the regression equation $y = 10 + 3x$. What does the equation imply, and what are the predicted book sales for a spend of \$50?

✎ **Answer the questions.**

21) What does the slope of a regression line represent in a simple linear regression equation?

22) In the regression equation $y = \beta_0 + \beta_1 x$, what is β_0?

23) How do you interpret a regression coefficient that is close to zero?

24) What is the purpose of calculating the coefficient of determination (R^2) in regression analysis?

✎ **Use the following information to answer the next five questions.**

A random sample of 10 local artists produced the following data, where x is the number of gallery showings the artist has had and y is the amount of money made, in thousands of dollars.

x	0	3	2	1	5	5	4	3	0	4
y	2	8	7	3	13	12	9	9	3	10

25) Draw a scatter plot of the data.

26) Use regression to find the equation for the line of best fit.

27) Draw the line of best fit on the scatter plot.

28) What is the slope of the line of best fit? What does it represent.

29) What is the y −intercept of the line of best fit? What does it represent.

✍ **Answer the questions.**

30) How do you interpret the direction of a scatter plot?

31) What does the shape of a scatter plot reveal about the data?

32) How can you assess the strength of the relationship in a scatter plot?

33) What is the purpose of a trendline (line of best fit) in a scatter plot?

✍ **Answer the questions based on the scenarios and the tables.**

The following table displays the number of hours students spend studying and their corresponding test scores.

Number of hours studied	1	2	3	4	5	6	7	8	9	10	11	12
Test scores	50	55	60	65	95	70	75	80	55	85	90	95

34) Create a scatter plot to represent the data.

35) Determine if this scatter plot shows a positive trend, a negative trend, or no trend.

36) Identify any outliers on the scatter plot.

Data records the temperature (°C) and the number of ice creams sold in a theme park.

Temperature (°C)	10	15	20	25	30	35	40	45	50	55
Ice cream sold	50	60	70	80	90	100	110	120	130	140

37) Construct a scatter plot to represent the data.

38) Determine if this scatter plot shows a positive trend, a negative trend, or no trend.

39) Detect any outliers on the scatter plot.

🔖 **Answer the questions about interpreting correlation coefficients.**

40) In a survey, the number of hours spent on social media and the level of satisfaction with social interactions were measured for a group of teenagers. The calculated correlation coefficient was -0.65. What does this indicate?

41) If the correlation coefficient between two variables is 0, what does it imply about the relationship between these variables?

42) A study finds a correlation coefficient of 0.45 between daily exercise duration and overall health score. How should this correlation be interpreted?

43) A study was conducted to determine the correlation between hours spent studying and scores on a math test. The following data was collected:

Hours (X)	1	2	3	4	5
Scores (Y)	50	55	65	70	80

Calculate the correlation coefficient.

🔖 **Calculate the correlation coefficient for the following data and interpret the result. Round your answer to the nearest thousandth.**

44) Emma wants to understand the relationship between her exercise frequency and weight loss. She records the number of weekly workouts (x) and her average weekly weight loss (y).

Number of weekly workouts	Average weekly weight loss (in pounds)
2	1
3	1.5
4	2.5
5	3
6	3.5

45) John tracks his daily study hours (x) and his test scores (y) to analyze his academic performance.

Daily study hours	Test scores
1	50
2	60
3	65
4	70
5	80

✎ Create a scatterplot for the following data and estimate the correlation coefficient.

46) A local library tracks the number of new memberships each month and the number of books borrowed. Create a scatterplot for the data showing the relationship between new memberships (X) and books borrowed (Y) and estimate the correlation coefficient.

X: 2, 3, 4, 5, 6

Y: 20, 30, 40, 50, 60

47) A study looks at the amount of time spent on social media and the level of reported happiness.
Create a scatterplot for the data showing the relationship between hours on social media (X) and happiness score (Y) and estimate the correlation coefficient.

X: 1, 2, 3, 4, 5

Y: 8, 6, 4, 2, 1

48) A transportation study investigates the correlation between the number of traffic lights on a street and the average speed of traffic. Create a scatterplot for the data showing the relationship between traffic lights (X) and average traffic speed (Y) and estimate the correlation coefficient.

X: 1, 2, 3, 4, 5

Y: 35, 35, 35, 35, 35

49) An ecologist examines the relationship between the number of rainy days in a month and the sighting of a certain bird species. Create a scatterplot for the data showing the relationship between rainy days (X) and bird sightings (Y) and estimate the correlation coefficient.

X: 3, 6, 9, 12, 15

Y: 30, 28, 26, 24, 22

🖎 **Use the following information to answer the next five questions.**

An agricultural research center is tracking the yield of a particular crop over the years. The yield depends on various factors, including weather conditions, soil quality, and farming practices. In the following table, x represents the year, and y represents the yield of the crop in tons per hectare.

X	Y	X	Y
1915	10.1	1969	36.7
1926	17.7	1975	49.3
1935	13.7	1979	72.6
1940	14.7	1980	82.4
1947	24.1	1986	109.6
1952	26.5	1991	130.7
1964	31.0	1999	166.6

50) Draw a scatter plot of the data.

51) Calculate the least-squares line. Write the equation in the form:

$$\hat{y} = a + bx$$

52) Draw the line on a scatter plot.

53) Find the correlation coefficient. Is it significant?

54) What is the estimated yield for the year 1990?

✍ **Determine whether the following relationship reflects both correlation and causation or not.**

55) Does the relationship between daily exercise and improved cardiovascular health indicate both correlation and causation?

56) Is there both correlation and causation between the hours spent practicing a musical instrument and the skill level achieved?

57) Does the relationship between drinking coffee and increased alertness reflect both correlation and causation?

58) Is there a correlation and causation relationship between using social media and feeling less lonely?

59) Does the relationship between high temperatures and increased ice cream sales reflect both correlation and causation?

60) Is there both correlation and causation between listening to classical music and improved concentration?

✍ **Determine if there are any outliers in the datasets.**

61) Identifying outliers in daily hours spent on smartphones by a sample group of teenagers.
Dataset: $\{8, 7, 5, 9, 6, 7, 2\}$

62) Examining outliers in monthly rainfall (in mm) data for a city.
Dataset: $\{120, 110, 130, 150, 115, 200, 105\}$

63) The weekly hours spent on exercise by individuals at a gym are: 100, 110, 107, 115, 208, 103, 105. Identify any outliers.

64) During a summer reading program, the number of pages read by participants in a week were: 32, 36, 45, 47, 34, 30, 150.
Determine if any values are outliers.

✎ Answer the questions.

65) If a regression model has an R −squared value of 1, what can be inferred about the model's predictions?

66) Can an R −squared value be negative, and what would it indicate if it were?

67) How should a student interpret an R −squared value of 0.65 in a study analyzing the relationship between hours studied and test scores?

68) In a study relating hours of online gaming to academic performance, researchers found an R −squared value of 0.10. How would you describe the relationship between online gaming and academic performance?

✎ Solve.

69) For a dataset comparing the number of hours studied and the scores obtained, with observed values $\{2, 3, 4, 5, 6\}$ and predicted values $\{1.9, 3.1, 4.0, 4.9, 5.8\}$, what is the R −squared value?

70) In analyzing the relationship between calories consumed and weight gained, with observed values $\{10, 20, 30, 40, 50\}$ and predicted values $\{12, 19, 29, 40, 52\}$, what is the R −squared value?

71) Considering the sales numbers for a product and the corresponding advertising budget, with observed values $\{100, 200, 300, 400, 500\}$ and predicted values $\{95, 205, 315, 385, 495\}$, what is the R −squared value?

72) For a study on the effects of sleep on cognitive function, with observed test scores $\{1, 2, 3, 4, 5\}$ and predicted scores based on hours of sleep $\{0.8, 2.1, 3.2, 3.9, 4.7\}$, what is the R −squared value?

✎ **Calculate the residuals and analyze if there's a pattern.**

73) A linear model predicts the final exam score (y) based on the number of study hours (x) with the equation $\hat{y} = 5x + 2$. The observed scores are $y = \{15, 20, 25\}$ for study hours $x = \{2, 3, 4\}$. Calculate the residuals and analyze if there's a pattern.

74) A company predicts sales (y) from advertising spend (x) with the model $y = 10x + 50$. The observed sales are $y = \{150, 200, 250\}$ for advertising spends $x = \{10, 15, 20\}$. What are the residuals and is there a pattern?

75) A health study predicts the blood pressure reduction (y) based on the number of weekly exercise hours (x) with the formula $\hat{y} = 2x + 5$. The observed reductions are $y = \{9, 11, 13\}$ for exercise hours $x = \{2, 3, 4\}$. Calculate the residuals and check for any pattern.

76) A financial model predicts the savings amount (y) based on the number of years worked (x) with the equation $\hat{y} = 4x + 20$. The observed savings are $y = \{44, 52, 60\}$ for years worked $x = \{5, 7, 9\}$. Are there any patterns in the residuals.

✎ **Solve.**

77) A student is analyzing the relationship between the number of hours spent on homework and their grades. Why is it important to perform a residual analysis in this scenario?

78) A researcher is studying the effect of fertilizer on plant growth. They've plotted residuals on a graph and noticed a pattern. What does the presence of a pattern in the residuals indicate about the model?

79) A dietician is trying to predict weight loss based on calorie intake and exercise but finds that the residuals are increasing as the number of calories increases. What can the dietician infer from the increasing residuals with calorie intake?

80) In a physics experiment, a student measures the distance a ball rolls on different surfaces and compares it to a theoretical model, finding residuals are mostly positive. What do mostly positive residuals suggest about the student's model or measurements?

✎ **Use the following information to answer the next nine questions.**

We have a dataset that tracks the average monthly data usage (in GB) for a group of cellular phone users over a period of time.

Year (Time)	Average monthly data usage (GB)	Year (Time)	Average monthly data usage (GB)
2011	340	2016	1,050
2012	499	2017	1,170
2013	592	2018	1,364
2014	757	2019	1,836
2015	927	2020	2,132

81) What are the independent and dependent variables?

82) Draw a scatter plot.

83) Use regression to find the line of best fit and the correlation coefficient.

84) Interpret the significance of the correlation coefficient.

85) Is there a linear relationship between the variables?

86) Find the coefficient of determination and interpret it.

87) What is the slope of the regression equation? What does it mean?

88) Use the line of best fit to estimate PCINC for 2010 and for 2035.

89) Determine whether there are any outliers.

✏ **Answer the questions.**

90) A real estate company is trying to predict house prices based on square footage, number of bedrooms, and age of the house.

What is multiple linear regression and how can it be used in this scenario?

91) A nutritionist wants to predict the body mass index (BMI) of individuals based on their calorie intake, daily protein intake, and exercise hours.

Why is it better to use multiple linear regression instead of simple linear regression for this prediction?

92) A health researcher is studying the impact of exercise hours, diet quality score, and sleep duration on overall health index.

What would the multiple linear regression model equation look like for predicting overall health index?

93) An economist is modeling the influence of education level, work experience, and region on individual income.

How would the multiple linear regression equation be written for predicting individual income?

94) A marketing analyst is assessing how advertising spend on different platforms (television, online, and radio) affects product sales.

Write the multiple linear regression model equation for predicting product sales based on advertising spend.

Chapter 10: Answers

1) If the graph is a straight line, the car is moving at a constant speed, representing a linear equation. If it's curved, the speed is not constant, and it's not a linear equation.

2) If the graph is a straight line, this indicates that the same fixed amount is being saved each month, which is a characteristic of a linear relationship. The constant saving rate corresponds to the slope, and any initial amount saved would be the $y-$intercept. A linear equation would be appropriate here.

3) If the price per pound is constant, the graph will be a straight line, which indicates a linear equation. The cost per pound is the slope, and any flat fee or minimum charge would show up as the $y-$intercept. A linear equation models this direct proportional relationship between weight and cost.

4) Because of the compounded interest, the savings would increase at a growing rate over time, resulting in a curve, not a straight line. Therefore, it's not a linear equation.

5) The independent variable (x) is the number of hours Oliver works each job. The dependent variable (y) is the amount, in dollars, Oliver earns for each job.
   The $y-$intercept is 40 ($a = 40$). This represents the flat rate charge of \$40 that Oliver applies at the start of each job ($x = 0$).
   The slope is 20 ($b = 20$). This indicates that Oliver earns an additional \$20 for each hour of work.

6) The independent variable (x) is the number of hours of each piano lesson. The dependent variable (y) is the total income Mia earns per student.
   The $y-$intercept is 30 ($a = 30$). The registration fee of \$30 is charged at the beginning ($x = 0$).
   The slope is 25 ($b = 25$). Mia earns \$25 for every hour of piano lessons she provides.

7) The independent variable (x) is the number of posters printed. The dependent variable (y) is the total cost to the customer.
   The $y-$intercept is 50 ($a = 50$). This is the setup fee charged to the customer before any posters are printed ($x = 0$).
   The slope is 10 ($b = 10$). This means that the cost increases by \$10 for each additional poster printed.

8) The independent variable (x) is the number of hours Julia spends cleaning. The dependent variable (y) is the total earnings per cleaning session.
The $y-$intercept is 35 ($a = 35$). This is the base fee Julia charges at the start of a cleaning session ($x = 0$).
The slope is 18 ($b = 18$). Julia earns an additional \$18 for every hour spent cleaning.

9) $y = 15 + 20x$ 11) $y = 20 + 18x$

10) $y = 5 + 12x$ 12) $y = 10 + 25x$

13) Interpretation: The $y-$intercept ($\beta_0 = 60$) suggests that without any study hours, the exam score starts at 60. The slope ($\beta_1 = 5$) indicates that for each additional hour spent studying, the exam score increases by 5 points.
Prediction: For $x = 10$, $y = 60 + 5(10) = 110$. Therefore, studying for 10 hours is predicted to result in an exam score of 110.

14) Interpretation: The $y-$intercept ($\beta_0 = 150$) suggests that at the reference temperature, the electricity usage is 150 units. The slope ($\beta_1 = 30$) indicates that for every degree increase in temperature, the electricity usage increases by 30 units.

Prediction: For $x = 20$, $y = 150 + 30(20) = 750$. So, with the temperature being 20 degrees above the reference, electricity usage is predicted to be 750 units.

15) Interpretation: The $y-$intercept ($\beta_0 = 10$) suggests that without any advertising, the product awareness score is at 10. The slope ($\beta_1 = 2$) indicates that for each additional hour of advertising, the product awareness score increases by 2 points.
Prediction: For ($x = 25$), $y = 10 + 2(25) = 60$. Therefore, 25 hours of advertising is predicted to achieve a product awareness score of 60.

16) Interpretation: The $y-$intercept ($\beta_0 = 200$) implies that if the store is not open at all, it would still make \$200 (possibly from online sales or other sources). The slope ($\beta_1 = 40$) means that each additional hour the store is open, revenue increases by \$40.
Prediction: For $x = 12$, $y = 200 + 40(12) = 680$. So, if the store is open for 12 hours, the predicted revenue is \$680.

17) Interpretation: The y−intercept ($\beta_0 = 200$) represents the base website traffic when no hours are spent on advertising. The slope ($\beta_1 = 50$) indicates that for each additional hour spent on online advertising, website traffic increases by 50 visitors.

Prediction: For 10 hours of advertising, $y = 200 + 50(10) = 700$. Therefore, the predicted website traffic is 700 visitors.

18) Interpretation: The y−intercept ($\beta_0 = 40{,}000$) suggests the starting salary for an employee with 0 years of experience. The slope ($\beta_1 = 2{,}000$) indicates that for each additional year of experience, the salary increases by $\$2{,}000$.

Prediction: At 5 years of experience, $y = 40{,}000 + 2{,}000(5) = 50{,}000$. Therefore, the expected salary is $\$50{,}000$.

19) Interpretation: The y−intercept ($\beta_0 = 3$) shows the base yield of crops without using any fertilizer. The slope ($\beta_1 = 0.5$) suggests that for each kilogram of fertilizer used, the crop yield increases by 0.5 tons.

Prediction: For $20\,kg$ of fertilizer, $y = 3 + 0.5(20) = 13$. The predicted crop yield is 13 tons.

20) Interpretation: The y−intercept ($\beta_0 = 10$) indicates the base number of books sold when no money is spent. The slope ($\beta_1 = 3$) means that for each dollar spent, three additional books are sold.

Prediction: If $\$50$ is spent, $y = 10 + 3(50) = 160$. So, the predicted number of books sold is 160.

21) The slope of a regression line represents the estimated change in the dependent variable (usually denoted as y) for each one-unit increase in the independent variable (denoted as x). It indicates the strength and direction of the relationship between the variables.

22) In the regression equation, β_0 is the y−intercept, which is the predicted value of the dependent variable y when the independent variable x is zero. It is where the regression line crosses the y−axis.

23) A regression coefficient close to zero suggests that there is a weak or no linear relationship between the independent and dependent variables. It means that changes in the independent variable do not significantly affect the dependent variable.

24) The coefficient of determination (R^2) measures the proportion of variation in the dependent variable that is predictable from the independent variable. It is a statistic that gives information about the goodness of fit of a model. An R^2 value of 1 indicates that the regression predictions perfectly fit the data, while an R^2 of 0 indicates that the model does not explain any of the variability in the response data around its mean.

25)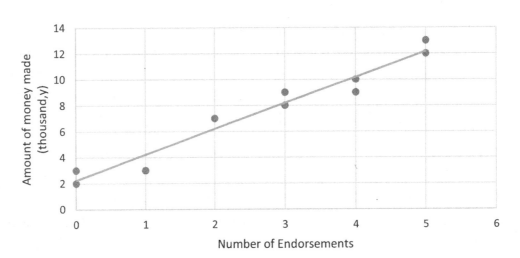

26) The equation for the line of best fit, based on the regression analysis, is $\hat{y} = 1.99x + 2.23$.

27) The line of best fit is drawn on the scatter plot in red.

28) The slope of the line of best fit is approximately 1.99. This represents that for each additional gallery showing, there is an average increase of approximately \$1,990 in the artist's earnings.

29) y−intercept of the line is approximately 2.23 (or \$2,230). This represents the estimated amount of money an artist would make if they had no gallery showings. It may be interpreted as a base amount of income from other sources besides gallery showings.

30) The direction of a scatter plot can be positive (upward-sloping), negative (downward-sloping), or no apparent direction. A positive direction suggests a positive relationship between variables, negative indicates a negative relationship, and no direction implies no significant relationship.

31) The shape of a scatter plot can reveal patterns such as linear, quadratic, or no discernible pattern. It helps determine the form of the relationship between variables.

32) The strength of the relationship in a scatter plot is assessed by how closely the points cluster around a trendline. A tight cluster indicates a strong relationship, while a scattered distribution suggests a weak relationship.

33) The trendline, also known as the line of best fit, is used to summarize and quantify the relationship between variables. It provides a mathematical model for the data and can be used for making predictions.

34)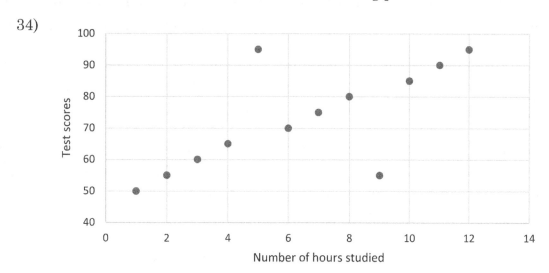

35) The scatter plot shows a positive trend. As the number of hours spent studying increases, test scores tend to rise.

36) The data point $(5, 95)$ appears to be an outlier since it has a significantly high test score for a relatively small number of hours studied.
The data point $(9, 55)$ also appears to be an outlier since it has a relatively low test score for a large number of hours studied.

37)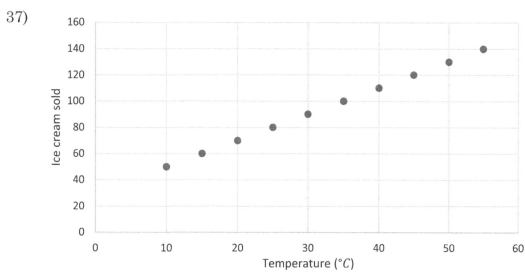

38) The scatter plot indicates a positive trend. As the temperature increases, the number of ice creams sold also increases.

39) There are no outliers in the scatter plot.

40) A correlation coefficient of -0.65 suggests a moderate to strong negative correlation. This means that as the number of hours spent on social media increases, the level of satisfaction with social interactions tends to decrease.

41) A correlation coefficient of 0 implies that there is no linear relationship between the two variables. This means that knowing the value of one variable does not help predict the value of the other.

42) A correlation coefficient of 0.45 indicates a moderate positive correlation. This suggests that there is a tendency for overall health scores to be higher with longer durations of daily exercise, though the relationship is not very strong.

43) The correlation coefficient (r) is calculated using the formula:
$$r = \frac{n(\sum XY) - (\sum X)(\sum Y)}{\sqrt{(n \sum X^2 - (\sum X)^2)(n \sum Y^2 - (\sum Y)^2)}}$$
$$r = \frac{5(1 \times 50 + 2 \times 55 + 3 \times 65 + 4 \times 70 + 5 \times 80) - (15)(320)}{\sqrt{(5(1^2 + 2^2 + 3^2 + 4^2 + 5^2) - 15^2)(5(50^2 + 55^2 + 65^2 + 70^2 + 80^2) - 320^2)}} = \frac{375}{50\sqrt{57}} \approx 0.99$$
After calculating, we find that r is approximately 0.99, indicating a strong positive correlation.

44) The correlation coefficient is calculated using the formula:
$$r = \frac{5(2 \times 1 + 3 \times 1.5 + 4 \times 2.5 + 5 \times 3 + 6 \times 3.5) - (20)(11.5)}{\sqrt{(5(2^2 + 3^2 + 4^2 + 5^2 + 6^2) - 20^2)(5(1^2 + 1.5^2 + 2.5^2 + 3^2 + 3.5^2) - 11.5^2)}} = \frac{32.5}{5\sqrt{43}} \approx 0.99$$
Interpretation: This high positive correlation suggests that as the number of weekly workouts increases, the average weekly weight loss also increases.

45) Using the correlation formula, the correlation coefficient (r) is approximately 0.99.
$$r = \frac{5(1 \times 50 + 2 \times 60 + 3 \times 65 + 4 \times 70 + 5 \times 80) - (15)(325)}{\sqrt{(5(1^2 + 2^2 + 3^2 + 4^2 + 5^2) - 15^2)(5(50^2 + 60^2 + 65^2 + 70^2 + 80^2) - 325^2)}} = \frac{350}{250\sqrt{2}} \approx 0.99$$
Interpretation: There's a strong positive correlation, indicating that an increase in study hours is associated with higher test scores.

46) The scatter plot for the data showing the relationship between new library memberships and the number of books borrowed has been created.

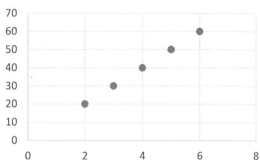

$$r = \frac{5(2\times20+3\times30+4\times40+5\times50+6\times60)-(20)(200)}{\sqrt{(5(2^2+3^2+4^2+5^2+6^2)-20^2)(5(20^2+30^2+40^2+50^2+60^2)-200^2)}} = \frac{500}{500} = 1$$

The correlation coefficient for these variables is 1.0, indicating a perfect positive linear relationship. This suggests that as the number of new memberships increases, the number of books borrowed increases proportionally.

47) The scatter plot for the data showing the relationship between hours spent on social media and reported happiness levels has been created.

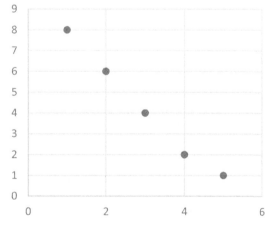

$$r = \frac{5(1\times8+2\times6+3\times4+4\times2+5\times1)-(15)(21)}{\sqrt{(5(1^2+2^2+3^2+4^2+5^2)-15^2)(5(8^2+6^2+4^2+2^2+1^2)-21^2)}} = \frac{-90}{10\sqrt{82}} \approx -0.994$$

The correlation coefficient for these variables is approximately -0.994, indicating a strong negative linear relationship. This suggests that as the amount of time spent on social media increases, the reported happiness score tends to decrease significantly.

48) The scatter plot for the data showing the relationship between the number of traffic lights on a street and the average speed of traffic has been created.

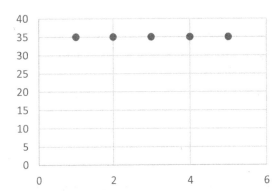

The correlation coefficient for these variables would be approximately 0, indicating no linear relationship between the number of traffic lights and the average speed of traffic.

49) The scatter plot for the data showing the relationship between the number of rainy days in a month and the sighting of a certain bird species has been created.

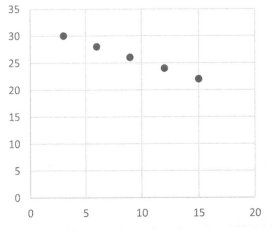

$$r = \frac{5(3\times30+6\times28+9\times26+12\times24+15\times22)-(45)(130)}{\sqrt{(5(3^2+6^2+9^2+12^2+15^2)-45^2)(5(30^2+28^2+26^2+24^2+22^2)-130^2)}} = \frac{-300}{300} = -1$$

The correlation coefficient for these variables is −1.0, indicating a strong negative linear relationship. This suggests that as the number of rainy days increases, the number of bird sightings tends to decrease significantly.

50) The scatter plot has been created, displaying the data points for each year against the crop yield.

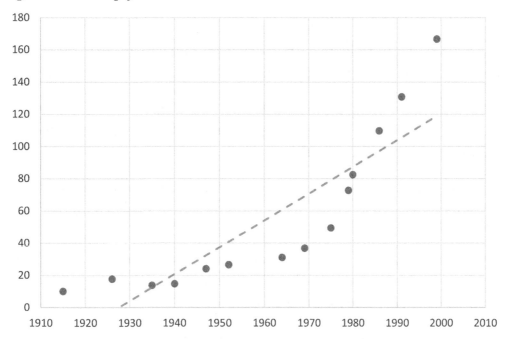

51) The equation for the least-squares regression line is $\hat{y} = -3202 + 1.661x$ where $\hat{y}$ is the predicted yield and x is the year.

52) The line has been drawn on the scatter plot, illustrating the trend of crop yield over the years.

53) The correlation coefficient is approximately 0.869, indicating a strong positive linear relationship between the year and crop yield. It is considered significant.

54) The estimated yield for the year 1990 is approximately 103.39 tons per hectare.

55) Yes, it does. Increased physical activity typically leads to better cardiovascular health.

56) Yes, this relationship generally reflects both correlation and causation. More practice usually leads to higher skill levels.

57) This relationship reflects correlation but not necessarily causation. While people who drink coffee often report increased alertness, other factors might contribute to this alertness.

58) This relationship shows correlation but not clear causation. People who feel lonely might use social media more, but it's not evident that social media use directly reduces loneliness.

59) This relationship reflects both correlation and causation. Warmer weather leads to more people buying ice cream.

60) This relationship shows correlation but not necessarily causation. People who listen to classical music might have better concentration, but other factors could contribute to this.

61) Outliers: None within this range.   63) Outliers: 208 is an outlier.

62) Outliers: 200 is an outlier.   64) Outliers: 150 is an outlier.

65) An R −squared value of 1 indicates that the regression model perfectly predicts the dependent variable. All points lie exactly on the regression line, with no variation unexplained by the model.

66) Yes, an R −squared value can be negative, although it's rare. It would indicate that the model is worse at predicting than using the mean of the dependent variable as a simple model.

67) An R −squared value of 0.65 means that 65% of the variation in test scores can be explained by the number of hours studied. This indicates a moderate to strong linear relationship between studying and test scores.

68) An R −squared value of 0.10 is quite low, indicating that only 10% of the variance in academic performance can be explained by hours of online gaming. This implies a very weak predictive relationship.

69) 0.993   71) 0.995

70) 0.99   72) 0.981

73) Residuals: $e_1 = 15 - (5 \times 2 + 2) = 15 - 12 = 3$.
$e_2 = 20 - (5 \times 3 + 2) = 20 - 17 = 3$.
$e_3 = 25 - (5 \times 4 + 2) = 25 - 22 = 3$.
All residuals are equal, suggesting the model predicts consistently across different values of x.

74) Residuals: $e_1 = 150 - (10 \times 10 + 50) = 150 - 150 = 0$.

$e_2 = 200 - (10 \times 15 + 50) = 200 - 200 = 0$.

$e_3 = 250 - (10 \times 20 + 50) = 250 - 250 = 0$.

There is no pattern in the residuals as they are all zero, indicating perfect predictions.

75) Residuals: $e_1 = 9 - (2 \times 2 + 5) = 9 - 9 = 0$.

$e_2 = 11 - (2 \times 3 + 5) = 11 - 11 = 0$.

$e_3 = 13 - (2 \times 4 + 5) = 13 - 13 = 0$.

There is no pattern to the residuals, and they are all zero, suggesting accurate predictions.

76) Residuals: $e_1 = 44 - (4 \times 5 + 20) = 44 - 40 = 4$.

$e_2 = 52 - (4 \times 7 + 20) = 52 - 48 = 4$.

$e_3 = 60 - (4 \times 9 + 20) = 60 - 56 = 4$.

The residuals are consistent, with no pattern indicating the model's predictions are consistently off by the same amount across different x values.

77) Residual analysis is important to validate the assumptions of a linear regression model. It helps to check if the relationship is indeed linear, if the errors are randomly distributed and have constant variance, and if there are no outliers that unduly influence the model.

78) If the residuals show a pattern, this indicates that the model is not capturing some aspect of the relationship, suggesting that the model may need to be improved, possibly by considering non-linear relationships or interaction effects.

79) Increasing residuals with higher calorie intake could imply that the relationship between calorie intake and weight loss is not purely linear or that there are other variables affecting weight loss that are not included in the model.

80) Mostly positive residuals suggest that the theoretical model consistently underestimates the distance the ball rolls. This could be due to systematic errors in measurement or an incomplete model that doesn't account for all the forces acting on the ball.

81) Independent Variable: Year (time). Dependent Variable: Average monthly data usage (GB).

82) A scatter plot has been drawn showing the relationship between the year and the data usage.

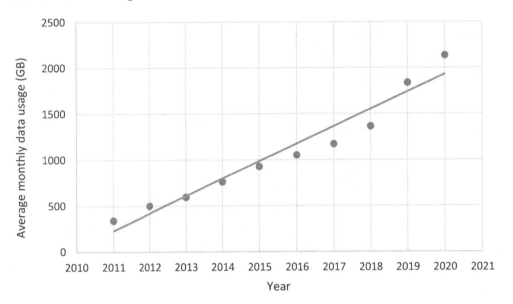

83) The line of best fit has been found using linear regression.
The correlation coefficient is 0.973, indicating a very strong positive relationship.

84) Since the correlation coefficient is close to 1, it signifies that there is a strong positive linear relationship between the year and the data usage.

85) Yes, there is a linear relationship between the variables, as suggested by the high correlation coefficient and visual evidence from the scatter plot.

86) The coefficient of determination (R^2) is 0.947, meaning that approximately 94.7% of the variation in data usage can be explained by the year.

87) The slope of the regression equation is 186.1. This means that for each year, the average data usage increases by about $186.1\ GB$.

88) The regression equation is: $\hat{y} = 186.1x - 374048$. The estimated average monthly data usage for the year 2010 is $13\ GB$. The estimated average monthly data usage for the year 2035 is $4665.5\ GB$.

89) The years 2011, 2012, 2013, 2019, and 2020 have significant residuals, indicating they may be outliers.

90) Multiple linear regression is a statistical technique that models the relationship between a dependent variable and two or more independent variables. In this scenario, it can be used to predict house prices (dependent variable) by using square footage, number of bedrooms, and age of the house (independent variables).

91) Multiple linear regression is better because BMI is likely influenced by more than one factor. By using multiple predictors such as calorie intake, protein intake, and exercise hours, the model can account for the combined effect of these variables, leading to more accurate predictions.

92) The model equation would be:
$Overall\ Health\ Index = \beta_0 + \beta_1 \times Exercise\ Hours + \beta_2 \times Diet\ Quality\ Score + \beta_3 \times Sleep\ Duration + \epsilon$

93) The equation would be:
$Income = \beta_0 + \beta_1 \times Education\ Level + \beta_2 \times Work\ Experience + \beta_3 \times Region + \epsilon$

94) The model would be framed as:
$Sales = \beta_0 + \beta_1 \times Television\ Spend + \beta_2 \times Online\ Spend + \beta_3 \times Radio\ Spend + \epsilon$

11 Analysis of Variance (ANOVA)

Topics that you'll learn in this chapter:

- ☑ F –Statistics Calculation in ANOVA
- ☑ The F Distribution
- ☑ One-Way ANOVA
- ☑ Test of Two Variances

325

F –Statistics Calculation in ANOVA

- You should have data for three or more groups.

- Sum of Squares Between Groups (SSB) measures how much each group mean deviates from the overall mean.
  $SSB = \sum n_i(\bar{y}_i - \bar{y})^2$, where n_i is the number of observations in group i, $\bar{y}_i$ is the mean of group i, and $\bar{y}$ is the overall mean.

- Sum of Squares Within Groups (SSW) measures the variation within each group.
  $SSW = \sum(y_{ij} - \bar{y}_i)^2$, where y_{ij} is an individual observation in group i.

- Degrees of Freedom:
  - For SSB, $dfB = number\ of\ groups - 1$
  - For SSW, $dfW = total\ number\ of\ observations - number\ of\ groups$

- Calculate Mean Squares:
  - Mean Square Between (MSB): $MSB = \frac{SSB}{dfB}$
  - Mean Square Within (MSW): $MSW = \frac{SSW}{dfW}$

- Calculate the F –Statistic: $F = \frac{MSB}{MSW}$

- A high F –value suggests that there are significant differences between the group means.

- Use an F – distribution table to find the critical F – value at a certain significance level (commonly 0.05) and compare.

Example:

In a study involving four groups of students, with each group consisting of 8 students, what is the comparison between the calculated F – value and the critical F –value? The SSB is 160, and SSW is 140.

Solution: Degrees of freedom for SSB is: $dfB = 4 - 1 = 3$. and Degrees of freedom for SSW is: $dfW = 32 - 4 = 28$.
Now, Calculate Mean Squares: $MSB = \frac{160}{3} \approx 53.33$, $MSW = \frac{140}{28} = 5$
So, $F = \frac{53.33}{5} \approx 10.67$, Critical F –value at the chosen significance level: 2.95

Since the calculated F –value (10.67) is greater than the critical F –value (2.95), this indicates that the differences among the group means are statistically significant. In other words, it is unlikely that these differences are due to random chance. This result suggests that at least one of the group means is significantly different from the others in the context of your study.

The F–Distribution

- The F–distribution is a probability distribution used in statistics to compare variances. It helps in determining whether the differences observed between data sets are significant or just due to random chance.
- Characteristics of the F–Distribution:
- Shape: It is skewed to the right and its exact shape changes depending on the degrees of freedom.
- Range: The values in an F– distribution are always positive, ranging from 0 to infinity.

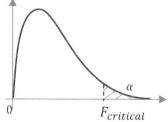

- Degrees of Freedom: It depends on two sets of degrees of freedom – one for the numerator and one for the denominator.
- Commonly used in ANOVA to compare the means of three or more groups, and in regression analysis to test the significance of the regression equation.
- F–distribution tables provide critical values for different degrees of freedom and significance levels (e.g., 0.05 or 5%).
- To use the table, you need the degrees of freedom for both the numerator and the denominator and the desired level of significance.

Example:

A high school teacher wants to compare the variances in test scores between two different teaching methods. Method A was used for a class of 12 students, and Method B for a class of 15 students. The variance in test scores for Method A is 16, and for Method B, it is 25.

Objective: To determine if there is a significant difference in variances of test scores between the two teaching methods.

Solution: First, Calculate the F–Statistic: $F = \frac{Variance\ of\ Method\ B}{Variance\ of\ Method\ A} = \frac{25}{16} = 1.56$

Degrees of Freedom: $df_{numerator} = df_{Method\ B} = 15 - 1 = 14$

$$df_{denominator} = df_{Method\ A} = 12 - 1 = 11$$

Using the F–distribution table, find the critical value for df_{14} and df_{11} at the desired significance level (e.g., 0.05): critical value = 2.56

$F = 1.56$ is smaller than the critical value, so there is no significant difference that can be concluded.

One-Way ANOVA

- It's a test that allows us to compare more than two groups at the same time to see if they are significantly different.
- "One-Way" means there is only one factor or independent variable with multiple levels.
- Compare the calculated $F-$ statistic with the critical value from $F-$distribution tables for a chosen significance level (commonly 0.05).
- A significant $F-$statistic (higher than the critical value) suggests that there are differences between the group means.

Example:

Imagine a study investigating the effectiveness of three different types of diets on weight loss. The study has 15 participants, divided into three groups (5 in each group), each group following a different diet plan.

The weight loss (in pounds) after two months is recorded for each participant. Here's the hypothetical data:

Diet A: $\{8, 7, 6, 9, 10\}$, Diet B: $\{5, 4, 6, 5, 3\}$, Diet C: $\{3, 2, 4, 3, 5\}$

Task: Use One-Way ANOVA to determine if there are any statistically significant differences in the effectiveness of these diet plans.

Solution: (H_0): There is no significant difference in weight loss among the three different diet plans.

Calculate Group Means and Overall Mean:

$$\bar{y}_A = \frac{8+7+6+9+10}{5} = 8.0 \ lb, \ \bar{y}_B = \frac{5+4+6+5+3}{5} = 4.6 \ lb, \ \bar{y}_C = \frac{3+2+4+3+5}{5} = 3.4 \ lb$$

$$\bar{y} = \frac{8\times5+4.6\times5+3.4\times5}{15} = 5.33 \ lb$$

Calculate (SSB) and (SSW):

$$SSB = 5((8.0 - 5.33)^2 + (4.6 - 5.33)^2 + (3.4 - 5.33)^2) = 5 \times 11.3867 = 56.9335$$

$$\sum(y_A - \bar{y}_A)^2 = 10, \ \sum(y_B - \bar{y}_B)^2 = 5.2, \ \sum(y_C - \bar{y}_C)^2 = 5.2, \ SSW = 10 + 5.2 + 5.2 = 20.4$$

Now, Calculate (MSB) and (MSW): $MSB = \dfrac{SSB}{number\ of\ groups-1} = \dfrac{56.9335}{3-1} = 28.46675$

$$MSW = \frac{SSW}{total\ number\ of\ observations-number\ of\ groups} = \frac{20.4}{15-3} \approx 1.7$$

Calculate the $F-$Statistic: $F = \dfrac{MSB}{MSW} = \dfrac{28.46675}{1.7} \approx 16.745$

The critical $F-$value from the $F-$distribution table at a 0.05 significance level for $df_{numerator} = 2$ and $df_{denominator} = 12$ is approximately 3.89. Since $16.745 > 3.89$, we reject the null hypothesis.

Test of Two Variances

- The Test of Two Variances, often called the F-test, is a simple yet powerful tool used to compare the variances of two different sets of data.

- Variance measures how spread out a set of numbers is. It's the average of the squared differences from the mean.

- A higher variance means more spread-out data.

- Purpose of the Test: To see if there is a significant difference in the spread (variance) of two groups.

- Hypotheses: H_0: The two groups have the same variance. H_1: The two groups have different variances.

  Calculating the F-Statistic: First, calculate the variance of each group. The F-statistic is the ratio of the higher variance to the lower variance.

  $F = \frac{Variance\ of\ Group\ 1}{Variance\ of\ Group\ 2}$ (assuming Group 1 has a higher variance).

- Each group's degrees of freedom is one less than its sample size $n - 1$.

- If the F-statistic is larger than the critical value at a chosen significance level (usually 0.05), it suggests the variances are different.

Example:

A teacher is interested in comparing the variability in test scores between two classes. Class A has a variance in scores of 20, while Class B's variance is 10. Both Class A and Class B consist of 15 students each. How does the calculated F-statistic compare to the critical F-value?

Solution: Calculate the F-statistic: $F = \frac{20}{10} = 2$.

Degrees of freedom for each class is $15 - 1 = 14$.

The critical F-value for $df_1 = 14$ and $df_2 = 14$ at the 0.05 significance level in an F-distribution table is approximately 2.48.

The calculated F-statistic (2) is less than the critical F-value (2.48). Therefore, the teacher cannot conclude that there is a significant difference in score variability between the two classes.

Chapter 11: Practices

✍ Use the following information to answer the next five questions

You are conducting a statistical analysis on a study evaluating the effectiveness of three different diets on weight loss. To determine if there's a significant difference in the average weight loss among these diets, you decide to use a one-way ANOVA test.

1) Identify one basic assumption necessary for conducting a one-way ANOVA test.

2) Mention another assumption required for this test.

3) State a third assumption for the one-way ANOVA test.

4) List a fourth assumption essential for the validity of this test.

5) Describe the final assumption needed for a one-way ANOVA test.

6) Formulate the null hypothesis for a one-way ANOVA test involving three diet groups.

7) State the alternative hypothesis for the same one-way ANOVA test.

8) Explain the circumstances under which a one-way ANOVA test is typically used.

✍ **Use the following information to answer the next questions**

In a botanical study, three different greenhouse environments are being compared for their effect on the growth rate of a particular plant species. The recorded growth rates (in millimeters per week) are analogous to the weights in the provided table.

	Greenhouse 1	Greenhouse 2	Greenhouse 3
1	216	202	170
2	198	213	165
3	240	284	182
4	187	228	197
5	176	210	201

9) What is the sum of squares factor?

10) What is the sum of squares error?

11) What is the df for the numerator?

12) What is the df for the denominator?

13) What is the mean square factor?

14) What is the mean square error?

15) What is the F statistic?

✎ **Use the following information to answer the next questions.**

In a science fair, four different experimental plant fertilizers are being evaluated for their effect on plant growth. The number of flowers produced by plants using each fertilizer type is recorded, as shown in the table below:

	Fertilizer 1	Fertilizer 2	Fertilizer 3	Fertilizer 4
Plant Set 1	1	2	0	3
Plant Set 2	2	3	1	4
Plant Set 3	0	2	1	4
Plant Set 4	3	4	0	3
Plant Set 5	2	4	0	2

16) What is the sum of squares between groups (SSB)?

17) What are the degrees of freedom (df) for the numerator?

18) What is the mean square between groups (MSB)?

19) What is the sum of squares within groups (SSW)?

20) What are the degrees of freedom (df) for the denominator?

21) What is the mean square within groups (MSW)?

22) What is the F statistic?

23) Based on the F statistic, is it likely or unlikely that the null hypothesis will be rejected?

✍ **Answer the questions based on the scenario.**

Five soccer teams conducted a random sample of players to measure their sprint speed over a distance of 40 meters. The results are shown in the table.

Team A	Team B	Team C	Team D	Team E
5.1	4.8	5.3	5.0	4.9
5.2	5.0	5.5	5.1	5.0
5.4	5.2	5.6	5.3	5.1

24) What is the df(num)? (degrees of freedom between groups)

25) What is the df(denom)? (degrees of freedom within groups)

26) What is the sum of squares and mean squares between groups?

27) What is the sum of squares and mean squares within groups?

28) What is the F statistic?

29) What is the p−value?

30) At the 5 percent significance level, is there a difference in the mean sprint speeds among the teams?

✍ **Answer the questions based on the scenario.**

Two students are studying for their finals and want to understand if there is any difference in their studying habits.

They track the number of hours they study each day for a month. The first student's study times have a variance of 5.4. The second student's study times have a variance of 9.1. The first student believes that her study times are more consistent than her colleague's.

They decide to test this hypothesis at the 10 percent significance level, assuming that study times follow a normal distribution.

31) State the null and alternative hypotheses.

32) What is s_1^2 in this problem? (variance of the first student).

33) What is s_2^2 in this problem? (variance of the second student).

34) What is n? (the number of observations for each student).

35) What is the F statistic? (the ratio of the variances).

36) What is the p −value? (probability of observing such a result if H_0 is true)

37) Is the claim accurate? (based on the p −value and the significance level)

🖎 **Solve.**

38) In an experiment with four different fertilizers applied to groups of 10 plants each, how does the calculated F-value compare to the critical F-value? The Sum of Squares Between treatments (SSB) is 200, and Sum of Squares Within treatments (SSW) is 180.

39) In a clinical trial comparing four different dosages of a medication, with each dosage tested on 7 patients, what is the comparison between the calculated F-value and the critical F-value? The SSB is 150, and SSW is 105.

40) Consider a study assessing the impact of three different types of sleep interventions on the quality of sleep. The study involves 15 participants, divided equally into three groups (5 in each group), with each group experiencing a different sleep intervention.

The increase in sleep quality scores (on a scale of 1 to 10) after a month is recorded for each participant. The hypothetical data is as follows:

Intervention A: $\{8, 7, 9, 6, 8\}$

Intervention B: $\{5, 6, 4, 5, 7\}$

Intervention C: $\{7, 8, 7, 6, 5\}$

Task: Use One-Way ANOVA to determine if there are any statistically significant differences in the effectiveness of these sleep interventions.

Use the following information to answer the next five questions.

Two chefs are comparing the variances of the time it takes them to prepare a signature dish. Each chef records the preparation times for 40 dishes. The first chef has a variance of 12.4, and the second chef has a variance of 18.6. They want to determine if there is a statistically significant difference between their variances in preparation times.

41) State the null and alternative hypotheses.

42) What is the F statistic.

43) At the 5 percent significance level, what can we say about the chefs' variances.

44) How many degrees of freedom are there for this F −test.

45) What is the p −value?

Chapter 11: Answers

1) Independence: Each group's data should be independent of the others.

2) Normality: The data in each group should be approximately normally distributed.

3) Homogeneity of Variances: All groups should have similar variances.

4) Random Sampling: The data should be collected from a random sample from the population.

5) Level of Measurement: The dependent variable should be measured at least at the interval level.

6) Null Hypothesis (H_0): There is no significant difference in average weight loss among the three diets.

7) Alternative Hypothesis (H_1): At least one diet leads to a significantly different average weight loss compared to the others.

8) A one-way ANOVA test is used when comparing the means of three or more independent groups to see if there is a statistically significant difference among them.

9) 4939.2

10) 7920.4

11) 2

12) 12

13) 2469.6

14) 660.03

15) 3.74

16) 25.75

17) 3

18) 8.58

19) 13.2

20) 16

21) 0.825

22) 10.40

23) Judging by the F statistic, it seems likely that the null hypothesis will be rejected, indicating that there are significant differences in the number of flowers produced by the plants using different fertilizers.

24) $df(num) = Number\ of\ groups - 1 = 5 - 1 = 4$

25) $df(denom) = Total\ number\ of\ observations - Number\ of\ groups$
    $= (3 \times 5) - 5 = 15 - 5 = 10$

26) $SSB \approx 0.45$, $MSB \approx 0.11$

27) $SSW \approx 0.24$, $MSW \approx 0.024$

28) 4.72

29) 0.021

30) The $p-$value is less than 0.05, we reject the null hypothesis and conclude that there is a significant difference in the mean sprint speeds among the teams.

31) Null hypothesis (H_0): The variances are equal, i.e., $\sigma_1^2 = \sigma_2^2$.
    Alternative hypothesis (H_1): The variances are not equal, i.e., $\sigma_1^2 \neq \sigma_2^2$.

32) $s_1^2 = 5.4$

33) $s_2^2 = 9.1$

34) $n = 30$ (assuming they recorded their study times for a month with 30 days).

35) $F = \dfrac{s_1^2}{s_2^2} = \dfrac{5.4}{9.1} \approx 0.59$

36) $P-$value ≈ 0.083

37) Given that the $p-$value (0.083) is less than the significance level of 0.10, we reject the null hypothesis. This suggests that there is a statistically significant difference in the consistency of their study times, supporting the first student's claim that her study times are more consistent than her colleague's.

38) Degrees of freedom for SSB: $dfB = 4 - 1 = 3$. Degrees of freedom for SSW: $dfW = 40 - 4 = 36$.
    Calculate Mean Squares: MSB $= \dfrac{200}{3} \approx 66.67$, MSW $= \dfrac{180}{36} = 5$.
    $F = \dfrac{66.67}{5} \approx 13.33$. With a critical $F-$value of 2.87, the calculated $F-$value (13.33) is significantly greater, indicating statistically significant differences in plant growth between the different fertilizers.

39) Degrees of freedom for SSB: $dfB = 4 - 1 = 3$. Degrees of freedom for SSW: $dfW = 28 - 4 = 24$.

Calculate Mean Squares: MSB $= \frac{150}{3} = 50$, MSW $= \frac{105}{24} \approx 4.38$.

$F = \frac{50}{4.38} \approx 11.42$. With a critical F-value of 3.01, the calculated F-value (11.42) is significantly higher, suggesting significant differences in patient responses to different medication dosages.

40) (dfB): 2, (dfW): 12, (SSB): 12.13, (SSW): 15.60, $F \approx 4.67$.

The critical F-value, found in an F-distribution table for 2 and 12 degrees of freedom at a commonly used significance level of 0.05, is 3.89.

The calculated F-statistic (4.67) is greater than the critical F-value, it indicates that there is a statistically significant difference in the effectiveness of the different sleep interventions.

41) Null Hypothesis (H_0): There is no difference in variances, $\sigma_1^2 = \sigma_2^2$.
Alternative Hypothesis (H_1): There is a difference in variances, $\sigma_1^2 \neq \sigma_2^2$.

42) $F = \frac{s_1^2}{s_2^2} = \frac{12.4}{18.6} \approx 0.667$

43) Since the p-value (0.895) is greater than the significance level of 0.05 (5 percent), we do not have enough evidence to reject the null hypothesis.

44) The degrees of freedom for the numerator (df_1) and denominator (df_2) are both $(n - 1)$, where n is the number of observations. So, $df_1 = df_2 = 40 - 1 = 39$.

45) p-value ≈ 0.895

Time to Test

Time to refine your statistics skills with a practice test.

Take a Statistics test to simulate the test day experience. After you've finished, score your test using the answer keys.

Before You Start

- You'll need a pencil and a calculator to take the test.

- For multiple questions, there are five possible answers. Choose which one is best.

- It's okay to guess. There is no penalty for wrong answers.

- Use the answer sheet provided to record your answers.

- **Scientific calculator is permitted for Statistics Test.**

- After you've finished the test, review the answer key to see where you went wrong.

Good Luck!

Statistics Practice
Test 1
2024

Total number of questions: 40
Total time: No time limit
Calculator is permitted for Statistics Test.

343

Statistics Practice Test Answer Sheet

Remove (or photocopy) this answer sheet and use it to complete the practice test.

Statistics Practice Test 1 Answer Sheet

1 Ⓐ Ⓑ Ⓒ Ⓓ Ⓔ	21 Ⓐ Ⓑ Ⓒ Ⓓ Ⓔ
2 Ⓐ Ⓑ Ⓒ Ⓓ Ⓔ	22 Ⓐ Ⓑ Ⓒ Ⓓ Ⓔ
3 Ⓐ Ⓑ Ⓒ Ⓓ Ⓔ	23 Ⓐ Ⓑ Ⓒ Ⓓ Ⓔ
4 Ⓐ Ⓑ Ⓒ Ⓓ Ⓔ	24 Ⓐ Ⓑ Ⓒ Ⓓ Ⓔ
5 Ⓐ Ⓑ Ⓒ Ⓓ Ⓔ	25 Ⓐ Ⓑ Ⓒ Ⓓ Ⓔ
6 Ⓐ Ⓑ Ⓒ Ⓓ Ⓔ	26 Ⓐ Ⓑ Ⓒ Ⓓ Ⓔ
7 Ⓐ Ⓑ Ⓒ Ⓓ Ⓔ	27 Ⓐ Ⓑ Ⓒ Ⓓ Ⓔ
8 Ⓐ Ⓑ Ⓒ Ⓓ Ⓔ	28 Ⓐ Ⓑ Ⓒ Ⓓ Ⓔ
9 Ⓐ Ⓑ Ⓒ Ⓓ Ⓔ	29 Ⓐ Ⓑ Ⓒ Ⓓ Ⓔ
10 Ⓐ Ⓑ Ⓒ Ⓓ Ⓔ	30 Ⓐ Ⓑ Ⓒ Ⓓ Ⓔ
11 Ⓐ Ⓑ Ⓒ Ⓓ Ⓔ	31 Ⓐ Ⓑ Ⓒ Ⓓ Ⓔ
12 Ⓐ Ⓑ Ⓒ Ⓓ Ⓔ	32 Ⓐ Ⓑ Ⓒ Ⓓ Ⓔ
13 Ⓐ Ⓑ Ⓒ Ⓓ Ⓔ	33 Ⓐ Ⓑ Ⓒ Ⓓ Ⓔ
14 Ⓐ Ⓑ Ⓒ Ⓓ Ⓔ	34 Ⓐ Ⓑ Ⓒ Ⓓ Ⓔ
15 Ⓐ Ⓑ Ⓒ Ⓓ Ⓔ	35 Ⓐ Ⓑ Ⓒ Ⓓ Ⓔ
16 Ⓐ Ⓑ Ⓒ Ⓓ Ⓔ	36 Ⓐ Ⓑ Ⓒ Ⓓ Ⓔ
17 Ⓐ Ⓑ Ⓒ Ⓓ Ⓔ	37 Ⓐ Ⓑ Ⓒ Ⓓ Ⓔ
18 Ⓐ Ⓑ Ⓒ Ⓓ Ⓔ	38 Ⓐ Ⓑ Ⓒ Ⓓ Ⓔ
19 Ⓐ Ⓑ Ⓒ Ⓓ Ⓔ	39 Ⓐ Ⓑ Ⓒ Ⓓ Ⓔ
20 Ⓐ Ⓑ Ⓒ Ⓓ Ⓔ	40 Ⓐ Ⓑ Ⓒ Ⓓ Ⓔ

Answer questions 1and 2, based on the following information. A bakery buys 150 cartons of eggs, with each carton containing 12 eggs. The probability that a carton contains at least one rotten egg is $\frac{1}{300}$. Assume the probability of finding a rotten egg is the same in all cartons and events are independent between cartons.

1) Let Y be the total number of cartons, with at least one rotten egg, in the purchase. Which of the following statements is correct?

A. Y follows Binomial ($n = 150, p = \frac{1}{300}$)

B. Y follows Binomial ($n = 150, p = \frac{1}{12}$)

C. Y follows Binomial ($n = 1800, p = \frac{1}{300}$)

D. Y follows Binomial ($n = 1800, p = \frac{1}{12}$)

2) What is the probability that none of the 150 cartons contain a rotten egg?

A. $\frac{149}{150}$

B. $\left(\frac{149}{150}\right)^{150}$

C. $\left(\frac{11}{12}\right)^{150}$

D. $1 - \left(1 - \frac{149}{150}\right)^{150}$

3) Imagine a random variable Z that denotes the number of times a particular event occurs in 10 attempts. The probability of this event occurring in each attempt is 0.25. The probability of Z being equal to m is given by $P(Z = m) = \binom{10}{m} (0.25)^m (0.75)^{10-m}$ for $m = 0, 1, \ldots, 10$. What is the mean of Z?

A. 0.25

B. 0.75

C. 2.50

D. 7.50

Answer questions 4 − 7, based on the following information. U is the time Maria takes to finish her coffee, and it has the following probability density function:

$$F(U) = \begin{cases} k & \text{if } a \leq U \leq 2a, \\ 0 & \text{otherwise,} \end{cases}$$

where a, k are positive constants.

4) What is $P(U = 2a)$?

   A. 0

   B. $\frac{1}{a}$

   C. $\frac{1}{2}$

   D. 1

5) Find $P(U > \frac{5}{3}a | U > \frac{3}{2}a)$.

   A. $\frac{5}{6}a$

   B. $\frac{2}{3}a$

   C. $\frac{5}{6}$

   D. $\frac{2}{3}$

6) $P(U^2 > \frac{16a^2}{9}) = $ _____.

   A. $\frac{1}{3}$

   B. $\frac{2}{3}$

   C. $\frac{4}{9}$

   D. 1

7) Let V be the time another person, John, takes to finish his coffee. Suppose V has the same distribution as U and V, U are independent. What is the chance that John finishes sooner than Maria?

A. $\frac{1}{4}$

B. $\frac{1}{2}$

C. $\frac{a}{4}$

D. $\frac{a}{2}$

Answer questions 8 and 9, based on the following information. In a study about coffee consumption habits, a survey was conducted among a group of office workers. A 90 percent confidence interval for the proportion, q, of workers who prefer black coffee is (0.55, 0.65).

8) Which of the following is (are) true?

I. The margin of error is 0.05

II. Increasing the sample size will reduce the margin of error

III. We are 90% certain q is no less than 0.55

A. I only

B. II only

C. III only

D. I and II

9) Estimate the size of the sample used to construct the confidence interval.

A. 100

B. 260

C. 500

D. 1200

Questions 10 and 11 are based on the following information. A coffee shop serves a special blend of coffee 15 times daily. Let Y be the number of times the blend is sold out on any regular day. The distribution of Y is given, and it is known that $E(Y) = 5$ and $SD(Y) = 1.8$.

10) We want to test if the average number of times the blend is sold out is higher on weekends. Assume on a particular weekend day, the blend is sold out 10 times. Based on the data, the p −value is _____ and the test should _____.

   A. < 0.01, reject H_0

   B. 0.975, not reject H_0

   C. < 0.05, reject H_0

   D. 0.925, reject H_0

11) Suppose additional data is collected, such that including the observation in question 15, there are 25 randomly chosen weekend days, with the sample average, $\bar{Y} = 5.8$ and sample standard deviation, $s = 2.5$, of the number of times the blend is sold out. Based on all given information, the most appropriate test statistic is _____ and the test should be _____.

   A. 8, two-tailed

   B. 0.48, one-tailed

   C. 1.60, two-tailed

   D. 2.24, one-tailed

12) In a research study to evaluate the efficacy of a new dietary supplement for boosting energy levels, some participants, who experience fatigue, are given the supplement, while others are not. Those not receiving the supplement are unaware of this fact. Select the term which best describes the group of participants not receiving the supplement.

   A. Double-blind experiment

   B. Placebo effect

   C. Control group

   D. Experimental group

13) Determine the accuracy of the following statements about statistical distributions:

    I. All exponential distributions have the same rate parameter.

    II. The median and the mode of any positively skewed distribution are always equal.

    II. The x −axis serves as a horizontal asymptote for all exponential distributions.

    IV. The line of symmetry for all uniform distributions is at the midpoint of their range.

    A. I and IV

    B. II and III

    C. II and IV

    D. IV only

14) What is the effect of increasing the level of confidence while keeping the sample size constant on the width of a confidence interval for a population proportion? Assume the population distribution is not known precisely.

Choose your answer from the options below.

    A. The margin of error will increase because the critical value will increase. The increased margin of error will cause the confidence interval to be wider.

    B. The margin of error will decrease because the critical value will decrease. The decreased margin of error will cause the confidence interval to be narrower.

    C. The margin of error will increase because the critical value will decrease. The increased margin of error will cause the confidence interval to be wider.

    D. The margin of error will decrease because the critical value will increase. The decreased margin of error will cause the confidence interval to be narrower.

15) Which of the following would likely show a bimodal distribution in a histogram?

    A. The final exam scores for a calculus course.

    B. The heights of adults in a city.

    C. The daily temperatures over a year in a temperate climate zone.

    D. The number of books people read per month.

16) Researchers are conducting a study to understand the average annual income of families in a certain city. They survey 1000 families in the city and ask about their annual income. The mean of the annual income of these 1000 families would be a _____.

A. Parameter

B. Population

C. Sample

D. Statistic

17) A medium-sized tech company conducted a survey among its employees and received 250 responses. The survey asked the employees to provide the following information:

▪ Department (e.g., Engineering, Marketing, HR)

▪ Employment Status (Full-Time, Part-Time, Contract)

▪ Years of Experience

▪ Satisfaction Rating (on a scale of 1 to 5)

What type of graph would be most appropriate to display the relationship between the variables 'Department' and 'Employment Status'?

A. A side-by-side histogram should be used since these are two numerical variables.

B. A side-by-side bar chart should be used since these are two categorical variables.

C. A side-by-side bar chart should be used since these are two numerical variables.

D. A side-by-side histogram should be used since these are two categorical variables.

18) A nutritionist wants to investigate if a new diet plan helps in weight loss. She randomly selects 80 individuals - 40 will follow the new diet plan, and 40 will follow their usual diet. The participants are monitored for three months to track their weight changes. what type of study is this?

A. Observational study

B. Case study

C. Controlled experiment

D. Neither

Questions 19 – 21 are based on the following information. A sports equipment manufacturer produces tennis balls that are designed to have a diameter of 2.57 inches. The manufacturer regularly conducts tests to ensure the quality of the balls. If the mean diameter is found to be significantly different from 2.57 inches, the production process must be adjusted. A recent simple random sample of 20 tennis balls showed a mean diameter of 2.54 inches with a standard deviation of 0.08 inches. Assume that the population distribution is approximately normal. Perform a hypothesis test on the accuracy of the production process at the 0.05 level of significance.

19) State the null and alternative hypotheses for the test.

$H_0: \mu = 2.57$, $H_a: \mu$ ___ 2.57

A. $\neq$

B. $>$

C. $<$

D. $\leq$

20) Compute the value of the test statistic. Round your answer to three decimal places.

Answer: _____

21) Draw a conclusion and interpret the decision.

A. We fail to reject the null hypothesis and conclude that there is insufficient evidence at a 0.05 level of significance that the mean diameter of the tennis balls is significantly different from 2.57 inches.

B. We reject the null hypothesis and conclude that there is sufficient evidence at a 0.05 level of significance that the mean diameter of the tennis balls is significantly different from 2.57 inches.

C. We reject the null hypothesis and conclude that there is insufficient evidence at a 0.05 level of significance that the mean diameter of the tennis balls is significantly different from 2.57 inches.

D. We fail to reject the null hypothesis and conclude that there is sufficient evidence at a 0.05 level of significance that the mean diameter of the tennis balls is significantly different from 2.57 inches.

Questions 22 and 23 are based on the following information. Consider the graph (graph below) of probability density functions (PDFs) for two random variables, W and Z.

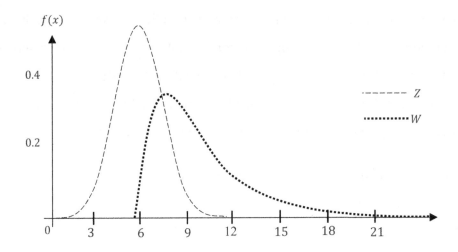

22) Which of the following statements is correct for W and Z?

   A. W and Z are both discrete

   B. W is continuous but Z is discrete

   C. Z is continuous but W is discrete

   D. W and Z are both continuous

23) Which of the following correctly describe(s) the relationship between W and Z?

   I. The mode of W is higher

   II. The variance of W is higher

   III. $P(W < 15) < P(Z < 3)$

   A. I only

   B. II only

   C. I and III only

   D. II and III only

24) A large company conducted a survey among its employees and received 500 responses. The survey asked the employees to provide the following information:

- Age
- Number of Training Sessions Attended in the Past Year
- Years of Service

What type of graph would be most appropriate to display the variable 'Number of Training Sessions Attended in the Past Year'?

A. A bar chart because the Number of Training Sessions Attended is a categorical variable.

B. A histogram because the Number of Training Sessions Attended is a numerical variable.

C. A bar chart because the Number of Training Sessions Attended is a numerical variable.

D. A histogram because the Number of Training Sessions Attended is a categorical variable.

25) Assume that the average heart rate for adults is 70 beats per minute with a standard deviation of 10 beats per minute. It is known that heart rate is not normally distributed. A sample of 36 adult heart rate measurements is taken from the population. What is the approximate z −value with interpretation for the probability that the average heart rate will be more than 73 beats per minute? Round to the nearest hundredth.

A. $z = 1.80$ which is greater than or equal to 2 standard deviations which is a significant result.

B. This probability cannot be determined because we do not know the distribution of the population.

C. $z = -1.80$ which is less than or equal to 2 standard deviations which is not a significant result.

D. $z = 1.80$ which is less than or equal to 2 standard deviations which is not a significant result.

26) What is the primary purpose of a single-blind experiment?

    A. To ensure that the results are statistically significant.

    B. To prevent bias in the participants' responses by keeping them unaware of their group assignment.

    C. To keep the researchers blind to the study's hypothesis.

    D. To eliminate the need for a control group in the experiment.

27) The following side-by-side bar graph shows the percentage of individuals adopting different fitness routines in the years 2010 and 2012. Use the bar graph to answer the question.

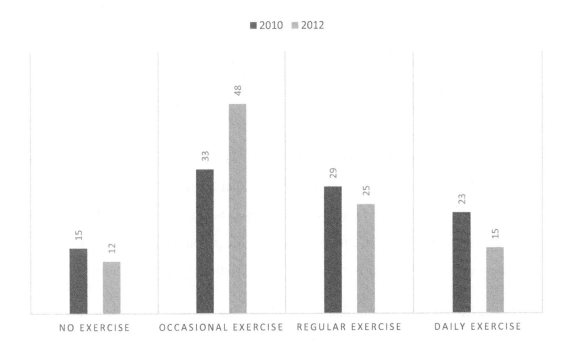

■ 2010　■ 2012

In which category was there more variability between 2010 and 2012?

    A. Regular Exercise

    B. No Exercise

    C. Occasional Exercise

    D. Daily Exercise

Answer questions 28 and 29, based on the following information.

Jackson enjoys reading books from his local library. Let Y be the number of books he checks out each visit. Suppose Y has the following probability distribution:

Y	0	1	2	3
$P(Y)$	0.1	0.3	0.2	0.4

28) Calculate $E(Y)$.

A. 0.5

B. 1.2

C. 1.4

D. 1.9

29) What is the average number of books Jackson checks out per visit when he checks out at least one book?

A. 1.0

B. 1.5

C. 2.0

D. 2.5

30) Based on the following probability density curve, answer the question.

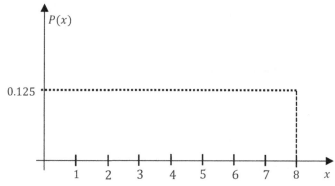

What is the probability that the random variable X is less than 6?

31) A survey is conducted to determine the preferred type of fruit between two groups of people: children and adults.

According to the following two-way table, why are percentages more useful than counts to compare fruit preferences between children and adults?

	Children	Adults
Apple	30	50
Banana	20	70

A. There are more people who prefer apples than bananas in the sample.

B. There are more adults than children in the sample.

C. You should only use counts in a two-way table.

D. You should only use percentages in a two-way table.

32) Choose the best statement to summarize the association shown between daily coffee consumption and productivity levels in the scatterplot below.

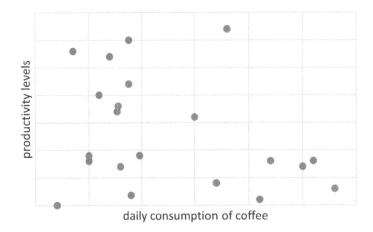

A. The scatterplot does not show a trend that would indicate an association between daily coffee consumption and productivity levels.

B. Coffee consumption causes productivity to increase.

C. As daily coffee consumption increases, productivity levels tend to increase.

D. As daily coffee consumption increases, productivity levels tend to decrease.

33) Match one of the histograms with its description.

The distribution of daily temperatures in a coastal city during summer is displayed in histogram _____.

A.

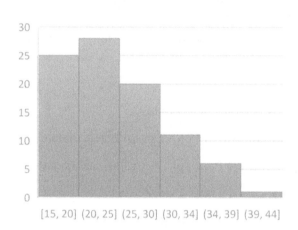

C.

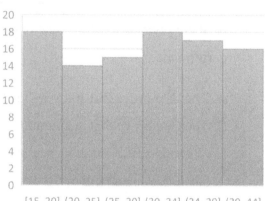

B.

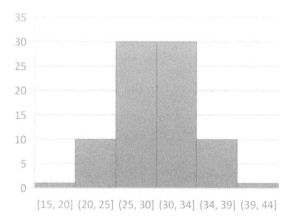

D.

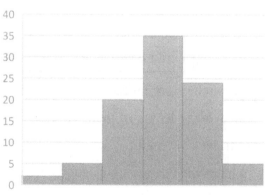

34) A study was conducted to examine the impact of different study durations on exam performance among students. A sample of 400 students provided the following data:

Study Duration

Performance	< 2 hours	2 − 5 hours	> 5 hours
Pass	80	120	60
Fail	40	60	40

Is there evidence of a relationship between the duration of studying and exam performance?

A. The data prove that studying longer improves exam performance.

B. The data prove that the duration of studying has no effect on exam performance.

C. There is sufficient evidence at the 1% significance level of a relationship between study duration and improved exam performance.

D. There is not sufficient evidence at the 10% level of a relationship between study duration and exam performance.

35) A study has been done types of trees and their average leaf length. Here's data and in table:

	Maple	Oak	Pine	Birch	Willow
Height (m)	5	10	15	20	25
Leaf Length (cm)	8	12	16	20	24

Researchers are investigating whether there is a correlation between the height of trees and the average length of their leaves. Five different tree species were measured for height and average leaf length.

What is the Pearson correlation coefficient for the given data? And what does the correlation coefficient suggest about the relationship between tree height and leaf length?

A. 0.0, No correlation

B. 0.5, Moderate positive correlation

C. 1.0, Perfect positive correlation

D. −1.0, Perfect negative correlation

36) A school is testing three different teaching methods to determine if there is a significant difference in student satisfaction. In the study, 180 students are randomly assigned to one of three groups, each receiving instruction by a different method. After a semester, students are surveyed for their satisfaction, and the results are as follows:

80 students preferred Method A, 50 preferred Method B, and 50 preferred Method C.

Is there sufficient evidence at the 5% significance level to conclude that there is a difference in student satisfaction among the three teaching methods?

A. No, with $\chi^2 = 12.2$, there is not sufficient evidence at the 5% level.

B. Yes, with $\chi^2 = 3.33$, there is sufficient evidence at the 5% level.

C. Yes, with $\chi^2 = 10.0$, there is sufficient evidence at the 5% level.

D. Yes, with $\chi^2 = 15.0$, there is sufficient evidence even at the 1% level.

37) Is it likely that more than 20% of people use public transportation for commuting? A random sample of 1500 people was surveyed and 25% of them said that they use public transportation for commuting. Find the 90% confidence interval for the proportion of people who use public transportation for commuting then choose the correct interpretation. (Round to the nearest tenth of a percent)

A. The population proportion of people who use public transportation is between 25% $\pm$ 2.1% with a confidence level of 90%. The interval includes 20% and therefore, it is likely that at least 20% of people use public transportation.

B. The population proportion of people who use public transportation is between 20% $\pm$ 2.1% with a confidence level of 90%. The interval includes 25% and therefore, it is likely that at least 25% of people use public transportation.

C. The population proportion of people who use public transportation is between 25% $\pm$ 1.05% with a confidence level of 90%. The interval does not include 20% and therefore, it is not likely that at least 20% of people use public transportation.

D. The population proportion of people who use public transportation is between 25% $\pm$ 1.9% with a confidence level of 90%. The interval is higher than 20% and therefore, it is likely that more than 20% of people use public transportation.

38) Imagine 3% of the population is allergic to a specific food ingredient. A new skin test can identify 90% of people who are allergic to this ingredient and also incorrectly identifies 10% of people who are not allergic as being allergic. What is the probability of testing positive for the allergy?

If a person tests positive for the allergy, what is the probability that the person is actually allergic to the ingredient?

A. 0.027, 0.218

B. 0.124, 0.218

C. 0.218, 0.124

D. 0.342, 0.027

39) In the context of clinical trials, what is the definition of a double-blinded experiment?

A. The participants are unaware of whether they are in the treatment or control groups.

B. Both the researchers conducting the experiment and the participants are unaware of who is in the treatment and control groups.

C. It is mandatory for both the researchers and participants to be aware of group assignments, as it is considered unethical to withhold this information.

D. Only the researchers are unaware of which participants are assigned to the treatment and control groups.

40) Complete the statement by filling in the blanks.

When interpreting the results of a hypothesis test, if the significance level (α) decreases, the likelihood of making a Type I error will _____ and the test becomes _____.

A. Increase; less strict.

B. Increase; more strict.

C. Decrease; less strict.

D. Decrease; more strict.

End of Statistics Practice Test 1

Statistics Practice
Test 2
2024

Total number of questions: 40
Total time: No time limit
Calculator is permitted for Statistics Test.

361

Statistics Practice Test Answer Sheet
Remove (or photocopy) this answer sheet and use it to complete the practice test.

Statistics Practice Test 2 Answer Sheet

1	Ⓐ Ⓑ Ⓒ Ⓓ Ⓔ	21	Ⓐ Ⓑ Ⓒ Ⓓ Ⓔ
2	Ⓐ Ⓑ Ⓒ Ⓓ Ⓔ	22	Ⓐ Ⓑ Ⓒ Ⓓ Ⓔ
3	Ⓐ Ⓑ Ⓒ Ⓓ Ⓔ	23	Ⓐ Ⓑ Ⓒ Ⓓ Ⓔ
4	Ⓐ Ⓑ Ⓒ Ⓓ Ⓔ	24	Ⓐ Ⓑ Ⓒ Ⓓ Ⓔ
5	Ⓐ Ⓑ Ⓒ Ⓓ Ⓔ	25	Ⓐ Ⓑ Ⓒ Ⓓ Ⓔ
6	Ⓐ Ⓑ Ⓒ Ⓓ Ⓔ	26	Ⓐ Ⓑ Ⓒ Ⓓ Ⓔ
7	Ⓐ Ⓑ Ⓒ Ⓓ Ⓔ	27	Ⓐ Ⓑ Ⓒ Ⓓ Ⓔ
8	Ⓐ Ⓑ Ⓒ Ⓓ Ⓔ	28	Ⓐ Ⓑ Ⓒ Ⓓ Ⓔ
9	Ⓐ Ⓑ Ⓒ Ⓓ Ⓔ	29	Ⓐ Ⓑ Ⓒ Ⓓ Ⓔ
10	Ⓐ Ⓑ Ⓒ Ⓓ Ⓔ	30	Ⓐ Ⓑ Ⓒ Ⓓ Ⓔ
11	Ⓐ Ⓑ Ⓒ Ⓓ Ⓔ	31	Ⓐ Ⓑ Ⓒ Ⓓ Ⓔ
12	Ⓐ Ⓑ Ⓒ Ⓓ Ⓔ	32	Ⓐ Ⓑ Ⓒ Ⓓ Ⓔ
13	Ⓐ Ⓑ Ⓒ Ⓓ Ⓔ	33	Ⓐ Ⓑ Ⓒ Ⓓ Ⓔ
14	Ⓐ Ⓑ Ⓒ Ⓓ Ⓔ	34	Ⓐ Ⓑ Ⓒ Ⓓ Ⓔ
15	Ⓐ Ⓑ Ⓒ Ⓓ Ⓔ	35	Ⓐ Ⓑ Ⓒ Ⓓ Ⓔ
16	Ⓐ Ⓑ Ⓒ Ⓓ Ⓔ	36	Ⓐ Ⓑ Ⓒ Ⓓ Ⓔ
17	Ⓐ Ⓑ Ⓒ Ⓓ Ⓔ	37	Ⓐ Ⓑ Ⓒ Ⓓ Ⓔ
18	Ⓐ Ⓑ Ⓒ Ⓓ Ⓔ	38	Ⓐ Ⓑ Ⓒ Ⓓ Ⓔ
19	Ⓐ Ⓑ Ⓒ Ⓓ Ⓔ	39	Ⓐ Ⓑ Ⓒ Ⓓ Ⓔ
20	Ⓐ Ⓑ Ⓒ Ⓓ Ⓔ	40	Ⓐ Ⓑ Ⓒ Ⓓ Ⓔ

Answer questions 1 and 2, based on the following information. In a different statistics course, the final exam score Y is also normally distributed. Maria scored in the $75th$ percentile on her exam.

1) Which of the following expressions calculates Maria's score, Y^* ?

   A. $P(Y \geq 75) = Y^*$

   B. $P(Y \leq 75) = Y^*$

   C. $P(Y \geq Y^*) = 0.75$

   D. $P(Y \leq Y^*) = 0.75$

2) In this course, students scoring at least 1.5 standard deviations below the mean are given a grade of D. Assume five students' scores are mutually independent. The probability that at least one of them receives a D is _____.

   A. 0.067^5

   B. $0.067(5)$

   C. $0.067(0.933)^4$

   D. $1 - 0.933^5$

3) A large company conducted a survey among its employees and received 500 responses. The survey asked the employees to provide the following information:

   ▪ Age

   ▪ Department (e.g., HR, Finance, Marketing, IT)

   ▪ Years of Service

   What type of graph would be most appropriate to display the variable 'Department'?

   A. A bar chart because Department is a categorical variable.

   B. A histogram because Department is a numerical variable.

   C. A bar chart because Department is a numerical variable.

   D. A histogram because Department is a categorical variable.

4) A factory produces bottles of soda and bottles of juice. The average volume of a bottle of soda is supposed to be 12.6 fluid ounces with an allowable deviation of 0.05 ounces. The average volume of a bottle of juice is supposed to be 16.07 fluid ounces with an allowable deviation of 0.06 ounces.

A quality control inspector randomly selects a bottle of soda from the production line and finds its volume to be 12.02 fluid ounces. Then, the inspector randomly selects a bottle of juice and finds its volume to be 16.04 fluid ounces.

Which description most accurately reflects the situation on the production line?

A. The soda bottle line is closer to the specifications given because its z −score is closer to the standard than the juice bottle line.

B. The soda bottle line is closer to the specifications given because its z −score is further from the standard than the juice bottle line.

C. The juice bottle line is closer to the specifications given because its z −score is closer to the standard than the soda bottle line.

D. The juice bottle line is closer to the specifications given because its z −score is further from the standard than the soda bottle line.

5) A company claims that 85% of its customers are satisfied with their products and services. In a random survey of 150 customers, 130 reported being satisfied. Establish a 95% confidence interval estimate of the proportion of all customers who are satisfied with the company's products and services.

A. 0.866 ± 0.054

B. 0.866 ± 0.038

C. 0.866 ± 0.044

D. 0.866 ± 0.071

Questions 6 and 7 are based on the following information. A clinical trial is conducted to compare the effectiveness of two therapies. Therapy X is a standard treatment, and the aim is to demonstrate that therapy Y, a new treatment, is more effective. In the trial, 150 patients each are randomly assigned one of the two therapies, X or Y. Among the 150 patients given therapy X, 45 showed improvement. Among the 150 patients given therapy Y, 60 showed improvement. Assume all data are independent.

6) Based on the data, which of the following tests should be used?

    A. Two sample test for proportions, one-sided

    B. One sample test for proportions, one-sided

    C. One sample test for proportions, two-sided

    D. t −test, one-sided

7) Based on the data, the test statistic is given by $\frac{D-E}{\sqrt{F}}$, where the most appropriate values of D, E, F are:

    A. $D = 0.4, E = 0.3, F = \frac{(0.4)(0.6)}{150} + \frac{(0.3)(0.7)}{150}$

    B. $D = 0.4, E = 0.3, F = \frac{(0.4)(0.6)+(0.3)(0.7)}{300}$

    C. $D = 0.4, E = 0.3, F = \frac{(0.35)(0.65)}{300}$

    D. $D = 60, E = 45, F = 150(0.4)(0.6) + 150(0.3)(0.7)$

8) In the context of drug testing, what does an open-label experiment aim to achieve?

    A. To determine the drug's effectiveness without any placebo control.

    B. To compare the drug's effects with a placebo without informing the participants.

    C. To ensure that neither the participants nor the researchers can influence the results.

    D. To evaluate how knowing the treatment affects the participants' responses.

Questions 9 − 11 are based on the following information. A survey suggests that 75% of adults use social media. A researcher believes this percentage is too low. To test this, the researcher conducts a simple random sample of 200 adults and finds that 160 of them use social media. Is there evidence to support the researcher's claim that more than 75% of adults use social media? Use a 0.05 level of significance.

9) State the null and alternative hypotheses for the test.

$H_0: p = 0.75$, $H_a: p$ ___ 0.75

A. $<$

B. $>$

C. $\geq$

D. $\neq$

10) Compute the value of the test statistic. Round your answer to two decimal places. Answer: _____

11) Draw a conclusion and interpret the decision.

A. We fail to reject the null hypothesis and conclude that there is insufficient evidence at a 0.05 level of significance that more than 75% of adults use social media.

B. We reject the null hypothesis and conclude that there is insufficient evidence at a 0.05 level of significance that more than 75% of adults use social media.

C. We fail to reject the null hypothesis and conclude that there is sufficient evidence at a 0.05 level of significance that more than 75% of adults use social media.

D. We reject the null hypothesis and conclude that there is sufficient evidence at a 0.05 level of significance that more than 75% of adults use social media.

Answer questions 12 − 14, based on the following information. Marina cultivates fruit trees as a hobby. Each tree produces M pieces of fruit (in a month). The PDF, $P(M = m)$ and CDF, $F(m)$, are given below:

Data Table:

m	0	1	2	3	4	5
$P(M = m)$	0.05	0.15	0.25	0.30	___	___
$F(m)$	___	___	___	___	0.95	___

12) The probability that a tree will produce 4 pieces of fruit is _____.

A. 0.05

B. 0.1

C. 0.2

D. 0.25

13) Suppose $E(M) = 2.8$, $Var(M) = 1.44$. Furthermore, suppose there are in total ten trees. Then the probability that there are more than 35 pieces of fruit in a month among the ten trees, assuming all events are independent, is, approximately _____.

A. 0.032

B. 0.05

C. 0.075

D. 0.1

14) Each piece of fruit has a probability $r = 0.25$ of containing a viable seed. The probability of 3 viable seeds from one tree is _____.

A. 0.0874

B. 0.0425

C. 0.0215

D. 0.0185

15) The graph illustrates the test scores of two different classes, Class *A* and Class *B*, on the same math test.

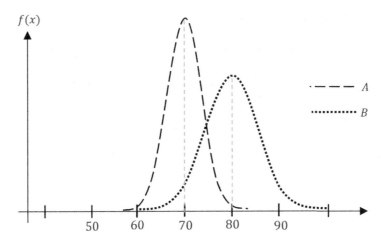

Based on the graph above, which statement best describes the graph?

A. Class *A* and Class *B* have average test scores that differ by 10 points and different variability in scores.

B. Class *A* and Class *B* have average test scores that differ by 10 points and similar variability in scores.

C. Class *A* and Class *B* have similar average test scores, but the variability in scores differs by 10 points.

D. Class *A* and Class *B* have similar average test scores and similar variability in scores.

16) The distribution of the number of books read by students per month is unimodal and symmetric with a mean of 4 books and a standard deviation of 2 books. If Maria had a $z-$score of -0.5, explain what this value means in terms of the number of books she reads.

A. Maria reads 0.5 books less than the average student.

B. The number of books Maria reads is 0.5 standard deviations below the mean.

C. Maria reads 0.5 books more than the average student.

D. The number of books Maria reads is 0.5 standard deviations above the mean.

Answer questions 9 and 10, based on the following information. Suppose D, E, and F are events such that: $P(D) = 0.3$, $P(E) = 0.6$, $P(D \cap E) = 0.18$, $P(F) = 0.4$, $P(D|F) = 0.5$, $P(E \cap F) = 0$.

17) Find the probability that at least one of the two events, D or E, happened.

    A. 0.3

    B. 0.6

    C. 0.72

    D. 0.78

18) Which of the following is not true, based on the given information?

    A. E and F are mutually exclusive.

    B. $P(E|F) + P(E|\overline{F}) = 1$.

    C. D and F are independent.

    D. $P(D|F) + P(D|\overline{F}) = 1$.

19) The average reading time for novels was measured for all novels released in the past year in the U.S. The mean reading time of all novels was found to be 6 hours with a standard deviation of 0.5 hours. Suppose a random sample of 30 novels was recorded from all novels released this year. The mean reading time of the novels in the sample was found to be 5.8 hours with a standard deviation of 0.6 hours.

If we create a sampling distribution of sample means, what would be the mean and standard deviation of that distribution given the sample size of 30?

    A. The mean reading time would be 6 hours with a standard deviation of 0.5 hours.

    B. The mean reading time would be 6 hours with a standard deviation of 0.6 hours.

    C. The mean reading time would be 6 hours with a standard deviation of 0.09 hours.

    D. The mean reading time would be 5.8 hours with a standard deviation of 0.6 hours.

20) A health researcher wants to determine if a new brand of vitamin supplement increases the average energy levels of individuals. The manufacturer claims that their supplement can increase average energy levels to 8 out of 10 on an energy scale. The researcher tested this claim by giving the supplement to 30 individuals and measuring their energy levels. The following are the summary statistics:

Mean $(\bar{x}) = 7.6$, Standard Deviation $(s) = 0.8$

Test the hypothesis that the supplement increases average energy levels to less than 8. Report the test statistic, p−value, your decision regarding the null hypothesis, and your conclusion about the original claim. Round all values to the nearest thousandth.

A. $t = -2.739$; $p = 0.005$; Reject the null hypothesis; there is strong evidence to suggest that the supplement increases average energy levels to less than 8.

B. $t = -2.739$; $p = 0.002$; Fail to reject the null hypothesis; there is not strong evidence to suggest that the supplement increases average energy levels to less than 8.

C. $z = 2.739$; $p = 0.998$; Fail to reject the null hypothesis; there is not strong evidence to suggest that the supplement increases average energy levels to less than 8.

D. $z = 2.739$; $p = 0.002$; Reject the null hypothesis; there is strong evidence to suggest that the supplement increases average energy levels to less than 8.

21) Which of the following scenarios best represents a single-blind experiment?

A. A taste test in which the participants do not know the brand of the product they are tasting, but the researchers do.

B. A study in which neither the participants nor the researchers know who receives the real medication or a placebo.

C. An experiment where both the researchers and participants are fully aware of the treatment each participant receives.

D. A study where only the data analysts are kept blind to the group assignments of participants.

22) Which scatterplot corresponds to the given correlation coefficient.

$$r = 0.95$$

A.

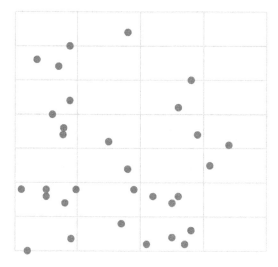

C.

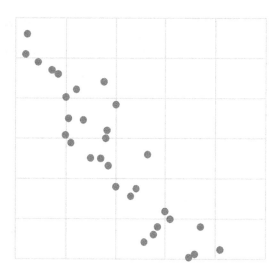

B.

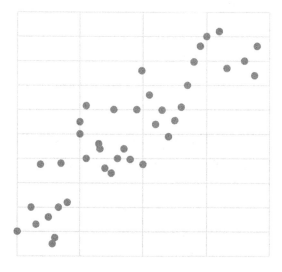

D.

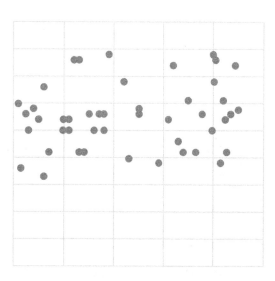

23) A research organization aims to estimate the difference in the proportion of U.S. citizens who favor a new environmental policy between younger (under 30) and older (over 60) age groups. They surveyed 3000 U.S. citizens and found a 90% confidence interval for the difference in proportions between the younger and older age groups as (-0.03 to 0.06), where population 1 is the younger group and population 2 is the older group. Select the correct interpretation of this result.

A. The interval contains zero, indicating that the younger group is more likely than the older group to favor the new environmental policy.

B. The interval does not contain zero, indicating no significant difference in proportions between the younger and older groups.

C. The interval contains zero, indicating no significant difference in proportions between the younger and older groups.

D. The interval contains zero, indicating that the older group is more likely than the younger group to favor the new environmental policy.

24) A quality control manager at a factory believes that the failure rate of their product is different from the failure rate claimed by the company. The manager's null hypothesis is that the failure rate of their products is $q = 0.05$ (the company's claimed failure rate). Suppose a hypothesis test is conducted with a significance level of 0.05. Symbolically, the null and alternative hypotheses are as follows: H_0: $q = 0.05$ and H_a: $q \neq 0.05$. Choose the statement that best describes the significance level in the context of the hypothesis test.

A. The significance level of 0.05 is the probability of concluding that the failure rate is equal to 0.05 when in fact it is not 0.05.

B. The significance level of 0.05 is the probability of concluding that the failure rate is different than 0.05 when in fact the failure rate is equal to 0.05.

C. The significance level of 0.05 is the z −statistic that we will use to compare the observed outcome to the null hypothesis.

D. The significance level of 0.05 is the failure rate we believe is the true failure rate.

25) A nutritionist believes that the average calorie intake of athletes in sport A is greater than that of athletes in sport B. She collects random samples of 50 athletes from each sport and records their daily calorie intake. The standard deviations for the two samples are 200 calories for sport A and 180 calories for sport B. If the average calorie intake from the sample of sport A athletes is 150 calories higher than that of sport B athletes, what conclusion is justified from a two-sample hypothesis test where:

$H_0: \mu_1 - \mu_2 = 0$ (There is no significant difference in average calorie intake between the two sports)

$H_a: \mu_1 - \mu_2 > 0$ (The average calorie intake of sport A athletes is greater than that of sport B athletes)

A. The observed difference in average calorie intake is significant.

B. The observed difference in average calorie intake is not significant.

C. A conclusion is not possible without knowing the mean calorie intake in each sample.

D. A conclusion is not possible without knowing both the sample means and the two original.

26) A survey was conducted on a group of 80 university students to determine whether they had bought any books related to their course in the last semester.

	Male	Female
Purchased books	15	35
Did not purchase books	10	20

Of the male university students surveyed, what percentage had purchased course-related books in the last semester?

A. 40%

B. 60%

C. 75%

D. 25%

27) The stemplot below shows the number of hours spent studying per week by two groups of students, Group *A* and Group *B*, during a semester.

Group *A*	Stem	Group *B*
5	1	7
4 4	2	2 3 9
2 3 6 7	3	0 1 4 5
8 9	4	6
	5	
1	6	8
4 7	7	9

Based on the stemplot, consider the following statements about the study hours of Group *A* and Group *B*:

I. The distributions have the same mean.

II. The distributions have the same range.

III. The distributions have the same standard deviation.

Which of the following are true statements?

A. II only

B. I and II

C. II and III

D. I, II, and III

28) Answer the question about the Law of Large Numbers. A fair dice is rolled 600 times. What can you say about getting the outcome of exactly 100 sixes?

A. Since the probability of rolling a six is $\frac{1}{6}$ for each roll, you should expect exactly 100 sixes in 600 rolls.

B. You should not expect exactly 100 sixes in 600 rolls, but the proportion of sixes should approach $\frac{1}{6}$ as the number of rolls increases.

C. You should expect between 80 and 120 sixes in 600 rolls.

D. Getting 100 sixes is no more likely than getting any other number of sixes in 600 rolls.

29) A survey on pet ownership found that in households with pets, 45% owned a dog, 30% owned a cat, and 10% owned a bird. Suppose that four households are selected randomly and with replacement.

What is the probability that at least one of the four randomly selected households owns a bird? (Round to the nearest thousandth)

A. 0.344

B. 0.900

C. 0.657

D. 0.010

30) The boxplots below summarize the distribution of final exam scores for two different subjects, History and Geography, among students in a high school.

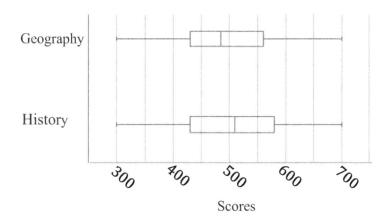

Which of the following statements are true?

I. The range of the Geography scores equals the range of the History scores.

II. The highest Geography score equals the median History score.

III. The History scores appear to be roughly symmetric, while the Geography scores appear to be skewed to the left.

A. I only

B. III only

C. I and II

D. II and III

31) A nutritionist in a suburban community believes that the type of breakfast consumed affects student performance in school. She plans an experiment in which an SRS of 30 high school sophomores will be given a high-protein breakfast, an SRS of 30 high school freshmen will be given a high-carbohydrate breakfast, and an SRS of 30 high school juniors with no specific breakfast guidance will serve as a control group. After one semester, the average test scores from each group will be compared. Is this a good experimental design?

A. Yes

B. No, because while this design may point out an association between breakfast type and test scores, it cannot establish a cause-and-effect relationship.

C. No, because without blinding, there is a strong chance of a placebo effect.

D. No, because the students' year in high school is a lurking variable which may well be confounded with the variables under consideration.

32) A marine biologist has recorded various data points for fish species observed during a research survey. This table represents the type of data that the marine biologist collected:

Species Name	Length (cm)	Habitat Depth (m)	Tagged	Swim Speed $\left(\frac{km}{h}\right)$
Salmon	75	200	Yes	8
Clownfish	10	2	Yes	1.5
Barracuda	120	10	No	36
Anglerfish	40	1000	No	1

How many variables has the biologist collected in this study?

A. 3

B. 4

C. 5

D. 6

33) The average time spent on homework by students in a particular school is 2 hours. Suppose the standard deviation of time spent on homework is 0.5 hours and the distribution of time spent on homework is approximately normally distributed. Approximately what percentage of students spend at least 2.5 hours on homework? Round to the nearest whole percent.

A. 30%

B. 20%

C. 70%

D. None of these.

34) Fifteen parents at a community meeting were asked the ages of their eldest child. The results are shown below.

8, 17, 13, 26, 4, 19, 12, 18, 14, 9, 21, 7, 11, 20, 16

Calculate the Interquartile Range (IQR) for this set of data.

A. 5

B. 9

C. 10

D. 19

35) Suppose there is a correlation of $r = 0.85$ between the number of books read by students over the summer and their scores on a standardized reading comprehension test at the beginning of the school year. Which of the following is a reasonable conclusion?

A. 85% of students who read books score high on the reading comprehension test.

B. 85% of the variation in reading comprehension test scores can be explained by the number of books read.

C. 15% of the variation in reading comprehension test scores cannot be explained by the number of books read over the summer.

D. 72.25% of the variation in reading comprehension test scores can be explained by the number of books read over the summer.

36) A tech company produces smartphones, and they source their components from two different suppliers. Supplier A provides 70% of the components, and the defect rate for their components is 0.02. Supplier B provides the remaining 30% of the components, and the defect rate for their components is 0.03. What proportion of the components can be expected to be defective?

If a defective component is found, what is the probability that it came from Supplier A?

A. 0.022, 0.700

B. 0.022, 0.667

C. 0.023, 0.609

D. 0.023, 0.750

37) The National Education Board (NEB) wants to estimate the percentage of high school teachers who feel the need for additional training in online teaching tools. To determine this percentage with a margin of error of $\pm 5\%$ at a 99% confidence level, what size sample should they survey?

A. 10

B. 66

C. 664

D. 845

38) A coffee machine is designed to fill cups with a specific amount of coffee. The machine's precision is such that the standard deviation in the amount of coffee delivered is 0.2 ounces. What should be the mean setting for the machine so that a 10 −ounce cup will overflow less than 1% of the time? Assume a normal distribution for ounces delivered.

A. 9.23 ounces

B. 9.53 ounces

C. 10.77 ounces

D. 10.70 ounces

39) A university claims that 60% of its students graduate within four years. A concerned group of students believes the actual graduation rate is lower. They conduct a survey of 250 students and find that only 140 students graduated within four years. Is this strong evidence to claim that the university's graduation rate is lower than 60%?

A. Yes, because the P −value is less than 0.05.

B. Yes, because the P −value is greater than 0.10.

C. No, because the P −value is less than 0.05.

D. No, because the P −value is greater than 0.10.

40) The graph below represents the cumulative grade distribution for a final exam in a large introductory statistics course, plotted against the scores out of a total of 100 points.

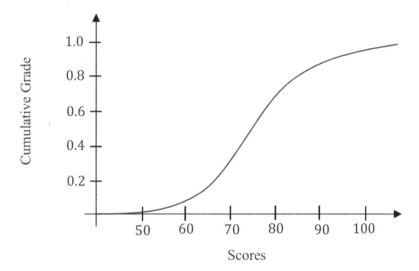

What is the median score of the final exam?

A. 60 points

B. 65 points

C. 70 points

D. 75 points

End of Statistics Practice Test 2

Statistics Practice Tests Answer Keys

Now, it's time to review your results to see where you went wrong and what areas you need to improve.

Statistics Practice Test 1				Statistics Practice Test 2			
1	A	21	A	1	D	21	A
2	B	22	D	2	D	22	B
3	C	23	B	3	A	23	C
4	A	24	B	4	C	24	B
5	D	25	D	5	A	25	A
6	B	26	B	6	A	26	B
7	B	27	C	7	A	27	A
8	D	28	D	8	D	28	B
9	B	29	C	9	B	29	A
10	A	30	75%	10	1.63	30	A
11	C	31	B	11	A	31	D
12	C	32	A	12	C	32	C
13	C	33	D	13	A	33	B
14	A	34	D	14	D	34	C
15	C	35	C	15	A	35	D
16	D	36	C	16	B	36	C
17	B	37	D	17	C	37	C
18	C	38	B	18	D	38	B
19	A	39	B	19	C	39	D
20	-1.677	40	D	20	A	40	D

Statistics Practice Tests 1 Explanations

1. Choice A is correct.

This is because the event we are considering is finding at least one rotten egg in a carton of eggs, which has a probability of $\frac{1}{300}$. Since there are 150 cartons, and the probability of finding a rotten egg is independent for each carton, the distribution of Y, the total number of cartons with at least one rotten egg, follows a binomial distribution with parameters $n = 150$ (number of trials or cartons) and $p = \frac{1}{300}$ (probability of success, which in this case is finding a rotten egg in a carton).

2. Choice B is correct.

This is calculated by considering the probability of not finding a rotten egg in a single carton, which is $1 - \frac{1}{300} = \frac{149}{150}$. Since there are 150 cartons and the events are independent, the probability that none of the 150 cartons contain a rotten egg is the product of the individual probabilities, which is $\left(\frac{149}{150}\right)^{150}$. This calculation follows from the properties of the binomial distribution, where we are calculating the probability of 0 successes (no cartons with rotten eggs) in 150 trials (cartons).

3. Choice C is correct.

We first recognize that the random variable Z follows a binomial distribution with parameters $n = 10$ (number of attempts) and $p = 0.25$ (probability of success on each attempt). The mean (or expected value) of a binomial distribution is given by the formula:

$$Mean = n \times p$$

Where: n is the number of trials, p is the probability of success on each trial, Let's calculate the mean for Z:

$$Mean_Z = 10 \times 0.25 = 2.50$$

So, the mean of the random variable Z is 2.50.

4. Choice A is correct.

This is because we are dealing with a continuous probability distribution. The probability of the variable taking on any single specific value in a continuous distribution is always zero. In this case, the probability that U equals exactly $2a$ is 0. because there are infinitely many points U could take in the interval from a to $2a$. The probability is spread across this entire interval, not concentrated at any point.

5. Choice D is correct.

This is a conditional probability question. We are given that U is greater than $\frac{3}{2}a$ and we need to find the probability that U is also greater than $\frac{5}{3}a$. The interval where U can lie is from $\frac{3}{2}a$ to $2a$. The portion of this interval where U is greater than $\frac{5}{3}a$ is from $\frac{5}{3}a$ to $2a$. The length of this portion over the length of the whole interval is:

$$\frac{2a - \frac{5}{3}a}{2a - \frac{3}{2}a} = \frac{2}{3}$$

6. Choice B is correct.

This question asks for the probability that U^2 is greater than $\frac{16a^2}{9}$. First, find the square root of $\frac{16a^2}{9}$, which is $(\frac{4a}{3})$. Now, we need the probability that U is greater than $\frac{4a}{3}$. The valid range for U is from a to $2a$, so the probability is:

$$\frac{2a - \frac{4a}{3}}{2a - a} = \frac{2}{3}$$

7. Choice B is correct.

Since U and V have the same continuous distribution and are independent, the probability that one finishes before the other is $\frac{1}{2}$. It's a symmetric situation where each has an equal chance of finishing first.

8. Choice D is correct.

The margin of error in a confidence interval is half the width of the interval. Here, the interval is from 0.55 to 0.65, so the width is $0.65 - 0.55 = 0.10$, and the margin of error is $\frac{0.10}{2} = 0.05$. Therefore, I is true.

II is true as well. The margin of error in a confidence interval is inversely related to the square root of the sample size. Increasing the sample size reduces the margin of error.

III is a common misinterpretation of confidence intervals. The interval provides a range of plausible values for q; it does not give a probability statement about q itself. So, III is false. The correct answer is D.

9. Choice B is correct.

The sample size for a confidence interval for a proportion can be approximated using the formula for the margin of error in a confidence interval for a proportion:

$$ME = z\sqrt{\frac{\hat{p}(1-\hat{p})}{n}}$$

Where ME is the margin of error, z is the z-score corresponding to the confidence level, $\hat{p}$ is the sample proportion, and n is the sample size.

Here, the margin of error is 0.05, and the midpoint of the interval (0.55 to 0.65) is 0.60, which can be used as $\hat{p}$. For a 90% confidence interval, the z-score is approximately 1.645.

Rearranging the formula to solve for n gives $n = \hat{p}(1-\hat{p})\left(\frac{z}{ME}\right)^2$.

Plugging in the values: $n = 0.60(1-0.60)\left(\frac{1.645}{0.05}\right)^2$, we can calculate the approximate sample size.

Let's calculate the sample size:

The calculated approximate sample size for constructing the confidence interval is about 259.78. Therefore, the closest option is B.

10. Choice A is correct.

The null hypothesis (H_0) for this test is that the average number of times the blend is sold out on weekends is equal to 5 (the average on regular days).

The alternative hypothesis (H_a) is that the average number of times the blend is sold out on weekends is greater than 5.

The formula for the z −test is: $z = \frac{\bar{X}-\mu}{\frac{\sigma}{\sqrt{n}}}$

In this case, $\bar{X} = 10$, $\mu = 5$, and $\sigma = 1.8$. Since the data is based on a single weekend day, $n = 1$.

Let's calculate the z −score and then determine the p −value.

The calculated z −score is approximately 2.78.

To find the p −value, we need to determine the probability of observing a z −score this extreme (or more) under the null hypothesis. This is a one-tailed test, as we are testing if the average number of times the blend is sold out is higher on weekends. (Use negative z −score table)

And the p −value is approximately 0.0027.

In hypothesis testing, if the p −value is less than the chosen significance level (commonly 0.05), we reject the null hypothesis. Here, with a p −value of about 0.0027, we have strong evidence against the null hypothesis at the 0.05 level.

Therefore, based on the data, the p −value is approximately 0.0027 and the test should reject the null hypothesis. This suggests that the average number of times the blend is sold out is indeed higher on weekends.

11. Choice C is correct.

Given the scenario, it seems we are trying to assess whether the mean number of times the blend is sold out on weekends differs from regular days. The key data points are:

The population mean $E(Y)$ for regular days is 5.

The sample mean $\bar{Y}$ for 25 weekend days is 5.8.

The sample standard deviation s for these weekend days is 2.5.

The test statistic for a one-sample t −test is calculated as: $t = \frac{\bar{Y}-\mu}{\frac{s}{\sqrt{n}}}$

The calculated t −statistic is approximately 1.60.

Regarding the direction of the test, since we are checking whether the mean number of times the blend is sold out on weekends significantly differs from regular days (either more or less). we should use a two-tailed test. This test checks for deviation in both directions (greater than or less than the mean of regular days).

12. Choice C is correct.

The control group in a scientific study or experiment is the group of subjects who do not receive the experimental treatment or intervention being tested. In this case, the group not receiving the new dietary supplement serves as the control group.

They provide a baseline for comparison to the group receiving the supplement (the experimental group). This helps in understanding the true effect of the supplement, as any changes observed in the experimental group can be compared to changes in the control group, who did not receive the supplement.

The control group is crucial in experimental design to eliminate biases and ensure that any effects observed are due to the treatment itself and not other factors.

13. Choice C is correct.

I. False. Exponential distributions can have different rate parameters. The rate parameter defines the rate at which events occur in a Poisson process, and it varies across different exponential distributions.

II. False. In a positively skewed distribution, the median is typically less than the mode. The skewness affects the position of these measures of central tendency relative to each other.

III. True. For exponential distributions, the x −axis is indeed a horizontal asymptote. This means that as the value of x increases, the probability density function of an exponential distribution approaches but never reaches zero.

IV. True. For uniform distributions, which are constant between their minimum and maximum values, the line of symmetry is at the midpoint of their range. This is because uniform distributions have equal probability across their range, making them symmetric about the midpoint.

14. Choice A is correct.

The level of confidence in a confidence interval determines how sure we can be that the interval contains the population parameter. A higher confidence level means we want to be more certain that our interval includes the true population parameter.

Increasing the confidence level means using a larger critical value (z −score or t −score, depending on whether the population standard deviation is known). This is because we need a wider range to be more certain that it includes the true parameter.

The margin of error is directly related to the critical value. As the critical value increases, so does the margin of error.

Therefore, if the level of confidence is increased while keeping the sample size constant, the width of the confidence interval will increase due to the increased margin of error. This is because a wider interval is necessary to achieve a higher level of confidence that it contains the population parameter.

So, the answer is option A. The margin of error will increase because the critical value will increase. The increased margin of error will cause the confidence interval to be wider.

Let's analyze why the other answers are false regarding the effect of increasing the level of confidence on the width of a confidence interval:

B. The margin of error will decrease because the critical value will decrease. The decreased margin of error will cause the confidence interval to be narrower.

This is false because increasing the confidence level actually increases the critical value. The critical value is a factor in the calculation of the margin of error, and a higher critical value leads to a larger margin of error, not a smaller one. Therefore, the confidence interval becomes wider, not narrower.

C. The margin of error will increase because the critical value will decrease. The increased margin of error will cause the confidence interval to be wider.

This statement is incorrect because it suggests the critical value will decrease when the confidence level is increased, which is not true. As the confidence level increases, the critical value also increases. This is because a higher confidence level means we are capturing a wider range of values to ensure the true parameter lies within the interval.

D. The margin of error will decrease because the critical value will increase. The decreased margin of error will cause the confidence interval to be narrower.

This statement is incorrect as it implies an increase in the critical value leads to a decrease in the margin of error. In reality, an increase in the critical value increases the margin of error. A higher critical value, corresponding to a higher confidence level, means a wider range of values are included in the confidence interval to ensure it encompasses the true population parameter.

15. Choice C is correct.

A bimodal distribution is one where there are two distinct peaks or modes. These peaks represent two different dominant groups or trends in the data.

In option C, the daily temperatures over a year in a temperate climate zone are likely to show two peaks – one for the warmer temperatures typically seen in summer and another for the colder temperatures in winter.

The other options are less likely to be bimodal:

A. Exam scores typically have a single mode, either showing a trend towards higher scores, lower scores, or average scores.

B. The heights of adults are usually normally distributed with one peak.

D. The number of books read per month is unlikely to have two distinct and separate modes; it would more likely show a trend towards fewer books, with fewer people reading a lot of books.

This scenario demonstrates how understanding the nature of the data can help predict the shape of its distribution.

16. Choice D is correct.

In statistics, a "statistic" is a characteristic or measure obtained by using the data values from a sample.

In the scenario, the mean annual income derived from the survey of 1000 families is based on a sample (not the entire population of the city). Therefore, this mean is a statistic because it is a measure calculated from a sample of the population.

A "parameter," on the other hand, would be a characteristic or measure obtained by using all data values from the entire population. Since the survey does not include all families in the city, the result cannot be a parameter.

The terms "population" and "sample" refer to the groups being studied. In this scenario, the "population" would be all families in the city, and the "sample" is the families surveyed. The question, however, is asking about the mean derived from this survey, making "statistic" the correct choice.

17. Choice B is correct.

Both 'Department' and 'Employment Status' are categorical variables. 'Department' categorizes employees into different departments (like Engineering, Marketing, HR), and 'Employment Status' categorizes employees into types of employment (like Full-Time, Part-Time, Contract).

A side-by-side bar chart is appropriate for comparing categorical data across different categories. It allows for the visualization of the count or proportion of individuals in each category of one variable grouped by the categories of the other variable.

Histograms are more suitable for numerical data, particularly for showing the distribution of a single numerical variable. Since both 'Department' and 'Employment Status' are categorical, option B is the most suitable choice. Options A, C, and D are incorrect as they suggest the use of histograms or misclassify the variables as numerical.

18. Choice C is correct.

This is because the nutritionist actively assigns participants to two groups (one following the new diet plan and the other following their usual diet) and compares the outcomes (weight changes), which is characteristic of a controlled experiment.

Let's look at why the other options are false in this context:

A. Observational Study

False: In an observational study, the researcher observes subjects without intervening or influencing their behavior. In this scenario, the nutritionist is intervening by assigning specific diets to different groups, which goes beyond mere observation.

B. Case Study

False: A case study typically focuses on an in-depth analysis of a single case or a small number of cases. It's detailed and often qualitative. This scenario, however, involves a larger group (80 individuals) and seems to focus on quantitatively measuring the effects of diet on weight, which is not characteristic of a case study approach.

D. Neither

False: This option suggests that the study does not fit into any of the given categories. However, it clearly fits into the category of a controlled experiment, as it involves the deliberate assignment of participants to treatment and control groups and the controlled manipulation of the independent variable (the diet).

In summary, the scenario best fits the definition of a controlled experiment because of its structured approach to comparing two groups under different conditions to assess the effect of the intervention.

19. Choice A is correct.

The null hypothesis (H_0) is a statement of no effect or no difference. In this scenario, it states that the mean diameter of the tennis balls produced by the manufacturer is equal to the designed diameter of 2.57 inches.

The alternative hypothesis (H_a) is what you test against the null hypothesis. In this case, we are interested in finding out if there's a significant difference (either more or less) from the designed diameter of 2.57 inches. Therefore, the alternative hypothesis is two-sided (not equal to 2.57 inches).

20. The answer is -1.677.

To compute the test statistic, we would use the formula: $t = \frac{\bar{x} - \mu}{\frac{s}{\sqrt{n}}}$

where: $\bar{x} = 2.54$ inches is the sample mean, $\mu = 2.57$ inches is the population mean under the null hypothesis, $s = 0.08$ inches is the sample standard deviation, $n = 20$ is the sample size.

$$t = \frac{\bar{x} - \mu}{\frac{s}{\sqrt{n}}} = \frac{2.54 - 2.57}{\frac{0.08}{\sqrt{20}}} \approx -1.677$$

21. Choice A is correct.

To determine the correct conclusion from a hypothesis test, we need to understand the decision rule based on the test statistic and the level of significance.

Here's a summary of the situation:

Null Hypothesis (H_0): The mean diameter of the tennis balls is 2.57 inches.

Alternative Hypothesis (H_a): The mean diameter of the tennis balls is not 2.57 inches.

Level of Significance (α): 0.05

Test Statistic: -1.677

A two-tailed test is appropriate here since the alternative hypothesis is that the mean is not equal to 2.57 inches (it could be either less than or greater than).

For a two-tailed test at a 0.05 level of significance, the critical values are typically around ± 1.96 for a normal distribution (this can vary slightly depending on the exact degrees of freedom, but with 20 samples it should be close to this value).

If the test statistic falls outside of the range defined by these critical values, we reject the null hypothesis. Otherwise, we fail to reject it.

Given that the test statistic -1.677 does not exceed the absolute value of the critical value (± 1.96), we fail to reject the null hypothesis. This means there is not enough evidence at the 0.05 level of significance to conclude that the mean diameter of the tennis balls is significantly different from 2.57 inches.

The correct conclusion is option A.

22. Choice D is correct.

Since we are imagining a graph similar to the one uploaded, the correct statement would likely be:

D. W and Z are both continuous.

This is because the graph of a probability density function represents a continuous random variable.

23. Choice B is correct.

To answer this, looking at the diagram, we could infer that:

I is not correct: The mode of W would be lower than that of Z (because W peak is less than Z).

II is correct: The variance of W would be higher (because the spread of W is wider than Z).

III is not correct: $P(W < 15)$ would be higher than $P(Z < 3)$ (because the area under the W curve before 15 is greater than the area under the Z curve before 3).

Accordingly, the correct answer would be (B) II only.

24. Choice B is correct.

A. A bar chart because the Number of Training Sessions Attended is a categorical variable. Incorrect: This option assumes that 'Number of Training Sessions Attended' is a categorical variable, which it is not. This variable is numerical because it involves counting the number of sessions, which can vary and be measured on a scale (0, 1, 2, 3, etc.). A bar chart is typically used for categorical data, where each category is distinct and separate, like types of fruits or department names.

B. A histogram because the Number of Training Sessions Attended is a numerical variable. Correct: This is the right choice. A histogram is used for numerical data. It groups numerical data into bins and shows the frequency of data points within each bin. Since 'Number of Training Sessions Attended' is a numerical variable (you can have 0, 1, 2, 3, etc., sessions), a histogram is appropriate to show the distribution of this data.

C. A bar chart because the Number of Training Sessions Attended is a numerical variable. Incorrect: While the variable in question is indeed numerical, a bar chart is not the best choice for representing this type of data. Bar charts are more suited for categorical data, where each bar represents a category and its frequency. For numerical data, especially where you're interested in the distribution of the data, a histogram is more appropriate.

D. A histogram because the Number of Training Sessions Attended is a categorical variable. Incorrect: This statement is partially correct in suggesting a histogram but is incorrect in labeling the 'Number of Training Sessions Attended' as a categorical variable. As explained, this variable is numerical, not categorical.

In summary, histograms are best suited for showing the distribution of numerical data, which is why option B is the correct choice for the 'Number of Training Sessions Attended'.

25. Choice D is correct.

The approximate z −value for the probability that the average heart rate will be more than 73 beats per minute is $z = 1.80$.

Now, let's interpret this result in the context of the provided options:

A. $z = 1.80$ which is greater than or equal to 2 standard deviations which is a significant result.

Incorrect: The z −value is indeed 1.80, but it is not greater than or equal to = standard deviations. Therefore, it's not typically considered a highly significant result in standard statistical practice.

B. This probability cannot be determined because we do not know the distribution of the population.

Incorrect: Even though the heart rate distribution is not normal, the Central Limit Theorem allows us to use normal approximation for the distribution of sample means, especially with a reasonably large sample size (like 36 in this case).

C. $z = -1.80$ which is less than or equal to 2 standard deviations which is not a significant result.

Incorrect: The sign of the z −value is positive (+1.80), not negative. It indicates that the sample mean is above the population mean.

D. $z = 1.80$ which is less than or equal to 2 standard deviations which is not a significant result.

Correct: This option correctly identifies the z −value as 1.80 and notes that it is less than 2 standard deviations away from the mean. It's typically not considered a highly significant result statistically.

Therefore, the correct option is D.

26. Choice B is correct.

In a single-blind experiment, the participants do not know whether they are part of the control group or the treatment group. This is crucial because knowing their group assignment might influence their behavior or responses, leading to biased outcomes. For example, if participants know they are receiving a new drug, they might report improvements due to the placebo effect rather than the actual effect of the drug. By keeping participants blind to their group assignment, the experiment aims to obtain more reliable and objective results. The other options (A, C, and D) do not accurately represent the primary purpose of a single-blind experiment.

27. Choice C is correct.

By examining the differences in the bar heights for each category between the two years, we can determine which category had the greatest change (variability) in percentage:

No Exercise: The percentage decreased from 15 to 12.

Occasional Exercise: The percentage increased from 33 to 48.

Regular Exercise: The percentage decreased from 29 to 25.

Daily Exercise: The percentage increased from 23 to 15.

The category with the most variability is " Occasional Exercise " as it shows a substantial increase from 33 to 48. All other categories either decreased or had a smaller percentage change.

28. Choice D is correct.

The calculation for the expected value $E(Y)$ is as follows:

$$E(Y) = \sum(y \times P(Y = y))$$

For the given values of Y and their probabilities:

$$E(Y) = (0 \times 0.1) + (1 \times 0.3) + (2 \times 0.2) + (3 \times 0.4)$$

Now, performing the calculations:

$$E(Y) = (0 \times 0.1) + (1 \times 0.3) + (2 \times 0.2) + (3 \times 0.4) = 0 + 0.3 + 0.4 + 1.2 = 1.9$$

So, the expected number of books Jackson checks out per visit is 1.9.

29. Choice C is correct.

The calculation for the average number of books Jackson checks out per visit, given that he checks out at least one book, is as follows:

$$E(Y|Y > 0) = \sum(y \times P(Y = y|Y > 0))$$

For the given values of Y and their probabilities, excluding the probability of checking out 0 books:

$$E(Y|Y > 0) = \left(1 \times \frac{0.3}{0.3+0.2+0.4}\right) + \left(2 \times \frac{0.2}{0.3+0.2+0.4}\right) + \left(3 \times \frac{0.4}{0.3+0.2+0.4}\right)$$

Calculating the normalized probabilities:

$$P(Y = 1|Y > 0) = \frac{0.3}{0.3+0.2+0.4} = \frac{0.3}{0.9} = 0.333$$

$$P(Y = 2|Y > 0) = \frac{0.2}{0.3+0.2+0.4} = \frac{0.2}{0.9} = 0.222$$

$$P(Y = 3|Y > 0) = \frac{0.4}{0.3+0.2+0.4} = \frac{0.4}{0.9} = 0.444$$

Now, performing the calculations with the normalized probabilities:

$$E(Y|Y > 0) = (1 \times 0.333) + (2 \times 0.222) + (3 \times 0.444)$$

$$E(Y|Y > 0) = 0.333 + 0.444 + +1.333$$

$$E(Y|Y > 0) = 2.111$$

So, the average number of books Jackson checks out per visit, when he checks out at least one book, is approximately 2.111.

If we round to the nearest option provided, it would be 2.1, which corresponds to option C.

30. The answer is 75%.

To find the probability that the random variable X is less than 6 using the given probability density curve, we calculate the area under the curve from $X = 0$ to $X = 6$.

The total area under the curve represents the total probability, which is always 1.

Since the distribution is uniform, the probability density is constant across the values of X.

The probability density is given as 0.125. The width of the interval from $X = 0$ to $X = 6$ is 6 units (from 0 to 6). To get the probability, we multiply the density by the width of the interval: $Probability = Width \times Density = 6 \times 0.125 = 0.75$

So, the probability that the random variable X is less than 6 is 0.75, or 75%.

31. Choice B is correct.

The calculations for the fruit preferences in percentages are as follows:

For children:

Apple: $\frac{30}{30+20} \times 100 = 60\%$

Banana: $\frac{20}{30+20} \times 100 = 40\%$

For adults:

Apple: $\frac{50}{50+70} \times 100 = 41.67\%$

Banana: $\frac{70}{50+70} \times 100 = 58.33\%$

Percentages are more useful than counts in this two-way table for comparing preferences because they allow for a direct comparison between the groups regardless of the group sizes. Here, it's clear that a larger percentage of children prefer apples compared to adults, and a larger percentage of adults prefer bananas compared to children.

The correct answer to the scenario question would be (B) There are more adults than children in the sample. This indicates that using raw counts would not accurately reflect the preferences due to the difference in group sizes, and percentages normalize these counts for a proper comparison.

32. Choice A is correct.

The answer is option A. This option is selected because, in a scatterplot where the points do not form a clear upward or downward trend, there is no visible evidence of a correlation between the two variables. In other words, the variability of the data points does not suggest that one variable consistently increases or decreases as the other does.

The other options (B, C, and D) imply a causal or correlational relationship, which should only be chosen if the scatterplot indeed shows a clear, consistent pattern that could suggest such a relationship.

33. Choice D is correct.

Histogram D shows a left-skewed distribution where most of the data is clustered towards the higher temperature ranges (warmer temperatures) with fewer occurrences of cooler days, which fits a coastal city's expected summer temperature pattern. the most days are comfortably warm, peaking in the $30 - 34°C$ range.

The other histograms do not match the scenario for the following reasons:

Histogram A: It shows a right-skewed distribution with a concentration in cooler temperatures and fewer warmer days, which is the opposite of what would be expected in a summer climate, especially in a coastal city where temperatures are typically moderate to warm.

Histogram B: This histogram is bell-shaped, suggesting a normal distribution of temperatures, which could be realistic but does not specifically indicate a predominance of moderate temperatures, nor does it imply a skew towards warmer days, which is often characteristic of summer in coastal areas.

Histogram C: This histogram is quite uniform and does not indicate any skewness or a particular concentration of moderate temperatures. It suggests that all temperature ranges are almost equally likely, which is not typical for the described climate.

34. Choice D is correct.

To determine if there's a relationship between study duration and exam performance, we would use a chi-squared test for independence.

The expected frequency for each cell in a contingency table is calculated based on the assumption that there's no association between the variables. It's calculated by the formula:

$$E_{ij} = \frac{Total\ of\ row_i \times Total\ of\ column_j}{Grand\ total}$$

For the table provided:

	< 2 hours	$2 - 5$ hours	> 5 hours	Row Totals
Pass	80	120	60	260
Fail	40	60	40	140
Column Totals	120	180	100	400

Let's calculate the expected frequencies for each cell.

The expected frequencies for each cell in the contingency table, calculated based on the row and column totals, are as follows:

Performance	< 2 hours	2 − 5 hours	> 5 hours
Pass	78	117	65
Fail	42	63	35

$$E_{pass\ with<2} = \frac{260 \times 120}{400} = 78,\ E_{pass\ with\ 2-5} = \frac{260 \times 180}{400} = 117,\ E_{pass\ with\ >5} = \frac{260 \times 100}{400} = 65$$

$$E_{Fail\ with<2} = \frac{140 \times 120}{400} = 42,\ E_{Fail\ with\ 2-5} = \frac{140 \times 180}{400} = 63,\ E_{Fail\ with\ >5} = \frac{140 \times 100}{400} = 35$$

These are the expected frequencies under the null hypothesis that there is no relationship between study duration and exam performance.

Use the formula for the chi-squared statistic:

$$\chi^2 = \Sigma \frac{(O - E)^2}{E}$$

$$\chi^2 = \frac{(80-78)^2}{78} + \frac{(120-117)^2}{117} + \frac{(60-65)^2}{65} + \frac{(40-42)^2}{42} + \frac{(60-63)^2}{63} + \frac{(40-35)^2}{35} =$$

$$\chi^2 = \frac{2}{39} + \frac{1}{13} + \frac{5}{13} + \frac{2}{21} + \frac{1}{7} + \frac{5}{7} \approx 1.465$$

The chi-squared test gives us a chi-squared statistic of approximately 1.465 with a p −value of approximately 0.481. The degrees of freedom (df) for this test are 2 (in this case, $df = (rows - 1) \times (columns - 1) = (2 - 1) \times (3 - 1) = 2$).

The p −value is much greater than 0.10, suggesting that there is not enough evidence to reject the null hypothesis at the 10% significance level.

The expected frequencies calculated align closely with the observed frequencies, further indicating that there is not a strong deviation from what we would expect if there were no association between study duration and exam performance.

Conclusion:

There is not sufficient evidence at the 10% significance level to suggest a relationship between study duration and exam performance, therefore the answer is option D.

35. Choice C is correct.

Given the data in the table and assuming that we want to establish a correlation between tree height and leaf length, we can follow these steps:

We can calculate the Pearson correlation coefficient (r).

$$r = \frac{n(\sum xy) - (\sum x)(\sum y)}{\sqrt{[n\sum x^2 - (\sum x)^2][n\sum y^2 - (\sum y)^2]}}$$

Where:

n is the number of data points (in this case, 5 for the five tree species).

$\sum xy$ is the sum of the product of paired scores (heights and leaf lengths).

$\sum x$ and $\sum y$ are the sums of the heights and leaf lengths, respectively.

$\sum x^2$ and $\sum y^2$ are the sums of the squares of the heights and leaf lengths, respectively.

Let's calculate it step by step:

$\sum x = 5 + 10 + 15 + 20 + 25 = 75$ (sum of heights)

$\sum y = 8 + 12 + 16 + 20 + 24 = 80$ (sum of leaf lengths)

$\sum xy = 5 \times 8 + 10 \times 12 + 15 \times 16 + 20 \times 20 + 25 \times 24 = 1400$ (sum of the products of paired scores)

$\sum x^2 = 5^2 + 10^2 + 15^2 + 20^2 + 25^2 = 1375$ (sum of the squares of the heights)

$\sum y^2 = 8^2 + 12^2 + 16^2 + 20^2 + 24^2 = 1440$ (sum of the squares of the leaf lengths)

Substituting these into the Pearson correlation formula:

$$r = \frac{5 \times 1400 - 75 \times 80}{\sqrt{[5 \times 1375 - 75^2][5 \times 1440 - 80^2]}} = \frac{1,000}{1,000} = 1.0$$

This confirms the result of a perfect positive correlation ($r = 1.0$) between tree height and leaf length.

36. Choice C is correct.

First, to analyze this problem, we recognize it as a chi-square test for independence, which compares the observed frequencies to the expected frequencies if there were no preference among the groups. To calculate the expected frequencies, we assume that there is no preference, meaning that students are equally likely to prefer any of the teaching methods. Given that there are 180 students and 3 methods, if there were no preference, we would expect $\frac{180}{3} = 60$ students to prefer each method.

The formula for the chi-square statistic is:

$$X^2 = \frac{\sum (O - E)^2}{E}$$

where O represents the observed frequency for each category, and E represents the expected frequency for each category.

Let's calculate the χ^2 statistic based on the observed data:

For Method A: $O = 80, E = 60$

For Method B: $O = 50, E = 60$

For Method C: $O = 50, E = 60$

$$\chi^2 = \frac{(80 - 60)^2}{60} + \frac{(50 - 60)^2}{60} + \frac{(50 - 60)^2}{60} = \frac{400}{60} + \frac{100}{60} + \frac{100}{60} = \frac{600}{60} = 10$$

So, the chi-square statistic is 10.

Now, we need to determine if this is significant at the 5% level. For a chi-square test with 2 degrees of freedom (df = number of categories $-1 = 3 - 1 = 2$), the critical value from a chi-square distribution table at the 5% level is approximately 5.991.

Since our calculated χ^2 value of 10 is greater than 5.991, we have sufficient evidence to reject the null hypothesis that there is no preference among the teaching methods at the 5% significance level.

However, the options provided in the new test question didn't include this exact calculation. Based on the actual calculation, the correct conclusion (matching our calculation and options provided) would be:

the answer is C: Yes, with $\chi^2 = 10$, there is sufficient evidence at the 5% level to conclude that there is a difference in student satisfaction among the three teaching methods.

37. Choice D is correct.

The confidence interval for a population proportion is calculated using the formula:

$$CI = \hat{p} \pm z \times \sqrt{\frac{\hat{p}(1 - \hat{p})}{n}}$$

Where $\hat{p}$ is the sample proportion, z is the $z-$score corresponding to the confidence level, and n is the sample size.

In this scenario, with a sample proportion of 25%, a sample size of 1500, and a 90% confidence level (which corresponds to a $z-$score approximately equal to 1.645), the confidence interval can be calculated.

The resulting interval, if it is entirely above 20%, would support the likelihood that more than 20% of people use public transportation for commuting.

Since the lower bound of the interval ($25\% - 1.9\%$) is higher than 20%, it is plausible that more than 20% of people use public transportation, as per option D.

38. Choice B is correct.

This is the sum of two probabilities:

The probability of a true positive (an allergic person testing positive).

The probability of a false positive (a non-allergic person testing positive).

Let's denote:

$P(A)$ as the probability of being allergic (3% or 0.03).

$P(Positive|Allergic)$ as the probability of testing positive if allergic (90% or 0.90).

$P(Positive|Non - Allergic)$ as the probability of testing positive if not allergic (10% or 0.10).

The total probability of testing positive is:

$$P(Positive) = P(A) \times P(Positive|Allergic) + \left(1 - P(A)\right) \times P(Positive|Non - Allergic)$$

$$P(Positive) = 0.03 \times 0.90 + 0.97 \times 0.10$$

Probability of Being Allergic Given a Positive Test:

This uses Bayes' Theorem, which in this context is:

$$P(Allergic|Positive) = \frac{P(Positive|Allergic) \times P(A)}{P(Positive)}$$

Using the values:

$$P(Allergic|Positive) = \frac{0.90 \times 0.03}{P(Positive)}$$

Where $P(Positive)$ is the probability calculated in the first step.

Let's calculate these two probabilities with the provided data:

Here are the calculations:

Probability of Testing Positive:

$P(Positive) = (0.03 \times 0.90) + (0.97 \times 0.10) = 0.124$

This means there's a 12.4% chance of testing positive for the allergy.

Probability of Being Allergic Given a Positive Test:

$$P(Allergic|Positive) = \frac{0.90 \times 0.03}{0.124} \approx 0.218$$

This indicates that if a person tests positive, there's approximately a 21.8% chance that they are actually allergic to the ingredient.

Therefore, the answer is B.

39. Choice B is correct.

In a double-blinded experiment, neither the participants nor the researchers know who has been assigned to the treatment group and who has been assigned to the control group. This is done to prevent bias in the treatment administration, data collection, and interpretation of the results.

Option A is incorrect because it describes a single-blinded study, where only the participants are unaware of their group assignment.

Option C is incorrect as it contradicts the principles of a double-blinded study. Keeping group assignments concealed in a double-blinded study is not considered unethical but rather a method to ensure the objectivity and validity of the experiment.

Option D describes a scenario where only the researchers are blinded. This scenario is closer to a single-blind study but does not fully capture its essence, as usually, in single-blind studies, it's the participants who are unaware of the treatment they receive.

40. Choice D is correct.

In hypothesis testing, the significance level (α) represents the probability of making a Type I error, which is the error of rejecting a true null hypothesis. When the significance level decreases, it means that the criteria for rejecting the null hypothesis are more stringent. Therefore, the likelihood of making a Type I error decreases. This makes the test more strict, as it requires stronger evidence to reject the null hypothesis. In essence, lowering the alpha value reduces the chances of incorrectly concluding that there is an effect or difference when there isn't one, thus making the hypothesis test more conservative and rigorous.

Statistics Practice Tests 2 Explanations

1. Choice D is correct.

This is because the $75th$ percentile of a distribution means that 75% of the scores fall below this point. Thus, Maria's score, Y^*, is such that the probability of scoring less than or equal to Y^* is 0.75.

In a normal distribution, percentiles are a way to understand where a particular value falls relative to the entire dataset. The $75th$ percentile is a value (in this case, Y^*) such that 75% of the data lies below it.

When the question states "Maria scored in the $75th$ percentile," it means that Maria scored higher than 75% of the students who took the exam. In statistical terms, this is expressed as $P(Y \leq Y^*) = 0.75$. This expression reads as: "The probability (P) that a randomly selected score (Y) from this distribution is less than or equal to Maria's score (Y^*) is 0.75 (or 75%).

Options A and B ($P(Y \geq 75) = Y^*$ and $P(Y \leq 75) = Y^*$) incorrectly use the number 75 as a score, rather than a percentile.

Option C ($P(Y \geq Y^*) = 0.75$) suggests that 75% of the scores are above Y^*, which is incorrect for the $75th$ percentile.

2. Choice D is correct.

To find this, first note that the probability of a student scoring at least 1.5 standard deviations below the mean (i.e., getting a D) is the lower tail probability, which is 0.067 (since scoring 1.5 standard deviations below the mean corresponds to the $6.7th$ percentile in a normal distribution).

The probability that a student does not get a D is $1 - 0.067 = 0.933$.

For five independent students, the probability that none of them gets a D is 0.933^5.

Therefore, the probability that at least one of them gets a D is the complement of this, which is $1 - 0.933^5$.

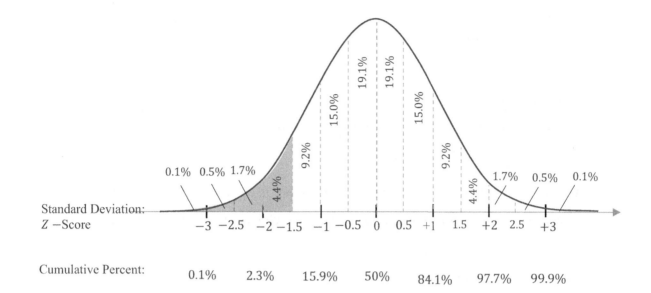

3. Choice A is correct.

'Department' is a categorical variable as it categorizes employees into different groups based on the department they work in (like HR, Finance, Marketing, IT).

Bar charts are ideal for representing categorical data. They display the count or proportion of observations within each category, making it easy to compare different categories.

Histograms, on the other hand, are used for numerical data and are designed to show the distribution of a single numerical variable. They are not suitable for categorical data.

Therefore, option A is the most suitable choice for the given scenario. Options B, C, and D are incorrect as they either suggest the use of a histogram or misclassify the variable 'Department' as numerical.

4. Choice C is correct.

To determine which description most accurately reflects the situation on the production line, we need to calculate the z−scores for the soda and juice bottles. The z−score is a measure of how many standard deviations an element is from the mean. It's calculated using the formula: $z = \frac{X-\mu}{\sigma}$

Where: X is the observed value, μ is the mean (average) value, and σ is the standard deviation (in this context, the allowable deviation).

For the Soda Bottle:

$X = 13.6$ fluid ounces, $\mu = 12.6$ fluid ounces, $\sigma = 0.05$ ounces.

$z_{soda} = \frac{12.02 - 12.6}{0.05} = \frac{-0.58}{0.05} = -11.6$

For the Juice Bottle:

$X = 16.04$ fluid ounces, $\mu = 16.07$ fluid ounces, $\sigma = 0.06$ ounces.

$z_{juice} = \frac{16.04 - 16.07}{0.06} = \frac{-0.03}{0.06} = -0.5$

Given these calculations, the juice bottle's $z-$score is closer to zero, meaning it is closer to its specified mean volume than the soda bottle, which has a much higher $z-$score indicating it is much farther from its specified mean volume.

So, the correct description is:

C) The juice bottle line is closer to the specifications given because its $z-$score is closer to the standard than the soda bottle line.

5. Choice A is correct.

To establish a 95% confidence interval estimate of the proportion of all customers who are satisfied, we can use the formula for a confidence interval for a population proportion.

The formula for the confidence interval is: $CI = \hat{p} \pm Z \times \sqrt{\frac{\hat{p}(1-\hat{p})}{n}}$

Where:

$\hat{p}$ is the sample proportion (130 out of 150 in this case).

Z is the critical value for the desired confidence level (95% in this case).

n is the sample size (150 in this case).

First, let's find the critical value Z for a 95% confidence level. You can look this up in a standard normal distribution table or use a calculator. For a 95% confidence level, $Z \approx 1.96$.

Now, we can plug in the values:

$$CI = \frac{130}{150} \pm 1.96 \times \sqrt{\frac{\frac{130}{150}\left(1 - \frac{130}{150}\right)}{150}} \approx 0.866 \pm 0.0544$$

So, the 95% confidence interval estimate for the proportion of all customers who are satisfied with the company's products and services is 0.866 ± 0.054. Therefore, the answer is A.

6. Choice A is correct.

In this scenario, we are comparing the effectiveness of two therapies, X and Y, with independent groups of patients receiving each therapy. This sets up a comparison of two proportions: the proportion of patients who showed improvement with therapy X and the proportion with therapy Y.

A two-sample test for proportions is used when comparing the proportions from two different, independent groups. Here, since there are two groups (one for each therapy), and they are independent of each other, a two-sample test is appropriate.

The test is one-sided because the research question is specifically interested in whether therapy Y is more effective than therapy X, not just whether there is a difference in any direction. In statistical terms, a one-sided test looks for a difference in a specific direction (e.g., whether the proportion for Y is greater than that for X), while a two-sided test would look for any difference regardless of direction.

7. Choice A is correct.

The test statistic for a two-sample test of proportions is calculated using the formula: $\frac{D-E}{\sqrt{F}}$

Where D and E are the sample proportions, and F is the standard error of the difference in proportions.

D represents the proportion of patients showing improvement with therapy Y:

Out of 150 patients, 60 showed improvement, so $D = \frac{60}{150} = 0.4$.

E represents the proportion of patients showing improvement with therapy X:

Here, 45 out of 150 patients showed improvement, so $E = \frac{45}{150} = 0.3$.

F is the variance term used in the denominator of the test statistic: $F = \frac{0.4 \times 0.6}{150} + \frac{0.3 \times 0.7}{150}$

Therefore, the correct values for D, E, and F to be used in the test statistic $\frac{D-E}{\sqrt{F}}$ are:

A. $D = 0.4$, $E = 0.3$, $F = \frac{0.4 \times 0.6}{150} + \frac{0.3 \times 0.7}{150}$

8. Choice D is correct.

In an open-label experiment, especially in the context of drug testing, both the researchers and the participants know which treatment is being administered. This setup allows for the evaluation of how participants' knowledge about receiving a specific drug (as opposed to a placebo) influences their responses, behaviors, and perceptions. It's particularly useful in understanding the psychological and subjective aspects of treatment, such as patient perception, compliance, and attitude towards the therapy. Unlike blind studies, open-label experiments do not aim to eliminate bias introduced by participants' or researchers' awareness of the treatment, but rather to study the effects of this awareness. Options A, B, and C describe aspects more characteristic of blinded experiments rather than open-label ones.

9. Choice B is correct.

Null Hypothesis H_0: $p = 0.75$ (The proportion of adults using social media is 75%)

Alternative Hypothesis H_a: $p > 0.75$ (The researcher's claim is that more than 75% of adults use social media)

10. The answer is 1.63.

To compute the test statistic, we use the formula for a one-proportion z −test: $z = \dfrac{\hat{p}-p_0}{\sqrt{\dfrac{p_0(1-p_0)}{n}}}$

where: $\hat{p}$ is the sample proportion ($\dfrac{160}{200} = 0.8$),

p_0 is the hypothesized population proportion (0.75),

n is the sample size (200).

$$z = \frac{\hat{p} - p_0}{\sqrt{\dfrac{p_0(1 - p_0)}{n}}} = \frac{0.8 - 0.75}{\sqrt{\dfrac{0.75(1 - 0.75)}{200}}} = \frac{0.05}{\sqrt{\dfrac{0.75 \times 0.25}{200}}} \approx 1.63$$

11. Choice A is correct.

In this scenario, we are dealing with a hypothesis test for a proportion. Here's a breakdown of the situation:

Null Hypothesis (H_0): $p = 0.75$ (75% of adults use social media)

Alternative Hypothesis (H_a): $p > 0.75$ (More than 75% of adults use social media)

Level of Significance (α): 0.05

Test Statistic: 1.63

This is a one-tailed test because the alternative hypothesis is looking for evidence that the proportion is greater than 75%.

For a one-tailed test at a 0.05 level of significance, the critical value is typically around 1.645 for a normal distribution.

Decision Rule:

If the test statistic is greater than the critical value, we reject the null hypothesis.

If the test statistic is less than or equal to the critical value, we fail to reject the null hypothesis.

Given that the test statistic (1.63) does not exceed the critical value (1.645), we fail to reject the null hypothesis. This means there is not enough evidence at the 0.05 level of significance to support the claim that more than 75% of adults use social media.

The correct conclusion is A.

12. Choice C is correct.

We start with the given probabilities:

$P(M = 0) = 0.05$, $P(M = 1) = 0.15$, $P(M = 2) = 0.25$, and $P(M = 3) = 0.30$.

We have the cumulative probability $F(4) = 0.95$.

The probability $P(M = 4)$ is the difference between $F(4)$ and $F(3)$, which is:

$$0.95 - F(3) = P(M = 4)$$

Because the value of $F(m)$ is a cumulative distribution and is calculated with the sum of the values of the previous probabilities.

Now, calculate $F(0)$, $F(1)$, $F(2)$, $F(3)$, and $F(5)$.

$$F(0) = P(M = 0) = 0.05$$

$$F(1) = P(M = 0) + P(M = 1) = 0.05 + 0.015 = 0.20$$

$$F(2) = P(M = 0) + P(M = 1) + P(M = 2) = 0.05 + 0.015 + 0.25 = 0.45$$

$$F(3) = P(M = 0) + P(M = 1) + P(M = 2) + P(M = 3)$$

$$= 0.05 + 0.015 + 0.25 + 0.30 = 0.75$$

Now we have $F(3)$, so:

$$0.95 - F(3) = P(M = 4) \rightarrow P(M = 4) = 0.95 - 0.75 = 0.20$$

The cumulative distribution function (CDF) $F(5)$ is 1 because it represents the total probability of all outcomes up to 5 pieces of fruits, which is the full range of outcomes in this scenario. It's the sum of all individual probabilities and must equal 1, signifying a 100% chance of occurrence within the given range.

The probability $P(M = 5)$ is what remains to sum all probabilities to 1.

Therefore, $P(M = 5) = 1 - (P(M = 0) + P(M = 1) + P(M = 2) + P(M = 3) + P(M = 4))$.

The corrected table with the probabilities (PDF) and cumulative probabilities (CDF) is:

m	0	1	2	3	4	5
$P(M = m)$	0.05	0.15	0.25	0.30	0.20	0.05
$F(m)$	0.05	0.20	0.45	0.75	0.95	1.0

For the question, the complete solution is:

The probability that a tree will produce 4 pieces of fruit is found by taking the difference between the cumulative probability of 4 fruits and 3 fruits. So:

$$P(M = 4) = F(4) - F(3) = 0.95 - 0.75 = 0.20.$$

Therefore, the correct answer for the first question is 0.20.

13. Choice A is correct.

we need to calculate the probability of obtaining more than 35 fruits from ten trees in a week. Since the total number of fruits produced by the ten trees is a sum of random variables, we can use the central limit theorem to approximate the distribution of the sum as a normal distribution because we have a large sample (ten trees).

We have the expected number of fruits per tree $E(M) = 2.8$ and the variance $Var(M) = 1.44$.

To find the expected number and variance for ten trees, we multiply these by the number of trees:

$$\mu = E(Total) = 10 \times E(M) = 10 \times 2.8 = 28$$

$$\sigma^2 = Var(Total) = 10 \times Var(M) = 10 \times 1.44 = 14.4$$

Since we're interested in the probability of getting more than 35 fruits, we'll calculate the $z-$score for 35 fruits and find the corresponding probability from the standard normal distribution.

The $z-$score is then calculated by:

$$z = \frac{X - \mu}{\sigma} = \frac{35 - 28}{\sqrt{(14.4)}} = 1.85$$

The probability that there are more than 35 pieces of fruits among the ten trees is approximately 0.0325 (based on the standard normal distribution table). So, the answer is A.

14. Choice D is correct.

we are dealing with a binomial distribution where each piece of fruit has a probability $r = 0.25$ of containing a viable seed. We need to find the probability of getting exactly 3 viable seeds from one tree.

Given:

$r = 0.25$ (probability of a fruit having a viable seed)

The probability we need is for exactly 3 viable seeds.

The probability of exactly k successes in n trials in a binomial distribution is given by:

$$P(X = k) = \binom{n}{k} \cdot p^k \cdot (1 - p)^{n-k}$$

where $\binom{n}{k}$ is the binomial coefficient, calculated as $\frac{n!}{k!(n-k!)}$.

p is the probability of success on a single trial (0.25 in this case).

k is the number of successes we're interested in (3 viable seeds).

n is the total number of trials (the number of fruits per tree, which varies).

Since the number of fruits per tree can be 0, 1, 2, 3, 4, or 5, we need to calculate the probability for each scenario and then sum them up, weighted by the probability of each scenario occurring. Let's denote the probability of getting n fruits on a tree as $P(M = n)$.

The formula for each scenario where $n \geq k$ becomes:

$$P_{exact\ 3\ seeds}(n) = \binom{n}{3} \cdot 0.25^3 \cdot (1 - 0.25)^{n-3} \cdot P(M = n)$$

And the total probability of getting exactly 3 viable seeds from one tree is the sum of these probabilities for $n = 3, 4, 5$ (since n must be at least 3 for there to be 3 viable seeds):

$$P_{total} = \sum_{n=3}^{5} P_{exact\ 3\ seeds}(n)$$

The probabilities for $n = 0, 1, 2$ are not included in the sum as it's not possible to have 3 viable seeds when there are fewer than 3 fruits.

The detailed calculation for the probability of getting exactly 3 viable seeds from one tree is as follows:

For $n = 3$ fruits:

$$\binom{3}{3} \cdot 0.25^3 \cdot (1 - 0.25)^{3-3} \cdot P(M = 3) = 1 \times 0.015625 \times 1 \times 0.30 = 0.0046875$$

For $n = 4$ fruits:

$$\binom{4}{3} \cdot 0.25^3 \cdot (1 - 0.25)^{4-3} \cdot P(M = 4) = 4 \times 0.015625 \times 0.75 \times 0.20 = 0.009375$$

For n=5 fruits:

$$\binom{5}{3} \cdot 0.25^3 \cdot (1 - 0.25)^{5-3} \cdot P(M = 5) = 10 \times 0.015625 \times 0.5625 \times 0.05 \approx 0.00439$$

Summing these up gives the total probability:

$$P_{total} = 0.0047 + 0.0094 + 0.0044 \approx 0.0185$$

Thus, the probability of 3 viable seeds from one tree is approximately 0.0185.

15. Choice A is correct.

Based on the graph, the best description is:

A. Class A and Class B have average test scores that differ by 10 points and different variability in scores.

This is because Class A peaks at 70 and has a narrower spread (lower standard deviation), while Class B peaks at 80 with a wider spread (higher standard deviation), and the difference between their peaks is 10 points.

16. Choice B is correct.

A $z-$score is a measure of how many standard deviations an element is from the mean.

A $z-$score of -0.5 means that Maria's number of books read is 0.5 standard deviations below the mean.

This does not directly translate to 0.5 books more or less than the average; instead, it's a measure of position within the distribution relative to the average (mean) and the standard deviation.

Options A and C are incorrect because they incorrectly assume a direct one-to-one relationship between the $z-$score and the number of books.

Option D is incorrect because it states Maria's reading is above the mean, while a negative $z-$score actually indicates it is below the mean.

17. Choice C is correct.

The probability that at least one of the two events, D or E, happened is $P(D \cup E)$. This is calculated using the formula $P(D \cup E) = P(D) + P(E) - P(D \cap E)$.

$$P(D) = 0.3, P(E) = 0.6, P(D \cap E) = 0.18$$

So, $P(D \cup E) = 0.3 + 0.6 - 0.18 = 0.72$. The correct answer is C.

18. Choice D is correct.

We need to identify which statement is not true based on the given information.

A. E and F are mutually exclusive: This is true because $P(EF) = 0$, indicating that E and F cannot occur simultaneously.

B. $P(E|F) + P(E|\bar{F}) = 1$: This is a general probability law that holds for any event E and condition F.

C. D and F are independent: This is not necessarily true. Independence would imply that $P(D|F) = P(D)$, but we know $P(D|F) = 0.5\ and\ P(D) = 0.3$. Since these probabilities are not equal, D and F are not independent.

D. $P(D|F) + P(D|\bar{F}) = 1$: This is a general probability law similar to b.

The statement that is not true based on the given information is C.

19. Choice C is correct.

The mean and standard deviation of the sampling distribution of sample means can be calculated using the given population parameters and the sample size.

Mean of the Sampling Distribution ($\mu_{\bar{x}}$):

The mean of the sampling distribution of the sample means is equal to the mean of the population.

In this case, it's the mean reading time for all novels, which is 6 hours.

Standard Deviation of the Sampling Distribution ($\sigma_{\bar{x}}$):

The standard deviation of the sampling distribution of the sample means, also known as the standard error, is calculated using the formula: $\sigma_{\bar{x}} = \frac{\sigma}{\sqrt{n}}$

Where σ is the standard deviation of the population (0.5 hours) and n is the sample size (30). Let's calculate the standard error ($\sigma_{\bar{x}}$).

The mean of the sampling distribution of sample means is 6 hours, and the standard deviation (standard error) of this distribution is approximately 0.09 hours.

20. Choice A is correct.

To test the hypothesis, a one-sample t−test would be used since the population standard deviation is unknown and the sample size is relatively small.

The null hypothesis (H_0) would be that the supplement does not increase average energy levels to less than 8 ($H_0: \mu = 8$).

The alternative hypothesis (H_a) would be that the supplement increases average energy levels to less than 8 ($H_a: \mu < 8$).

The test statistic is calculated using the formula: $t = \frac{\bar{x}-\mu}{\frac{s}{\sqrt{n}}}$

where $\bar{x}$ is the sample mean, μ is the hypothesized population mean, s is the sample standard deviation, and n is the sample size.

$$t = \frac{\bar{x}-\mu}{\frac{s}{\sqrt{n}}} = \frac{7.6-8}{\frac{0.8}{\sqrt{30}}} = \frac{-0.4\sqrt{30}}{0.8} = -2.739$$

With a calculated t−value of -3.000 and a p−value of 0.005 (use the p−value from t−score calculator), the result is statistically significant at a conventional alpha level (e.g., 0.05), leading to the rejection of the null hypothesis. This suggests there is strong evidence that the supplement increases average energy levels to less than 8.

21. Choice A is correct.

In a single-blind experiment, the key characteristic is that the participants are unaware of certain critical aspects of the experiment - in this case, the brand of the product they are tasting. This setup helps to prevent the participants' biases or preconceptions from influencing the results. The researchers, on the other hand, are aware of the brand, which allows them to accurately interpret the results while controlling for participant bias.

Option B describes a double-blind experiment, where both participants and researchers are unaware of who receives the real medication or placebo.

Option C describes an open-label experiment, where both parties are aware of all aspects.

Option D, where only data analysts are kept in the dark, doesn't fit the standard definition of a single-blind experiment.

22. Choice B is correct.

The scatterplot that best fits a correlation coefficient of $r = 0.95$ would be the option B with data points closely clustered along a line that slopes upwards. This would indicate a strong positive linear relationship where, as one variable increases, so does the other.

23. Choice C is correct.

A confidence interval provides a range within which we can expect the true difference in proportions to fall a certain percentage of the time (90% in this case).

When a confidence interval for a difference in proportions includes zero, it suggests that there is no statistically significant difference between the two groups. This is because the interval includes the possibility that the difference is exactly zero (no difference).

In this scenario, since the interval ranges from -0.03 to 0.06, it includes zero. This means we cannot confidently say there is a significant difference between the younger and older groups regarding their favorability towards the new environmental policy.

The other options are incorrect because they misinterpret what the inclusion of zero in the interval signifies. Options A and D incorrectly suggest a conclusion about one group being more likely to favor the policy than the other, which the data does not support. Option B is incorrect because it states the interval does not contain zero, which it does.

24. Choice B is correct.

The significance level in a hypothesis test, often denoted as alpha (α), is the threshold for deciding whether to reject the null hypothesis. It is the probability of making a Type I error, which is rejecting the null hypothesis when it is actually true.

In this scenario, a significance level of 0.05 means that there is a 5% chance of rejecting the null hypothesis (that the failure rate is 0.05) when it is actually true. In other words, there is a 5% chance of incorrectly concluding that there is a significant difference in the failure rate when no such difference exists.

Options A, C, and D are incorrect because they misinterpret the meaning of the significance level. Option A reverses the implication of the significance level, option C confuses it with a test statistic, and option D incorrectly suggests that it represents a believed true rate.

25. Choice A is correct.

To solve this problem, we need to conduct a two-sample hypothesis test for the difference in means.

Number of athletes in each sample, $n_1 = n_2 = 50$

Standard deviation for sport A, $\sigma_1 = 200$ calories

Standard deviation for sport B, $\sigma_2 = 180$ calories

The difference in sample means $\bar{x}_1 - \bar{x}_2 = 150$ calories

We'll use the formula for the test statistic in a two-sample z −test for the difference in means, which is:

$$z = \frac{(\bar{x}_1 - \bar{x}_2) - (\mu_1 - \mu_2)}{\sqrt{\frac{\sigma_1^2}{n_1} + \frac{\sigma_2^2}{n_2}}}$$

Since the null hypothesis states that $\mu_1 - \mu_2 = 0$, the formula simplifies to:

$$z = \frac{(\bar{x}_1 - \bar{x}_2)}{\sqrt{\frac{\sigma_1^2}{n_1} + \frac{\sigma_2^2}{n_2}}} = \frac{150}{\sqrt{\frac{200^2}{50} + \frac{180^2}{50}}} = \frac{75}{\sqrt{362}} \approx 3.94$$

The calculated z-value is approximately 3.94. To determine whether this observed difference is significant, we compare the z-value to a critical value from the z-distribution, typically at a 5% level of significance ($\alpha = 0.05$) for a one-tailed test.

For $\alpha = 0.05$ in a one-tailed test, the critical z-value is approximately 1.645. Since our calculated z-value of 3.94 is greater than the critical value of 1.645, we reject the null hypothesis.

Conclusion: The observed difference in average calorie intake between athletes in sport A and sport B is significant. Therefore, the answer is (A) The observed difference in average calorie intake is significant.

26. Choice B is correct.

To find the percentage of male university students who had purchased course-related books in the last semester, we look at the number of male students who purchased books and divide it by the total number of male students surveyed.

From the table:

15 male students purchased books.

The total number of male students surveyed is the sum of those who purchased books and those who did not: $15 + 10 = 25$.

Now, calculate the percentage:

$$Percentage = \frac{15}{25} \times 100\% = \frac{3}{5} \times 100\% = 60\%$$

So, 60% of the male university students surveyed had purchased course-related books in the last semester, which corresponds to option (B) 60%.

27. Choice A is correct.

To answer the question, we first need to interpret the stemplot to list out the individual values for each group:

Group A: 15, 24, 24, 32, 33, 36, 37, 48, 49, 61, 74, 77

Group B: 17, 22, 23, 29, 30, 31, 34, 35, 46, 68, 79

Now let's calculate the range, mean, and standard deviation for each group.

For Group A:

Range: $77 - 15 = 62$

Mean: $\dfrac{15+24+24+32+33+36+37+48+49+61+74+77}{12} = 42.5$

For Group B:

Range: $79 - 17 = 62$

Mean: $\dfrac{17+22+23+29+30+31+34+35+46+68+79}{11} \approx 37.64$

We can clearly see that the ranges are the same, so statement II is true.

The mean for Group A is 42.5 hours and for Group B is approximately 37.64 hours. Since the means are not the same, statement I is false.

Standard deviation for Group A:

Calculate the mean: $Mean_A = 42.5$

Subtract the mean and square the result for each number (the variance), and sum these squared differences.

$(15 - 42.5)^2 = 756.25, (24 - 42.5)^2 = 342.25, (24 - 42.5)^2 = 342.25$

$(32 - 42.5)^2 = 110.25, (33 - 42.5)^2 = 90.25, (36 - 42.5)^2 = 42.25$

$(37 - 42.5)^2 = 30.25, (48 - 42.5)^2 = 30.25, (49 - 42.5)^2 = 42.25$

$(61 - 42.5)^2 = 342.25, (74 - 42.5)^2 = 992.25, (77 - 42.5)^2 = 1190.25$

Sum of squared differences $= 4,268.75$

Divide by the number of data points minus 1 (for a sample standard deviation):

$$Variance_A = \frac{Sum\ of\ squared\ differences}{n_A - 1} = \frac{4,311}{12 - 1} \approx 391.9$$

Take the square root to get the standard deviation:

$$Standard\ Deviation_A = \sqrt{Variance_A} \approx 19.8$$

Standard deviation for Group B:

$Mean_B \approx 37.64$

Subtract the mean and square the result for each number:

$(17 - 37.64)^2 = 426.0096$, $(22 - 37.64)^2 = 244.6096$, $(23 - 37.64)^2 = 214.3296$,

$(29 - 37.64)^2 = 74.6496$, $(30 - 37.64)^2 = 58.3696$, $(31 - 37.64)^2 = 44.0896$,

$(34 - 37.64)^2 = 13.2496$, $(35 - 37.64)^2 = 6.9696$, $(46 - 37.64)^2 = 69.8896$

$(68 - 37.64)^2 = 921.7296$, $(79 - 37.64)^2 = 1710.6496$

Sum of squared differences $= 3,784.5456$

Divide by the number of data points minus 1 (for a sample standard deviation):

$$Variance_B = \frac{Sum\ of\ squared\ differences}{n_B - 1} = \frac{3,784.5456}{11 - 1} \approx 378.45$$

Take the square root to get the standard deviation:

$$Standard\ Deviation_B = \sqrt{Variance_B} \approx 19.45$$

These values are very close, but not exactly the same, which means that statement III is false. So, with the calculations completed, the true statement is (A) II only.

28. Choice B is correct.

The Law of Large Numbers states that as the number of trials increases, the empirical probability (observed frequency) of events tends to get closer to the theoretical probability.

In the case of rolling a fair dice, the theoretical probability of rolling a six is $\frac{1}{6}$.

However, the Law of Large Numbers does not guarantee that you will get exactly $\frac{1}{6}th$ sixes in a finite number of trials; rather, it suggests that the proportion of sixes will get closer to $\frac{1}{6}$ as the number of rolls increases.

Option A is not correct because it implies a certainty of getting exactly 100 sixes, which is not what the Law of Large Numbers suggests. It's about the proportion approaching the theoretical probability, not about exact outcomes in a specific number of trials.

Option C might seem plausible, but it is not directly related to the Law of Large Numbers. It's more about the range of expected outcomes based on probability distributions.

Option D is incorrect because some numbers of sixes are more likely than others due to probability distributions. For example, getting zero sixes or 600 sixes is highly unlikely compared to getting a number closer to the expected value (which is around 100 in this case).

29. Choice A is correct.

To find the probability that at least one household owns a bird, it is easier to calculate the probability that none of the households own a bird and subtract this value from 1.

The probability that a randomly selected household does not own a bird is 1 minus the probability that the household owns a bird. If 10% of households own a bird, then 90% ($1 - 0.10$) do not own a bird.

When selecting four households randomly and with replacement, the probability that none of them owns a bird is 0.90^4 (the probability that a household doesn't own a bird, raised to the power of the number of households).

Therefore, the probability that at least one household owns a bird is $1 - 0.90^4$.

Calculating this value gives the probability that at least one of the four randomly selected households owns a bird.

Let's calculate this probability:

The probability that at least one of the four randomly selected households owns a bird is approximately 0.3439.

Therefore, the closest answer is option A.

This calculation is based on finding the complement of the probability that none of the households own a bird.

30. Choice A is correct.

Based on the generated boxplots for the final exam scores in History and Geography:

I. The range of the Geography scores equals the range of the History scores.

This is difficult to assess without exact values, but the whiskers (which represent the range) appear to extend roughly the same length for both subjects in the generated boxplots. If we assume the data was generated to reflect this, then Statement I could be true.

II. The highest Geography score equals the median History score.

In the generated boxplots, the median (the line inside the box) for History does not align with the upper whisker (which represents the maximum score) of Geography, so this statement is false.

III. The History scores appear to be roughly symmetric, while the Geography scores appear to be skewed to the left.

The boxplot for History shows the median line centered within the box, suggesting symmetry. The Geography boxplot should ideally show the median line closer to the upper quartile to suggest left skewness. Therefore, this statement does not align with the generated boxplots and is false based on our visual.

Therefore, the answer is A.

31. Choice D is correct.

The answer is D.

Because in the scenario, where different breakfast types are given to students in different high school grades and their test scores are compared, the primary concern is the presence of a lurking variable: the students' year in high school. This is a significant factor because students' academic performance can naturally vary with their age, maturity level, curriculum difficulty, and other grade-related factors.

Sophomores, freshmen, and juniors are at different stages in their high school education. These stages come with varying academic challenges and learning experiences, which can independently affect test scores.

By assigning different breakfast types to different grades, the experiment design inadvertently links the variable of interest (type of breakfast) with the lurking variable (grade level). This confounding makes it difficult to determine if differences in test scores are due to the breakfast type or the inherent differences between students in different grades.

Any observed difference in test scores might be attributed to the grade level rather than the type of breakfast, making it challenging to establish a direct causal relationship between breakfast type and academic performance.

For a more robust experimental design, the nutritionist should ensure that each breakfast type is represented across all grade levels. This would help isolate the effect of the breakfast type from the effect of grade level, leading to more reliable conclusions about the impact of breakfast on academic performance.

32. Choice C is correct.

According to the table provided, the biologist has collected 5 variables in this study:

1) Species Name

2) Length (cm)

3) Habitat Depth (meters)

4) Tagged

5) Swim Speed (km/h)

33. Choice B is correct.

To answer this question, you would calculate the $z-$score for 2.5 hours and then find the corresponding percentile in a standard normal distribution table.

The $z-$score is calculated as follows:

$$z = \frac{X - \mu}{\sigma}$$

Where X is 2.5 hours, μ (the mean) is 2 hours, and σ (the standard deviation) is 0.5 hours. After calculating the $z-$score, you can find the percentage of students who spend less than 2.5 hours on homework and subtract this from 100% to find the percentage who spend at least 2.5 hours. Let's do this calculation:

Approximately 16% of students spend at least 2.5 hours on homework.

Therefore, the closest answer is B, 20%.

This calculation is based on the standard normal distribution, where we first find the percentile for spending less than 2.5 hours on homework and then subtract this from 100% to find the percentage spending at least that amount of time.

34. Choice C is correct.

The Interquartile Range (IQR) is a measure of variability, based on dividing a data set into quartiles. Quartiles divide a rank-ordered data set into four equal parts. The values that divide each part are known as the first quartile (Q_1), the second quartile (Q_2, or the median), and the third quartile (Q_3).

Here are the steps to calculate the IQR for the given ages:

Order the Data: First, arrange the ages in ascending order.

4, 7, 8, 9, 11, 12, 13, 14, 16, 17, 18, 19, 20, 21, 26

Find the Median (Q_2): The median is the middle number. Since there are 15 numbers, the median is the 8th number.

Median $Q_2 = 14$

Find the First Quartile (Q_1): Q_1 is the median of the first half of the data (excluding the median if the number of data points is odd, which it is in this case).

First half (excluding the overall median): 4, 7, 8, 9, 11, 12, 13

The median of this set is the $4th$ number.

$$Q_1 = 9$$

Find the Third Quartile (Q_3): Q_3 is the median of the second half of the data.

Second half (excluding the overall median): 16, 17, 18, 19, 20, 21, 26

The median of this set is the $4th$ number.

$$Q_3 = 19$$

Calculate the IQR: Subtract Q_1 from Q_3.

$$IQR = Q_3 - Q_1 = 19 - 9 = 10$$

The Interquartile Range (IQR) for the ages of the eldest child reported by the fifteen parents is 10 years.

This calculation shows the range within which the middle 50% of the ages fall, providing a sense of the age spread ignoring the extremes.

35. Choice D is correct.

To answer this question, we first need to understand what the correlation coefficient r indicates. The correlation coefficient measures the strength and direction of a linear relationship between two variables, in this case, the number of books read and reading comprehension test scores. A value of $r = 0.85$ suggests a strong positive linear relationship, meaning that, generally, as the number of books read increases, the reading comprehension test scores tend to increase as well.

Now, let's analyze the answer choices:

A. misinterpret the correlation by suggesting that it implies a direct causation or that it can be applied to percentages of students or outcomes, which is not accurate.

B. incorrectly suggests that the percentage correlation coefficient directly translates to the percentage of variation explained.

C. while it attempts to refer to the unexplained variance, does not directly correlate with how the coefficient of determination (r^2) is used to explain variance.

D. correctly applies the concept of the coefficient of determination (r^2). Squaring the correlation coefficient ($r = 0.85$) gives $r^2 = 0.7225$ or 72.25%. This means that 72.25% of the variation in reading comprehension test scores can be explained by the variation in the number of books read over the summer. The coefficient of determination (r^2) is used to indicate the proportion of the variance in the dependent variable that is predictable from the independent variable.

Therefore, the most reasonable conclusion based on the given correlation of $r = 0.85$ is:

D. 72.25% of the variation in reading comprehension test scores can be explained by the number of books read over the summer.

This answer demonstrates how to interpret the correlation coefficient and the coefficient of determination, highlighting the importance of understanding statistical concepts correctly.

36. Choice C is correct.

To calculate the proportion of defective components and the probability that a defective component came from Supplier A, we can follow a similar approach as in the previous question.

Proportion of Defective Components:

Using the law of total probability:

$$P(D) = P(D \cap A) + P(D \cap B) = P(D \mid A) \cdot P(A) + P(D \mid B) \cdot P(B)$$

$$= 0.02 \times 0.70 + 0.03 \times 0.30 = 0.014 + 0.009 = 0.023$$

So, the proportion of defective components can be expected to be 0.023.

Probability that a Defective Component Came from Supplier A:

Using Bayes' theorem:

$$P(A \mid D) = \frac{P(D \mid A) \cdot P(A)}{P(D)} = \frac{0.02 \times 0.70}{0.023} = \frac{0.014}{0.023} \approx 0.609$$

So, the probability that a defective component came from Supplier A is approximately 0.609.

Therefore, the correct answer is C.

37. Choice C is correct.

To calculate the sample size needed for the National Education Board (NEB) survey, we'll use the formula for determining sample size for estimating a population proportion: $n = \frac{Z^2 \times \hat{p} \times (1 - \hat{p})}{E^2}$

Given:

The margin of error (E) is $\pm 5\%$, or 0.05.

For a 99% confidence level, the Z−score (Z) is approximately 2.576.

If the NEB does not have a prior estimate of the proportion, we use $\hat{p} = 0.5$ to maximize the sample size.

Let's calculate the sample size.

$$n = \frac{2.576^2 \times 0.5 \times (1 - 0.5)}{0.05^2} = 663.5776$$

To estimate the percentage of high school teachers who feel the need for additional training in online teaching tools with a margin of error of $\pm 5\%$ at a 99% confidence level, the National Education Board should survey a sample size of approximately 663.58 teachers. Since you cannot survey a fraction of a person, always round up to the nearest whole number regardless of the decimal, meaning you would need approximately 664 participants to achieve the desired margin of error and confidence level.

So, the correct answer is C.

38. Choice B is correct.

We are given:

Desired overflow rate: less than 1% of the time.

Standard deviation $\sigma = 0.2$ ounces.

Cup size $= 10$ ounces.

We need to find the mean setting (μ) such that the probability of getting more than 10 ounces (overflowing the cup) is less than 1%.

In a normal distribution, we can find the $z-$score corresponding to the $99th$ percentile (since we want less than 1% overflow) and then use the formula for the $z-$score to find the mean:

$$z = \frac{X - \mu}{\sigma}$$

Where X is the value of interest (10 ounces). First, we find the $z-$score corresponding to the $99th$ percentile, and then solve for μ. Let's calculate it.

The calculated mean setting for the coffee machine to ensure that a $10-$ounce cup will overflow less than 1% of the time is approximately 9.53 ounces. This setting would make it highly unlikely for the coffee machine to overflow a $10-$ounce cup.

39. Choice D is correct.

To solve this problem, we will perform a hypothesis test for a population proportion.

Formulate Hypotheses:

Null Hypothesis (H_0): The university's graduation rate is 60% ($p = 0.60$).

Alternative Hypothesis (H_a): The university's graduation rate is lower than 60% ($p < 0.60$).

Choose the Significance Level:

Let's assume a significance level of $\alpha = 0.05$ for a one-tailed test.

Calculate the Test Statistic:

We will use the $z-$test for a population proportion. The formula for the $z-$test statistic is:

$$z = \frac{\hat{p} - p}{\sqrt{\dfrac{p(1 - p)}{n}}}$$

where: $\hat{p}$ is the sample proportion (140 out of 250), p is the hypothesized population proportion (0.60), n is the sample size (250).

Plugging in the values:

$$z = \frac{0.56 - 0.60}{\sqrt{\dfrac{0.60(1 - 0.60)}{250}}} \approx \frac{-0.04}{\sqrt{\dfrac{0.24}{250}}} \approx -1.29$$

Calculate the $p-$value

For a one-tailed test, we need to find the $p-$value associated with the calculated $z-$test statistic ($z = -1.29$).

Using the $z-$table or a calculator, the $p-$value for $z = -1.29$ is approximately 0.0985.

Comparing the $p-$value to the Significance Level:

Significance Level (α): 0.05

Since the $p-$value (0.0985) is greater than the significance level (0.05), we fail to reject the null hypothesis.

Based on the results of the hypothesis test, there is not strong evidence to claim that the university's graduation rate is lower than 60%.

The correct answer is:

D. No, because the $P-$value is greater than 0.10.

40. Choice D is correct.

The graph represents a cumulative distribution function (CDF) of final exam scores. To find the median, we look for the score corresponding to a cumulative proportion of 0.5 (the $50th$ percentile) on the vertical axis.

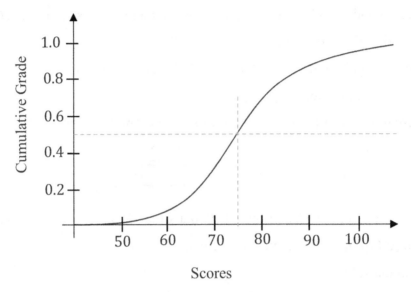

From the graph, it appears that the median value, where the red dashed line intersects the curve, is somewhere around a score of 75 out of 100. This is an estimate because the exact intersection point cannot be determined without the raw data or a more precise graph. Therefore, the answer is D.

Probability Tables

Z –Score Table: P –Values for Standard Normal Distribution

How to Read a Z –Score Table

A Z –score table typically displays the proportion of values (as a decimal) to the left of a Z –score in a standard normal distribution.

Step 1: Identify the First Part of Your Z –score. Begin by looking at the left column of the Z –score table. This column lists the first part of the Z –score (e.g., the integer and the first decimal digit). Scroll down this column to locate the initial part of your Z –score.

Step 2: Find the Second Part of Your Z –score. Next, move to the top row of the table. This row contains the second part of the Z –score (the remaining decimal digits). Traverse this row to find the second part of your Z –score.

Step 3: Determine the Intersection Value. The intersection of the row and column, corresponding to the first and second parts of your Z –score, respectively, will reveal the associated value. This value represents the proportion of the dataset that lies below your Z –score's corresponding value in a standard normal distribution.

There are two types of Z –score tables:

Positive Z –score Table: This is utilized when the Z –score is positive, indicating values above the mean. It helps in finding the probability or percentage of values that occur below a given positive Z –score within a standard normal distribution.

Negative Z –score Table: This table is used for negative Z –scores, which represent values below the mean. It assists in determining the probability or percentage of values that fall below a specific negative Z –score in a standard normal distribution.

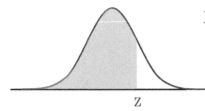

Positive Z –Score Table:

(Left-Tail Probabilities)

Z

z	0.00	0.01	0.02	0.03	0.04	0.05	0.06	0.07	0.08	0.09
0.0	0.50000	0.50399	0.50798	0.51197	0.51595	0.51994	0.52392	0.52790	0.53188	0.53586
0.1	0.53983	0.54380	0.54776	0.55172	0.55567	0.55966	0.56360	0.56749	0.57142	0.57535
0.2	0.57926	0.58317	0.58706	0.59095	0.59848	0.59871	0.60257	0.60642	0.61026	0.61409
0.3	0.61791	0.62172	0.62552	0.62930	0.63307	0.63683	0.64058	0.64431	0.64803	0.65173
0.4	0.65542	0.65910	0.66276	0.66640	0.67003	0.67364	0.67724	0.68082	0.68439	0.68793
0.5	0.69146	0.69497	0.69847	0.70194	0.70540	0.70884	0.71226	0.71566	0.71904	0.72240
0.6	0.72575	0.72907	0.73237	0.73565	0.73891	0.74215	0.74537	0.74857	0.75175	0.75490
0.7	0.75804	0.76115	0.76424	0.76730	0.77035	0.77337	0.77637	0.77935	0.78230	0.78524
0.8	0.78814	0.79103	0.79389	0.79673	0.79955	0.80234	0.80511	0.80785	0.81057	0.81327
0.9	0.81594	0.81859	0.82121	0.82381	0.82639	0.82894	0.83147	0.83398	0.83646	0.83891
1.0	0.84134	0.84375	0.84614	0.84849	0.85083	0.85314	0.85543	0.85769	0.85993	0.86214
1.1	0.86433	0.86650	0.86864	0.87076	0.87286	0.87493	0.87698	0.87900	0.88100	0.88298
1.2	0.88493	0.88686	0.88877	0.89065	0.89251	0.89435	0.89617	0.89796	0.89973	0.90147
1.3	0.90320	0.90490	0.90658	0.90824	0.90988	0.91149	0.91308	0.91466	0.91621	0.91774
1.4	0.91924	0.92073	0.92220	0.92364	0.92507	0.92647	0.92785	0.92922	0.93056	0.93189
1.5	0.93319	0.93448	0.93574	0.93699	0.93822	0.93943	0.94062	0.94179	0.94295	0.94408
1.6	0.94520	0.94630	0.94738	0.94845	0.94950	0.95053	0.95154	0.95254	0.95352	0.95449
1.7	0.95543	0.95637	0.95728	0.95818	0.95907	0.95994	0.96080	0.96164	0.96246	0.96327
1.8	0.96407	0.96485	0.96562	0.96638	0.96712	0.96784	0.96856	0.96926	0.96995	0.97062
1.9	0.97128	0.97193	0.97257	0.97320	0.97381	0.97441	0.97500	0.97558	0.97615	0.97670
2.0	0.97725	0.97778	0.97831	0.97882	0.97932	0.97982	0.98030	0.98077	0.98124	0.98169
2.1	0.98214	0.98257	0.98300	0.98341	0.98382	0.98422	0.98461	0.98500	0.98537	0.98574
2.2	0.98610	0.98645	0.98679	0.98713	0.98745	0.98778	0.98809	0.98840	0.98870	0.98899
2.3	0.98928	0.98956	0.98983	0.99010	0.99036	0.99061	0.99086	0.99111	0.99134	0.99158
2.4	0.99180	0.99202	0.99224	0.99245	0.99366	0.99286	0.99305	0.99324	0.99343	0.99361
2.5	0.99379	0.99396	0.99413	0.99430	0.99446	0.99461	0.99477	0.99492	0.99506	0.99520
2.6	0.99534	0.99547	0.99560	0.99573	0.99585	0.99598	0.99609	0.99621	0.99632	0.99643
2.7	0.99653	0.99664	0.99674	0.99683	0.99693	0.99702	0.99711	0.99720	0.99728	0.99736
2.8	0.99744	0.99752	0.99760	0.99767	0.99774	0.99781	0.99788	0.99795	0.99801	0.99807
2.9	0.99813	0.99819	0.99825	0.99831	0.99836	0.99841	0.99846	0.99851	0.99856	0.99861
3.0	0.99865	0.99869	0.99874	0.99878	0.99882	0.99886	0.99889	0.99893	0.99896	0.99900
3.1	0.99903	0.99906	0.99910	0.99913	0.99916	0.99918	0.99921	0.99924	0.99926	0.99929
3.2	0.99931	0.99934	0.99936	0.99938	0.99940	0.99942	0.99944	0.99946	0.99948	0.99950
3.3	0.99952	0.99953	0.99955	0.99957	0.99958	0.99960	0.99961	0.99962	0.99964	0.99965
3.4	0.99966	0.99968	0.99969	0.99970	0.99971	0.99972	0.99973	0.99974	0.99975	0.99976
3.5	0.99977	0.99978	0.99978	0.99979	0.99980	0.99981	0.99981	0.99982	0.99983	0.99983
3.6	0.99984	0.99985	0.99985	0.99986	0.99986	0.99987	0.99987	0.99988	0.99988	0.99989
3.7	0.99989	0.99990	0.99990	0.99990	0.99991	0.99991	0.99992	0.99992	0.99992	0.99992
3.8	0.99993	0.99993	0.99993	0.99994	0.99994	0.99994	0.99994	0.99995	0.99995	0.99995
3.9	0.99995	0.99995	0.99996	0.99996	0.99996	0.99996	0.99996	0.99996	0.99997	0.99997
4.0	0.99997	0.99997	0.99997	0.99997	0.99997	0.99997	0.99998	0.99998	0.99998	0.99998

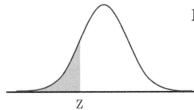

Negative Z –Score Table:

(Left-Tail Probabilities)

z	0.00	0.01	0.02	0.03	0.04	0.05	0.06	0.07	0.08	0.09
−0.0	0.50000	0.49601	0.49202	0.48803	0.48405	0.48006	0.47608	0.47210	0.46812	0.46414
−0.1	0.46017	0.45620	0.45224	0.44828	0.44433	0.44034	0.43640	0.43251	0.42858	0.42465
−0.2	0.42074	0.41683	0.41294	0.40905	0.40152	0.40129	0.39743	0.39358	0.38974	0.38591
−0.3	0.38209	0.37828	0.37448	0.37070	0.36693	0.36317	0.35942	0.35569	0.35197	0.34827
−0.4	0.34458	0.34090	0.33724	0.33360	0.32997	0.32636	0.32276	0.31918	0.31561	0.31207
−0.5	0.30854	0.30503	0.30153	0.29806	0.29460	0.29116	0.28774	0.28434	0.28096	0.27760
−0.6	0.27425	0.27093	0.26763	0.26435	0.26109	0.25785	0.25463	0.25143	0.24825	0.24510
−0.7	0.24196	0.23885	0.23576	0.23270	0.22965	0.22663	0.22363	0.22065	0.21770	0.21476
−0.8	0.21186	0.20897	0.20611	0.20327	0.20045	0.19766	0.19489	0.19215	0.18943	0.18673
−0.9	0.18406	0.18141	0.17879	0.17619	0.17361	0.17106	0.16853	0.16602	0.16354	0.16109
−1.0	0.15866	0.15625	0.15386	0.15151	0.14917	0.14686	0.14457	0.14231	0.14007	0.13786
−1.1	0.13567	0.13350	0.13136	0.12924	0.12714	0.12507	0.12302	0.12100	0.11900	0.11702
−1.2	0.11507	0.11314	0.11123	0.10935	0.10749	0.10565	0.10383	0.10204	0.10027	0.09853
−1.3	0.09680	0.09510	0.09342	0.09176	0.09012	0.08851	0.08692	0.08534	0.08379	0.08226
−1.4	0.08076	0.07927	0.07780	0.07636	0.07493	0.07353	0.07215	0.07078	0.06944	0.06811
−1.5	0.06681	0.06552	0.06426	0.06301	0.06178	0.06057	0.05938	0.05821	0.05705	0.05592
−1.6	0.05480	0.05370	0.05262	0.05155	0.05050	0.04947	0.04846	0.04746	0.04648	0.04551
−1.7	0.04457	0.04363	0.04272	0.04182	0.04093	0.04006	0.03920	0.03836	0.03754	0.03673
−1.8	0.03593	0.03515	0.03438	0.03362	0.03288	0.03216	0.03144	0.03074	0.03005	0.02938
−1.9	0.02872	0.02807	0.02743	0.02680	0.02619	0.02559	0.02500	0.02442	0.02385	0.02330
−2.0	0.02275	0.02222	0.02169	0.02118	0.02068	0.02018	0.01970	0.01923	0.01876	0.01831
−2.1	0.01786	0.01743	0.01700	0.01659	0.01618	0.01578	0.01539	0.01500	0.01463	0.01426
−2.2	0.01390	0.01355	0.01321	0.01287	0.01255	0.01222	0.01191	0.01160	0.01130	0.01101
−2.3	0.01072	0.01044	0.01017	0.00990	0.00964	0.00939	0.00914	0.00889	0.00866	0.00842
−2.4	0.00820	0.00798	0.00776	0.00755	0.00634	0.00714	0.00695	0.00676	0.00657	0.00639
−2.5	0.00621	0.00604	0.00587	0.00570	0.00554	0.00539	0.00523	0.00508	0.00494	0.00480
−2.6	0.00466	0.00453	0.00440	0.00427	0.00415	0.00402	0.00391	0.00379	0.00368	0.00357
−2.7	0.00347	0.00336	0.00326	0.00317	0.00307	0.00298	0.00289	0.00280	0.00272	0.00264
−2.8	0.00256	0.00248	0.00240	0.00233	0.00226	0.00219	0.00212	0.00205	0.00199	0.00193
−2.9	0.00187	0.00181	0.00175	0.00169	0.00164	0.00159	0.00154	0.00149	0.00144	0.00139
−3.0	0.00135	0.00131	0.00126	0.00122	0.00118	0.00114	0.00111	0.00107	0.00104	0.00100
−3.1	0.00097	0.00094	0.00090	0.00087	0.00084	0.00082	0.00079	0.00076	0.00074	0.00071
−3.2	0.00069	0.00066	0.00064	0.00062	0.00060	0.00058	0.00056	0.00054	0.00052	0.00050
−3.3	0.00048	0.00047	0.00045	0.00043	0.00042	0.00040	0.00039	0.00038	0.00036	0.00035
−3.4	0.00034	0.00032	0.00031	0.00030	0.00029	0.00028	0.00027	0.00026	0.00025	0.00024
−3.5	0.00023	0.00022	0.00022	0.00021	0.00020	0.00019	0.00019	0.00018	0.00017	0.00017
−3.6	0.00016	0.00015	0.00015	0.00014	0.00014	0.00013	0.00013	0.00012	0.00012	0.00011
−3.7	0.00011	0.00010	0.00010	0.00010	0.00009	0.00009	0.00008	0.00008	0.00008	0.00008
−3.8	0.00007	0.00007	0.00007	0.00006	0.00006	0.00006	0.00006	0.00005	0.00005	0.00005
−3.9	0.00005	0.00005	0.00004	0.00004	0.00004	0.00004	0.00004	0.00004	0.00003	0.00003
−4.0	0.00003	0.00003	0.00003	0.00003	0.00003	0.00003	0.00002	0.00002	0.00002	0.00002

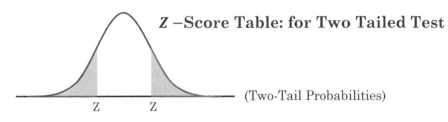

Z –Score Table: for Two Tailed Test

(Two-Tail Probabilities)

Z   Z

z	0.00	0.01	0.02	0.03	0.04	0.05	0.06	0.07	0.08	0.09
0.0	1.00000	0.99202	0.98404	0.97607	0.96809	0.96012	0.95216	0.94419	0.93624	0.92829
0.1	0.92034	0.91241	0.90448	0.89657	0.88866	0.88068	0.87280	0.86501	0.85715	0.84931
0.2	0.84148	0.83367	0.82587	0.81809	0.80303	0.80259	0.79486	0.78716	0.77948	0.38591
0.3	0.76418	0.75656	0.74897	0.74140	0.73386	0.72634	0.71885	0.71138	0.70395	0.69654
0.4	0.34458	0.68181	0.67449	0.66720	0.65994	0.65271	0.64552	0.63836	0.63123	0.62413
0.5	0.61708	0.61005	0.60306	0.59611	0.58920	0.58232	0.57548	0.56868	0.56191	0.55519
0.6	0.54850	0.54186	0.53526	0.52869	0.52217	0.51569	0.50925	0.50286	0.49650	0.49019
0.7	0.24196	0.47770	0.47152	0.46539	0.45930	0.45325	0.44725	0.44130	0.43539	0.42953
0.8	0.42372	0.41794	0.41222	0.40654	0.40091	0.39533	0.38979	0.38430	0.37886	0.37347
0.9	0.36812	0.36282	0.35757	0.35237	0.34722	0.34211	0.33706	0.33205	0.32709	0.32217
1.0	0.31732	0.31250	0.30773	0.30301	0.29834	0.29372	0.28914	0.28462	0.28014	0.27571
1.1	0.27134	0.26700	0.26271	0.25848	0.25429	0.25014	0.24605	0.24200	0.23800	0.23405
1.2	0.23014	0.22628	0.22246	0.21870	0.21498	0.21130	0.20767	0.20408	0.20055	0.19705
1.3	0.19360	0.19020	0.18684	0.18352	0.18025	0.17702	0.17383	0.17069	0.16759	0.16453
1.4	0.16152	0.15854	0.15561	0.15272	0.14987	0.14706	0.14429	0.14156	0.13887	0.13622
1.5	0.13362	0.13104	0.12851	0.12602	0.12356	0.12114	0.11876	0.11642	0.11411	0.11183
1.6	0.10960	0.10740	0.10523	0.10310	0.10101	0.09894	0.09691	0.09492	0.09296	0.09103
1.7	0.08914	0.08727	0.08543	0.08363	0.08186	0.08012	0.07841	0.07673	0.07508	0.07345
1.8	0.07186	0.07030	0.06876	0.06725	0.06577	0.06431	0.06289	0.06148	0.06011	0.05876
1.9	0.05744	0.05613	0.05486	0.05361	0.05238	0.05118	0.05000	0.04884	0.04770	0.04659
2.0	0.04550	0.04443	0.04338	0.04236	0.04135	0.04036	0.03940	0.03845	0.03753	0.03662
2.1	0.03572	0.03486	0.03401	0.03317	0.03235	0.03156	0.03077	0.03001	0.02926	0.02852
2.2	0.02781	0.02711	0.02642	0.02575	0.02509	0.02445	0.02382	0.02321	0.02261	0.02202
2.3	0.02145	0.02089	0.02034	0.01981	0.01928	0.01877	0.01827	0.01779	0.01731	0.01685
2.4	0.01640	0.01595	0.01552	0.01510	0.01269	0.01429	0.01389	0.01351	0.01314	0.01277
2.5	0.01242	0.01207	0.01174	0.01141	0.01109	0.01077	0.01047	0.01017	0.00988	0.00960
2.6	0.00932	0.00905	0.00879	0.00854	0.00829	0.00805	0.00781	0.00759	0.00736	0.00715
2.7	0.00693	0.00673	0.00653	0.00633	0.00614	0.00596	0.00578	0.00561	0.00544	0.00527
2.8	0.00511	0.00495	0.00480	0.00465	0.00451	0.00437	0.00424	0.00410	0.00398	0.00385
2.9	0.00373	0.00361	0.00350	0.00339	0.00328	0.00318	0.00308	0.00298	0.00288	0.00279
3.0	0.00270	0.00261	0.00253	0.00245	0.00237	0.00229	0.00221	0.00214	0.00207	0.00200
3.1	0.00194	0.00187	0.00181	0.00175	0.00169	0.00163	0.00158	0.00152	0.00147	0.00142
3.2	0.00137	0.00133	0.00128	0.00124	0.00120	0.00115	0.00111	0.00108	0.00104	0.00100
3.3	0.00097	0.00093	0.00090	0.00087	0.00084	0.00081	0.00078	0.00075	0.00072	0.00070
3.4	0.00067	0.00065	0.00063	0.00060	0.00058	0.00056	0.00054	0.00052	0.00050	0.00048
3.5	0.00047	0.00045	0.00043	0.00042	0.00040	0.00039	0.00037	0.00036	0.00034	0.00033
3.6	0.00032	0.00031	0.00029	0.00028	0.00027	0.00026	0.00025	0.00024	0.00023	0.00022
3.7	0.00022	0.00021	0.00020	0.00019	0.00018	0.00018	0.00017	0.00016	0.00016	0.00015
3.8	0.00014	0.00014	0.00013	0.00013	0.00012	0.00012	0.00011	0.00011	0.00010	0.00010
3.9	0.00010	0.00009	0.00009	0.00008	0.00008	0.00008	0.00007	0.00007	0.00007	0.00007
4.0	0.00006	0.00006	0.00006	0.00006	0.00006	0.00005	0.00005	0.00005	0.00005	0.00005

Z-Scores for Various Confidence Levels

Credible Level	α	$\dfrac{\alpha}{2}$	$Z-$Score
50.0%	0.500	0.2500	± 0.675
80.0%	0.200	0.1000	± 1.282
90.0%	0.100	0.0500	± 1.645
95.0%	0.050	0.0250	± 1.960
98.0%	0.020	0.0100	± 2.326
99.0%	0.010	0.0050	± 2.576
99.9%	0.001	0.0005	± 3.291

T –Distribution Table

Here's a step-by-step guide on how to use the t –distribution table:

Step 1: Determine Your Degrees of Freedom (df).

Step 2: Decide on the Significance Level or Probability. Determine the significance level (α) you need for your test. Common values are 0.05, 0.01, and 0.10.

- Note that for two-tailed tests, you will split the (α) value (e.g., 0.05 becomes 0.025 on each side).

Step 3: Find the Appropriate Value in the Table.

- Locate the row corresponding to your degrees of freedom.

- Move across to the column that corresponds to your chosen significance level.

- The number where the row and column intersect is the critical value (t –value) of the t –distribution.

Step 4: Interpret the t –Value. If the absolute value of your t –statistic is greater than the table value, it suggests significance (rejecting the null hypothesis in a hypothesis test).

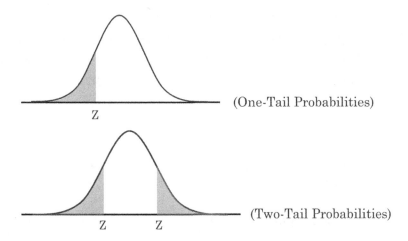

(One-Tail Probabilities)

(Two-Tail Probabilities)

One-taile

df	Significance level (α)								
	0.20	0.15	0.10	0.05	0.025	0.01	0.005	0.001	0.0005
1	1.376	1.963	3.078	6.314	12.706	31.821	63.657	318.31	636.62
2	1.061	1.386	1.886	2.920	4.303	6.965	9.925	22.327	31.599
3	0.978	1.250	1.638	2.353	3.182	4.541	5.841	10.214	12.924
4	0.941	1.190	1.533	2.132	2.776	3.747	4.604	7.173	8.610
5	0.920	1.156	1.476	2.015	2.571	3.365	4.032	5.894	6.869
6	0.906	1.134	1.440	1.943	2.447	3.143	3.707	5.208	5.959
7	0.896	1.119	1.415	1.895	2.365	2.998	3.499	4.785	5.408
8	0.889	1.108	1.397	1.860	2.306	2.896	3.355	4.501	5.041
9	0.883	1.100	1.383	1.833	2.262	2.821	3.250	4.297	4.781
10	0.879	1.093	1.372	1.812	2.228	2.764	3.169	4.144	4.587
11	0.876	1.088	1.363	1.796	2.201	2.718	3.106	4.025	4.437
12	0.873	1.083	1.356	1.782	2.179	2.681	3.055	3.930	4.318
13	0.870	1.079	1.350	1.771	2.160	2.650	3.012	3.852	4.221
14	0.868	1.076	1.345	1.761	2.145	2.624	2.977	3.787	4.140
15	0.866	1.074	1.341	1.753	2.131	2.602	2.947	3.733	4.073
16	0.865	1.071	1.337	1.746	2.120	2.583	2.921	3.686	4.015
17	0.863	1.069	1.333	1.740	2.110	2.567	2.898	3.646	3.965
18	0.862	1.067	1.330	1.734	2.101	2.552	2.878	3.610	3.922
19	0.861	1.066	1.328	1.729	2.093	2.539	2.861	3.579	3.883
20	0.860	1.064	1.325	1.725	2.086	2.528	2.845	3.552	3.850
21	0.859	1.063	1.323	1.721	2.080	2.518	2.831	3.527	3.819
22	0.858	1.061	1.321	1.717	2.074	2.508	2.819	3.505	3.792
23	0.858	1.060	1.319	1.714	2.069	2.500	2.807	3.485	3.768
24	0.857	1.059	1.318	1.711	2.064	2.492	2.797	3.467	3.745
25	0.856	1.058	1.316	1.708	2.060	2.485	2.787	3.450	3.725
26	0.856	1.058	1.315	1.706	2.056	2.479	2.779	3.435	3.707
27	0.855	1.057	1.314	1.703	2.052	2.473	2.771	3.421	3.689
28	0.855	1.056	1.313	1.701	2.048	2.467	2.763	3.408	3.674
29	0.854	1.055	1.311	1.699	2.045	2.462	2.756	3.396	3.660
30	0.854	1.055	1.310	1.697	2.042	2.457	2.750	3.385	3.646
40	0.851	1.050	1.030	1.684	2.021	2.423	2.704	3.307	3.551
50	0.849	1.047	1.299	1.676	2.009	2.403	2.678	3.261	3.496
60	0.848	1.045	1.296	1.671	2.000	2.390	2.660	3.232	3.460
70	0.847	1.044	1.294	1.667	1.994	2.381	2.648	3.211	3.435
80	0.846	1.043	1.292	1.664	1.990	2.374	2.639	3.195	3.416
100	0.845	1.042	1.290	1.660	1.984	2.364	2.626	3.174	3.390
1000	0.842	1.037	1.282	1.646	1.962	2.330	2.581	3.098	3.300

two-tail

df	Significance level (α)								
	0.40	0.30	0.20	0.10	0.05	0.02	0.01	0.002	0.001
1	1.376	1.963	3.078	6.314	12.706	31.821	63.657	318.31	636.62
2	1.061	1.386	1.886	2.920	4.303	6.965	9.925	22.327	31.599
3	0.978	1.250	1.638	2.353	3.182	4.541	5.841	10.214	12.924
4	0.941	1.190	1.533	2.132	2.776	3.747	4.604	7.173	8.610
5	0.920	1.156	1.476	2.015	2.571	3.365	4.032	5.894	6.869
6	0.906	1.134	1.440	1.943	2.447	3.143	3.707	5.208	5.959
7	0.896	1.119	1.415	1.895	2.365	2.998	3.499	4.785	5.408
8	0.889	1.108	1.397	1.860	2.306	2.896	3.355	4.501	5.041
9	0.883	1.100	1.383	1.833	2.262	2.821	3.250	4.297	4.781
10	0.879	1.093	1.372	1.812	2.228	2.764	3.169	4.144	4.587
11	0.876	1.088	1.363	1.796	2.201	2.718	3.106	4.025	4.437
12	0.873	1.083	1.356	1.782	2.179	2.681	3.055	3.930	4.318
13	0.870	1.079	1.350	1.771	2.160	2.650	3.012	3.852	4.221
14	0.868	1.076	1.345	1.761	2.145	2.624	2.977	3.787	4.140
15	0.866	1.074	1.341	1.753	2.131	2.602	2.947	3.733	4.073
16	0.865	1.071	1.337	1.746	2.120	2.583	2.921	3.686	4.015
17	0.863	1.069	1.333	1.740	2.110	2.567	2.898	3.646	3.965
18	0.862	1.067	1.330	1.734	2.101	2.552	2.878	3.610	3.922
19	0.861	1.066	1.328	1.729	2.093	2.539	2.861	3.579	3.883
20	0.860	1.064	1.325	1.725	2.086	2.528	2.845	3.552	3.850
21	0.859	1.063	1.323	1.721	2.080	2.518	2.831	3.527	3.819
22	0.858	1.061	1.321	1.717	2.074	2.508	2.819	3.505	3.792
23	0.858	1.060	1.319	1.714	2.069	2.500	2.807	3.485	3.768
24	0.857	1.059	1.318	1.711	2.064	2.492	2.797	3.467	3.745
25	0.856	1.058	1.316	1.708	2.060	2.485	2.787	3.450	3.725
26	0.856	1.058	1.315	1.706	2.056	2.479	2.779	3.435	3.707
27	0.855	1.057	1.314	1.703	2.052	2.473	2.771	3.421	3.689
28	0.855	1.056	1.313	1.701	2.048	2.467	2.763	3.408	3.674
29	0.854	1.055	1.311	1.699	2.045	2.462	2.756	3.396	3.660
30	0.854	1.055	1.310	1.697	2.042	2.457	2.750	3.385	3.646
40	0.851	1.050	1.030	1.684	2.021	2.423	2.704	3.307	3.551
50	0.849	1.047	1.299	1.676	2.009	2.403	2.678	3.261	3.496
60	0.848	1.045	1.296	1.671	2.000	2.390	2.660	3.232	3.460
70	0.847	1.044	1.294	1.667	1.994	2.381	2.648	3.211	3.435
80	0.846	1.043	1.292	1.664	1.990	2.374	2.639	3.195	3.416
100	0.845	1.042	1.290	1.660	1.984	2.364	2.626	3.174	3.390
1000	0.842	1.037	1.282	1.646	1.962	2.330	2.581	3.098	3.300

Chi-square Distribution Table

Here are two different ways to use the chi-square distribution table:

Method 1: Using the Chi-Square Table for Critical Values

This method is used to find the critical value of chi-square for a given significance level (α) and degrees of freedom (df).

Step 1: Determine Your Significance Level (α). Choose the desired level of significance, typically 0.01, 0.05, or 0.10. This represents the probability of making a Type I error (rejecting a true null hypothesis).

Step 2: Determine Degrees of Freedom (df).

Step 3: Locate the Critical Value. In the chi-square distribution table, find the row corresponding to your degrees of freedom (df). Then, look for the column that matches or is just larger than your chosen significance level (α).

Step 4: Read the Critical Value. The value at the intersection of the row and column you found in step 3 is your critical chi-square value ($\chi^2_{\alpha,df}$).

Step 5: Use in Hypothesis Testing. In hypothesis testing, if your calculated chi-square statistic is greater than the critical value, you can reject the null hypothesis.

Method 2: Using the Chi-Square Table for P–Values

This method is used to find the p–value associated with a calculated chi-square statistic.

Step 1: Calculate Chi-Square Statistic (χ^2).

Step 2: Determine Degrees of Freedom (df).

Step 3: Use the Chi-Square Distribution Table. Locate the row that corresponds to your degrees of freedom (df).

Step 4: Find the P–Value Column. Look for the column that contains values closest to your calculated chi-square statistic.

Step 5: Read the P–Value. The value at the top of the column you found in step 4 is your p–value.

Step 6: Interpret the Results: If the p–value is less than or equal to your chosen significance level (α), reject the null hypothesis.

					Significance level					
df	0.995	0.99	0.975	0.95	0.90	0.10	0.05	0.025	0.01	0.005
1	0.000	0.000	0.001	0.004	0.016	2.706	3.841	5.024	6.635	7.879
2	0.010	0.020	0.051	0.103	0.211	4.605	5.991	7.378	9.210	10.597
3	0.072	0.115	0.216	0.352	0.584	6.251	7.815	9.348	11.345	12.838
4	0.207	0.297	0.484	0.711	1.064	7.779	9.488	11.143	13.277	14.860
5	0.412	0.554	0.831	1.145	1.610	9.236	11.070	12.833	15.086	16.750
6	0.676	0.872	1.237	1.635	2.204	10.645	12.592	14.449	16.812	18.548
7	0.989	1.239	1.690	2.167	2.833	12.017	14.067	16.013	18.475	20.278
8	1.344	1.646	2.180	2.733	3.490	13.362	15.507	17.535	20.090	21.955
9	1.735	2.088	2.700	3.325	4.168	14.684	16.919	19.023	21.666	23.589
10	2.156	2.558	3.247	3.940	4.865	15.987	18.307	20.483	23.209	25.188
11	2.603	3.053	3.816	4.575	5.578	17.275	19.675	21.920	24.725	26.757
12	3.074	3.571	4.404	5.226	6.304	18.549	21.026	23.337	26.217	28.300
13	3.565	4.107	5.009	5.892	7.042	19.812	22.362	24.736	27.688	29.819
14	4.075	4.660	5.629	6.571	7.790	21.064	23.685	26.119	29.141	31.319
15	4.601	5.229	6.262	7.261	8.547	22.307	24.996	27.488	30.578	32.801
16	5.142	5.812	6.908	7.962	9.312	23.542	26.296	28.845	32.000	34.267
17	5.697	6.408	7.564	8.672	10.085	24.769	27.587	30.191	33.409	35.718
18	6.265	7.015	8.231	9.390	10.865	25.989	28.869	31.526	34.805	37.156
19	6.844	7.633	8.907	10.117	11.651	27.204	30.144	32.852	36.191	38.582
20	7.434	8.260	9.591	10.851	12.443	28.412	31.410	34.170	37.566	39.997
21	8.034	8.897	10.283	11.591	13.240	29.615	32.671	35.479	38.932	41.401
22	8.643	9.542	10.982	12.338	14.041	30.813	33.924	36.781	40.289	42.796
23	9.260	10.196	11.689	13.091	14.848	32.007	35.172	38.076	41.638	44.181
24	9.886	10.856	12.401	13.848	15.659	33.196	36.415	39.364	42.980	45.559
25	10.520	11.524	13.120	14.611	16.473	34.382	37.652	40.646	44.314	46.928
26	11.160	12.198	13.844	15.379	17.292	35.563	38.885	41.923	45.642	48.290
27	11.808	12.879	14.573	16.151	18.114	36.741	40.113	43.195	46.963	49.645
28	12.461	13.565	15.308	16.928	18.939	37.916	41.337	44.461	48.278	50.993
29	13.121	14.256	16.047	17.708	19.768	39.087	42.557	45.722	49.588	52.336
30	13.787	14.953	16.791	18.493	20.599	40.256	43.773	46.979	50.892	53.672
31	14.458	15.655	17.539	19.281	21.434	41.422	44.985	48.232	52.191	55.003
32	15.134	16.362	18.291	20.072	22.271	42.585	46.194	49.480	53.486	56.328
33	15.815	17.074	19.047	20.867	23.11	43.745	47.400	50.725	54.776	57.648
34	16.501	17.789	19.806	21.664	23.952	44.903	48.602	51.966	56.061	58.964
35	17.192	18.509	20.569	22.465	24.797	46.059	49.802	53.203	57.342	60.275
36	17.887	19.233	21.336	23.269	25.643	47.212	50.998	54.437	58.619	61.581

37	18.586	19.960	22.106	24.075	26.492	48.363	52.192	55.668	59.893	62.883
38	19.289	20.691	22.878	24.884	27.343	49.513	53.384	56.896	61.162	64.181
39	19.996	21.426	23.654	25.695	28.196	50.660	54.572	58.120	62.428	65.476
40	20.707	22.164	24.433	26.509	29.051	51.805	55.758	59.342	63.691	66.766
41	21.421	22.906	25.215	27.326	29.907	52.949	56.942	60.561	64.950	68.053
42	22.138	23.650	25.999	28.144	30.765	54.090	58.124	61.777	66.206	69.336
43	22.859	24.398	26.785	28.965	31.625	55.230	59.304	62.990	67.459	70.616
44	23.584	25.148	27.575	29.787	32.487	56.369	60.481	64.201	68.710	71.893
45	24.311	25.901	28.366	30.612	33.35	57.505	61.656	65.410	69.957	73.166
46	25.041	26.657	29.160	31.439	34.215	58.641	62.830	66.617	71.201	74.437
47	25.775	27.416	29.956	32.268	35.081	59.774	64.001	67.821	72.443	75.704
48	26.511	28.177	30.755	33.098	35.949	60.907	65.171	69.023	73.683	76.969
49	27.249	28.941	31.555	33.930	36.818	62.038	66.339	70.222	74.919	78.231
50	27.991	29.707	32.357	34.764	37.689	63.167	67.505	71.420	76.154	79.490
51	28.735	30.475	33.162	35.600	38.560	64.295	68.669	72.616	77.386	80.747
52	29.481	31.246	33.968	36.437	39.433	65.422	69.832	73.810	78.616	82.001
53	30.230	32.018	34.776	37.276	40.308	66.548	70.993	75.002	79.843	83.253
54	30.981	32.793	35.586	38.116	41.183	67.673	72.153	76.192	81.069	84.502
55	31.735	33.570	36.398	38.958	42.060	68.796	73.311	77.380	82.292	85.749
56	32.490	345.350	37.212	39.801	42.937	69.919	74.468	78.567	83.513	86.994
57	33.248	35.131	38.027	30.646	43.816	71.040	75.624	79.752	84.733	88.236
58	34.008	35.913	38.844	41.492	44.696	72.160	76.778	80.936	85.950	89.477
59	34.770	36.698	39.662	42.339	45.577	73.279	77.931	82.117	87.166	90.715
60	35.534	37.485	40.482	43.188	46.459	74.397	79.082	83.298	88.379	91.952
61	36.301	38.273	41.303	44.038	47.342	75.514	80.232	84.476	89.591	93.186
62	37.068	39.063	42.126	44.889	48.226	76.630	81.381	85.654	90.802	94.419
63	37.838	39.855	42.950	45.741	49.111	77.745	82.529	86.830	92.010	95.649
64	38.610	40.649	43.776	46.595	49.996	78.860	83.675	88.004	93.217	96.878
65	39.383	41.444	44.603	47.450	50.883	79.973	84.821	89.177	94.422	98.105
66	40.158	42.240	45.431	48.305	51.770	81.085	85.965	90.349	95.626	99.330
67	40.935	43.038	46.261	49.162	52.659	82.197	87.108	91.519	96.828	100.554
68	41.713	43.838	47.092	50.020	53.548	83.308	88.250	92.689	98.028	101.776
69	42.494	44.639	47.924	50.879	54.438	84.418	89.391	93.856	99.228	102.996
70	43.275	45.442	48.758	51.739	55.329	85.527	90.531	95.023	100.425	104.215
71	44.058	46.246	49.592	52.600	56.221	86.635	91.670	96.189	101.621	105.432
72	44.843	47.051	50.428	53.462	57.113	87.743	92.808	97.353	102.816	106.648
73	45.629	47.858	51.265	54.325	58.006	88.850	93.945	98.516	104.010	107.862
74	46.417	48.666	52.103	55.189	58.900	89.956	95.081	99.678	105.202	109.074

75	47.206	49.475	52.942	56.054	59.795	91.061	96.217	100.839	106.393	110.286
76	47.997	50.286	53.782	56.920	60.690	92.166	97.351	101.999	107.583	111.495
77	48.788	51.097	54.623	57.786	61.586	93.270	98.484	103.158	108.771	112.704
78	49.582	51.910	55.466	58.654	62.483	94.374	99.617	104.316	109.958	113.911
79	50.376	52.725	56.309	59.522	63.380	95.476	100.749	105.473	111.144	115.117
80	51.172	53.540	57.153	60.391	64.278	96.578	101.879	106.629	112.329	116.321
81	51.969	54.357	57.998	61.261	65.176	97.680	103.010	107.783	113.512	117.524
82	52.767	55.174	58.845	62.132	66.076	98.780	104.139	108.937	114.695	118.726
83	53.567	55.993	59.692	63.004	66.976	99.880	105.267	110.090	115.876	119.927
84	54.368	56.813	60.540	63.876	67.876	100.980	106.395	111.242	117.057	121.126
85	55.170	57.634	61.389	64.749	68.777	102.079	107.522	112.393	118.236	122.325
86	55.973	58.456	62.239	65.623	69.679	103.177	108.648	113.544	119.414	123.522
87	56.777	59.279	63.089	66.498	70.581	104.275	109.773	114.693	120.591	124.718
88	57.582	60.103	63.941	67.373	71.484	105.372	110.898	115.841	121.767	125.913
89	58.389	60.928	64.793	68.249	72.387	106.469	112.022	116.989	122.942	127.106
90	59.196	61.754	65.647	69.126	73.291	107.565	113.145	118.136	124.116	128.299
91	60.005	62.581	66.501	70.003	74.196	108.661	114.268	119.383	125.289	129.491
92	60.815	63.409	67.356	70.882	75.100	109.756	115.390	120.427	126.462	130.681
93	61.625	64.238	68.211	71.760	76.006	110.580	116.511	121.571	127.633	131.871
94	62.437	65.068	69.068	72.640	76.912	111.944	117.632	122.715	128.803	133.059
95	63.250	65.898	69.925	73.520	77.818	113.038	118.752	123.858	129.973	134.247
96	64.630	66.730	70.783	74.401	78.725	114.131	119.871	125.000	131.141	135.433
97	64.878	67.562	71.642	75.282	79.633	115.223	120.990	126.141	132.309	136.619
98	65.694	68.396	72.501	76.164	80.541	116.315	122.108	127.282	133.476	137.803
99	66.510	69.230	73.361	77.046	81.449	117.407	123.225	128.422	134.642	138.987
100	67.328	70.065	74.222	77.929	82.358	118.498	124.342	129.561	135.807	140.169

F −Distribution Table: Critical Values for *F* −test

There are two tables here. The first one gives critical values of F at the $p = 0.05$ level of significance.

The second table gives critical values of F at the $p = 0.01$ level of significance.

Find the Critical Value in the Table:

Step 1: Locate the row in the table corresponding to your between-groups degrees of freedom (dfB).

Step 2: Locate the column corresponding to your within-groups degrees of freedom (dfW).

Step 3: The intersection of this row and column gives you the critical value of F for your specific test conditions.

Critical values of F for the 0.05 significance level:

	1	2	3	4	5	6	7	8	9	10
1	161.50	199.50	215.71	224.58	230.16	233.99	236.77	238.88	240.54	241.88
2	18.51	19.00	19.16	19.25	19.30	19.33	19.35	19.37	19.39	19.40
3	10.13	9.55	9.28	9.12	9.01	8.94	8.89	8.85	8.81	8.79
4	7.71	6.64	6.59	6.39	6.26	6.16	6.09	6.04	6.00	5.96
5	6.61	5.79	5.41	5.19	5.05	4.95	4.88	4.82	4.77	4.74
6	5.99	5.14	4.76	4.53	4.39	4.28	4.21	4.15	4.10	4.06
7	5.59	4.74	4.35	4.12	3.97	3.87	3.79	3.73	3.68	3.64
8	5.32	4.46	4.07	3.84	3.69	3.58	3.50	3.44	3.39	3.35
9	5.12	4.26	3.86	3.63	3.48	3.37	3.29	3.23	3.18	3.14
10	4.97	4.10	3.71	3.48	3.33	3.22	3.14	3.07	3.02	2.98
11	4.84	3.98	3.59	3.36	3.20	3.10	3.01	2.95	2.90	2.85
12	4.75	3.89	3.49	3.26	3.11	3.00	2.91	2.85	2.80	2.75
13	4.67	3.81	3.41	3.18	3.03	2.92	2.83	2.77	2.71	2.67
14	4.60	3.74	3.34	3.11	2.96	2.85	2.76	2.70	2.65	2.60
15	4.54	3.68	3.29	3.06	2.90	2.79	2.71	2.64	2.59	2.54
16	4.49	3.63	3.24	3.01	2.85	2.74	2.66	2.59	2.54	2.49
17	4.45	3.59	3.20	2.97	2.81	2.70	2.61	2.55	2.49	2.45
18	4.41	3.56	3.16	2.93	2.77	2.66	2.58	2.51	2.46	2.41
19	4.38	3.52	3.13	2.90	2.74	2.63	2.54	2.48	2.42	2.38
20	4.35	3.49	3.10	2.87	2.71	2.60	2.51	2.45	2.39	2.35
21	4.33	3.47	3.07	2.84	2.69	2.57	2.49	2.42	2.37	2.32
22	4.30	3.44	3.05	2.82	2.66	2.55	2.46	2.40	2.34	2.30
23	4.28	3.42	3.03	2.80	2.64	2.53	2.44	2.38	2.32	2.28

24	4.26	3.40	3.01	2.78	2.62	2.51	2.42	2.36	2.30	2.26
25	4.24	3.39	2.99	2.76	2.60	2.49	2.41	2.34	2.28	2.24
26	4.23	3.37	2.98	2.74	2.59	2.47	2.39	2.32	2.27	2.22
27	4.21	3.35	2.96	2.73	2.57	2.46	2.37	2.31	2.25	2.20
28	4.20	3.34	2.95	2.71	2.56	2.45	2.36	2.29	2.24	2.19
29	4.18	3.33	2.93	2.70	2.55	2.43	2.35	2.28	2.22	2.18
30	4.17	3.32	2.92	2.69	2.53	2.42	2.33	2.27	2.21	2.17
31	4.16	3.31	2.91	2.68	2.52	2.41	2.32	2.26	2.20	2.15
32	4.15	3.30	2.90	2.67	2.51	2.40	2.31	2.24	2.19	2.14
33	4.14	3.29	2.89	2.66	2.50	2.39	2.30	2.24	2.18	2.13
34	4.13	3.28	2.88	2.65	2.49	2.38	2.29	2.23	2.17	2.12
35	4.12	3.27	2.87	2.64	2.49	2.37	2.29	2.22	2.16	2.11
36	4.11	3.26	2.87	2.63	2.48	2.36	2.28	2.21	2.15	2.11
37	4.11	3.25	2.86	2.63	2.47	2.36	2.27	2.20	2.15	2.10
38	4.10	3.25	2.85	2.62	2.46	2.35	2.26	2.19	2.14	2.09
39	4.09	3.24	2.85	2.61	2.46	2.34	2.26	2.19	2.13	2.08
40	4.09	3.23	2.84	2.61	2.45	2.34	2.25	2.18	2.12	2.08
41	4.08	3.23	2.83	2.60	2.44	2.33	2.24	2.17	2.12	2.07
42	4.07	3.22	2.83	2.59	2.44	2.32	2.24	2.17	2.11	2.07
43	4.07	3.21	2.82	2.59	2.43	2.32	2.23	2.16	2.11	2.06
44	4.06	3.21	2.82	2.58	2.43	2.31	2.23	2.16	2.10	2.05
45	4.06	3.20	2.81	2.58	2.42	2.31	2.22	2.15	2.10	2.05
46	4.05	3.20	2.81	2.57	2.42	2.30	2.22	2.15	2.09	2.04
47	4.05	3.20	2.80	2.57	2.41	2.30	2.21	2.14	2.09	2.04
48	4.04	3.19	2.80	2.57	2.41	2.30	2.21	2.14	2.08	2.04
49	4.04	3.19	2.79	2.56	2.40	2.29	2.20	2.13	2.08	2.03
50	4.03	3.18	2.79	2.56	2.40	2.29	2.20	2.13	2.07	2.03
51	4.03	3.18	2.79	2.55	2.40	2.28	2.20	2.13	2.07	2.02
52	4.03	3.18	2.78	2.55	2.39	2.28	2.19	2.12	2.07	2.02
53	4.02	3.17	2.78	2.55	2.39	2.28	2.19	2.12	2.06	2.02
54	4.02	3.17	2.78	2.54	2.39	2.27	2.19	2.12	2.06	2.01
55	4.02	3.17	2.77	2.54	2.38	2.27	2.18	2.11	2.06	2.01
56	4.01	3.16	2.77	2.54	2.38	2.27	2.18	2.11	2.05	2.01
57	4.01	3.16	2.77	2.53	2.38	2.26	2.18	2.11	2.05	2.00
58	4.01	3.16	2.76	2.53	2.37	2.26	2.17	2.10	2.05	2.00
59	4.00	3.15	2.76	2.53	2.37	2.26	2.17	2.10	2.04	2.00
60	4.00	3.15	2.76	2.53	2.37	2.25	2.17	2.10	2.04	1.99
61	4.00	3.15	2.76	2.52	2.37	2.25	2.16	2.09	2.04	1.99
62	4.00	3.15	2.75	2.52	2.36	2.25	2.16	2.09	2.04	1.99
63	3.99	3.14	2.75	2.52	2.36	2.25	2.16	2.09	2.03	1.99

64	3.99	3.14	2.75	2.52	2.36	2.24	2.16	2.09	2.03	1.98
65	3.99	3.14	2.75	2.51	2.36	2.24	2.15	2.08	2.03	1.98
66	3.99	3.14	2.74	2.51	2.35	2.24	2.15	2.08	2.03	1.98
67	3.98	3.13	2.74	2.51	2.35	2.24	2.15	2.08	2.02	1.98
68	3.98	3.13	2.74	2.51	2.35	2.24	2.15	2.08	2.02	1.97
69	3.98	3.13	2.74	2.51	2.35	2.23	2.15	2.08	2.02	1.97
70	3.98	3.13	2.74	2.50	2.35	2.23	2.14	2.07	2.02	1.97
71	3.98	3.13	2.73	2.50	2.34	2.23	2.14	2.07	2.02	1.97
72	3.97	3.12	2.73	2.50	2.34	2.23	2.14	2.07	2.01	1.97
73	3.97	3.12	2.73	2.50	2.34	2.23	2.14	2.07	2.01	1.96
74	3.97	3.12	2.73	2.50	2.34	2.22	2.14	2.07	2.01	1.96
75	3.97	3.12	2.73	2.49	2.34	2.22	2.13	2.06	2.01	1.96
76	3.97	3.12	2.73	2.49	2.34	2.22	2.13	2.06	2.01	1.96
77	3.97	3.12	2.72	2.49	2.33	2.22	2.13	2.06	2.00	1.96
78	3.96	3.11	2.72	2.49	2.33	2.22	2.13	2.06	2.00	1.95
79	3.96	3.11	2.72	2.49	2.33	2.22	2.13	2.06	2.00	1.95
80	3.96	3.11	2.72	2.49	2.33	2.21	2.13	2.06	2.00	1.95
81	3.96	3.11	2.72	2.48	2.33	2.21	2.13	2.06	2.00	1.95
82	3.96	3.11	2.72	2.48	2.33	2.21	2.12	2.05	2.00	1.95
83	3.96	3.11	2.72	2.48	2.32	2.21	2.12	2.05	2.00	1.95
84	3.96	3.11	2.71	2.48	2.32	2.21	2.12	2.05	1.99	1.95
85	3.95	3.10	2.71	2.48	2.32	2.21	2.12	2.05	1.99	1.94
86	3.95	3.10	2.71	2.48	2.32	2.21	2.12	2.05	1.99	1.94
87	3.95	3.10	2.71	2.48	2.32	2.21	2.12	2.05	1.99	1.94
88	3.95	3.10	2.71	2.48	2.32	2.20	2.12	2.05	1.99	1.94
89	3.95	3.10	2.71	2.47	2.32	2.20	2.11	2.04	1.99	1.94
90	3.95	3.10	2.71	2.47	2.31	2.20	2.11	2.04	1.99	1.94
91	3.95	3.10	2.71	2.47	2.31	2.20	2.11	2.04	1.98	1.94
92	3.95	3.10	2.70	2.47	2.31	2.20	2.11	2.04	1.98	1.94
93	3.94	3.09	2.70	2.47	2.31	2.20	2.11	2.04	1.98	1.93
94	3.94	3.09	2.70	2.47	2.31	2.20	2.11	2.04	1.98	1.93
95	3.94	3.09	2.70	2.47	2.31	2.20	2.11	2.04	1.98	1.93
96	3.94	3.09	2.70	2.47	2.31	2.20	2.11	2.04	1.98	1.93
97	3.94	3.09	2.70	2.47	2.31	2.19	2.11	2.04	1.98	1.93
98	3.94	3.09	2.70	2.47	2.31	2.19	2.10	2.03	1.98	1.93
99	3.94	3.09	2.70	2.46	2.31	2.19	2.10	2.03	1.98	1.93
100	3.94	3.09	2.70	2.46	2.31	2.19	2.10	2.03	1.98	1.93

Critical values of F for the 0.01 significance level:

	1	2	3	4	5	6	7	8	9	10
1	4052.19	4999.52	5403.34	5624.62	5763.65	5858.97	5928.33	5981.10	6022.50	6055.85
2	98.50	99.00	99.17	99.25	99.30	9933.00	99.36	99.37	99.39	99.40
3	34.12	30.82	29.46	28.71	28.24	2791.00	27.67	27.49	27.35	27.23
4	21.20	18.00	16.69	15.98	15.52	15.21	14.98	14.80	14.66	14.55
5	16.26	13.27	12.06	11.39	10.97	10.67	10.46	10.29	10.16	10.05
6	13.75	10.93	9.78	9.15	8.75	8.47	8.26	8.10	7.98	7.87
7	12.25	9.55	8.45	7.85	7.46	7.19	6.99	6.84	6.72	6.62
8	11.26	8.65	7.59	7.01	6.63	6.37	6.18	6.03	5.91	9.81
9	10.56	8.02	6.99	6.42	6.06	5.80	5.61	5.47	5.35	5.26
10	10.04	7.56	6.55	5.99	5.64	5.39	5.20	5.06	4.94	4.85
11	9.65	7.21	6.22	5.67	5.03	5.07	4.89	4.74	4.63	4.54
12	9.33	6.93	5.95	5.41	5.06	4.82	4.64	4.50	4.39	2.30
13	9.07	6.70	5.74	5.21	4.86	4.62	4.44	4.30	4.19	2.10
14	8.86	6.52	5.56	5.04	4.70	4.46	4.28	4.14	4.03	3.94
15	8.68	6.36	5.42	4.89	4.56	4.32	4.14	4.00	3.90	3.81
16	8.53	6.23	5.29	4.77	4.44	4.20	4.03	3.89	3.78	3.69
17	8.40	6.11	5.19	4.67	4.34	4.10	3.93	3.79	3.68	3.59
18	8.29	6.01	5.09	4.58	4.25	4.02	3.84	3.71	3.60	3.51
19	8.19	5.93	5.01	4.50	4.17	3.94	3.77	3.63	3.52	3.43
20	8.10	5.85	4.94	4.43	4.10	3.87	3.70	3.56	3.46	3.37
21	8.02	5.78	4.87	4.37	4.04	3.81	3.64	3.51	3.40	3.31
22	7.95	5.72	4.82	4.31	3.99	3.76	3.59	3.45	3.35	3.26
23	7.88	5.66	4.77	4.26	3.94	3.71	3.54	3.41	3.30	3.21
24	7.82	5.61	4.72	4.22	3.90	3.67	3.50	3.36	3.26	3.17
25	7.77	5.57	4.68	4.18	3.86	3.63	3.46	3.32	3.22	3.13
26	7.72	5.53	4.64	4.14	3.82	3.59	3.42	3.29	3.18	3.09
27	7.68	5.49	4.60	4.11	3.79	3.56	3.39	3.26	3.15	3.06
28	7.64	5.45	4.57	4.07	3.75	3.53	3.36	3.23	3.12	3.03
29	7.60	5.42	4.54	4.05	3.73	3.50	3.33	3.20	3.09	3.01
30	7.56	5.39	4.51	4.02	3.70	3.47	3.31	3.17	3.07	2.98
31	7.53	5.36	4.48	3.99	3.68	3.45	3.28	3.15	3.04	2.96
32	7.50	5.34	4.46	3.97	3.65	3.43	3.26	3.13	3.02	2.93
33	7.47	5.31	4.44	3.95	3.06	3.41	3.24	3.11	3.00	2.91
34	7.44	5.29	4.42	3.93	3.61	3.39	3.22	3.09	2.98	2.89
35	7.42	5.27	4.40	3.91	3.59	3.37	3.20	3.07	2.96	2.88
36	7.40	5.25	4.38	3.89	3.57	3.35	3.18	3.05	2.95	2.86
37	7.37	5.23	4.36	3.87	3.56	3.33	3.17	3.04	2.93	2.84
38	7.35	5.21	4.34	3.86	3.54	3.32	3.15	3.02	2.92	2.83

39	7.33	5.19	4.33	3.84	3.53	3.31	3.14	3.01	2.90	2.81
40	7.31	5.18	4.31	3.83	3.51	3.29	3.12	2.99	2.89	2.80
41	7.30	5.16	4.30	3.82	3.50	3.28	3.11	2.98	2.88	2.79
42	7.28	5.15	4.29	3.80	3.49	3.27	3.10	2.97	2.86	2.78
43	7.26	5.14	4.27	3.79	3.48	3.25	3.09	2.96	2.85	2.76
44	7.25	5.12	4.26	3.78	3.47	3.24	3.08	2.95	2.84	2.75
45	7.23	5.11	4.25	3.77	3.45	3.23	3.07	2.94	2.83	2.74
46	7.22	5.10	4.24	3.76	3.44	3.22	3.06	2.93	2.82	2.73
47	7.21	5.09	4.23	3.75	3.43	3.21	3.05	2.92	2.81	2.72
48	7.19	5.08	4.22	3.74	3.43	3.20	3.04	2.91	2.80	2.72
49	7.18	5.07	4.21	3.73	3.42	3.20	3.03	2.90	2.79	2.71
50	7.17	5.06	4.20	3.72	3.41	3.19	3.02	2.89	2.79	2.70
51	7.16	5.05	4.19	3.71	3.40	3.18	3.01	2.88	2.78	2.69
52	7.15	5.04	4.18	3.70	3.39	3.17	3.01	2.87	2.77	2.68
53	7.14	5.03	4.17	3.70	3.38	3.16	3.00	2.87	2.76	2.68
54	7.13	5.02	4.17	3.69	3.38	3.16	2.99	2.86	2.76	2.67
55	7.12	5.01	4.16	3.68	3.37	3.15	2.98	2.85	2.75	2.66
56	7.11	5.01	4.15	3.67	3.36	3.14	2.98	2.85	2.74	2.66
57	7.10	5.00	4.15	3.67	3.36	3.14	2.97	2.84	2.74	2.65
58	7.09	4.99	4.14	3.66	3.35	3.13	2.97	2.84	2.73	2.64
59	7.09	4.98	4.13	3.66	3.35	3.12	2.96	2.83	2.72	2.64
60	7.08	4.98	4.13	3.65	3.34	3.12	2.95	2.82	2.72	2.63
61	7.07	4.97	4.12	3.64	3.33	3.11	2.95	2.82	2.71	2.63
62	7.06	4.97	4.11	3.64	3.33	3.11	2.94	2.81	2.71	2.62
63	7.06	4.96	4.11	3.63	3.32	3.10	2.94	2.81	2.70	2.62
64	7.05	4.95	4.10	3.63	3.32	3.10	2.93	2.80	2.70	2.61
65	7.04	4.95	4.10	3.62	3.31	3.09	2.93	2.80	2.69	2.61
66	7.04	4.94	4.09	3.62	3.31	3.09	2.92	2.79	2.69	2.60
67	7.03	4.94	4.09	3.61	3.30	3.08	2.92	2.79	2.68	2.60
68	7.02	4.93	4.08	3.61	3.30	3.08	2.91	2.79	2.68	2.59
69	7.02	4.93	4.08	3.60	3.30	3.08	2.91	2.78	2.68	2.59
70	7.01	4.92	4.07	3.60	3.29	3.07	2.91	2.78	2.67	2.59
71	7.01	4.92	4.07	3.60	3.29	3.07	2.90	2.77	2.67	2.58
72	7.00	4.91	4.07	3.59	3.28	3.06	2.90	2.77	2.66	2.58
73	7.00	4.91	4.06	3.59	3.28	3.06	2.90	2.77	2.66	2.57
74	6.99	4.90	4.06	3.58	3.28	3.06	2.89	2.76	2.66	2.57
75	6.99	4.90	4.05	3.58	3.27	3.05	2.89	2.76	2.65	2.57
76	6.98	4.90	4.05	3.58	3.27	3.05	2.88	2.76	2.65	2.56
77	6.98	4.89	4.05	3.57	3.27	3.05	2.88	2.75	2.65	2.56
78	6.97	4.89	4.04	3.57	3.26	3.04	2.88	2.75	2.64	2.56

79	6.97	4.88	4.04	3.57	3.26	3.04	2.87	2.75	2.64	2.55
80	6.96	4.88	4.04	3.56	3.26	3.04	2.87	2.74	2.64	2.55
81	6.96	4.88	4.03	3.56	3.25	3.03	2.87	2.74	2.63	2.55
82	6.95	4.87	4.03	3.56	3.25	3.03	2.87	2.74	2.63	2.55
83	6.95	4.87	4.03	3.55	3.25	3.03	2.86	2.73	2.63	2.54
84	6.95	4.87	4.02	3.55	3.24	3.03	2.86	2.73	2.63	2.54
85	6.94	4.86	4.02	3.55	3.24	3.02	2.86	2.73	2.62	2.54
86	6.94	4.86	4.02	3.55	3.24	3.02	2.85	2.73	2.62	2.53
87	6.94	4.86	4.02	3.54	3.24	3.02	2.85	2.72	2.62	2.53
88	6.93	4.86	4.01	3.54	3.23	3.01	2.85	2.72	2.62	2.53
89	6.93	4.85	4.01	3.54	3.23	3.01	2.85	2.72	2.61	2.53
90	6.93	4.85	4.01	3.54	3.23	3.01	2.85	2.72	2.61	2.52
91	6.92	4.85	4.00	3.53	3.23	3.01	2.84	2.71	2.61	2.52
92	6.92	4.84	4.00	3.53	3.22	3.00	2.84	2.71	2.61	2.52
93	6.92	4.84	4.00	3.53	3.22	3.00	2.84	2.71	2.60	2.52
94	6.91	4.84	4.00	3.53	3.22	3.00	2.84	2.71	2.60	2.52
95	6.91	4.84	4.00	3.52	3.22	3.00	2.83	2.70	2.60	2.51
96	6.91	4.83	3.99	3.52	3.21	3.00	2.83	2.70	2.60	2.51
97	6.90	4.83	3.99	3.52	3.21	2.99	2.83	2.70	2.60	2.51
98	6.90	4.83	3.99	3.52	3.21	2.99	2.83	2.70	2.59	2.51
99	6.90	4.83	3.99	3.52	3.21	2.99	2.83	2.70	2.59	2.51
100	6.90	4.82	3.98	3.51	3.21	2.99	2.82	2.69	2.59	2.50

Build Your Math Skills: Our Top Book Picks!

Download eBooks (in PDF format) Instantly!

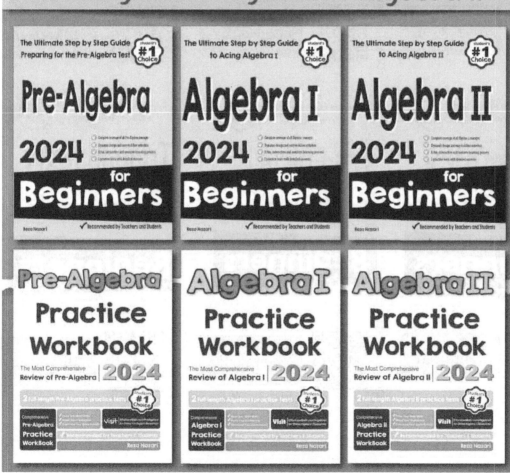

Our Most Popular Books!

Download at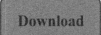

 Download

Download at Download

Download at Download

Download at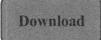

 Download

Download at

 Download

Download at Download

Our Most Popular Books!

Pre-Algebra Practice Workbook

The Most Comprehensive Review of Pre-Algebra | 2024

2 full-length Pre-Algebra practice tests

Students #1 Choice

Comprehensive Pre-Algebra Practice WorkBook

Recommended by Teachers & Students

Reza Nazari

Download at

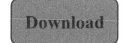

Download

Algebra I Practice Workbook

The Most Comprehensive Review of Algebra I | 2024

2 full-length Algebra I practice tests

Students #1 Choice

Comprehensive Algebra I Practice WorkBook

Recommended by Teachers & Students

Reza Nazari

Download at

Download

Algebra II Practice Workbook

The Most Comprehensive Review of Algebra II | 2024

2 full-length Algebra II practice tests

Students #1 Choice

Comprehensive Algebra II Practice WorkBook

Recommended by Teachers & Students

Reza Nazari

Download at

Download

Trigonometry Practice Workbook

The Most Comprehensive Review for Trigonometry | 2024

2 full-length Trigonometry practice tests

Test Takers #1 Choice

Comprehensive Trigonometry Practice WorkBook

Recommended by Teachers & Students

Reza Nazari

Download at

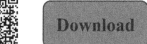

Download

Receive the PDF version of this book or get another FREE book!

Thank you for using our Book!

Do you LOVE this book?

Then, you can get the PDF version of this book or another book absolutely FREE!

Please email us at:

info@EffortlessMath.com

for details.

Author's Final Note

Congratulations on completing "***Statistics for Beginners***"! It's quite an achievement, and I'm truly honored that you chose this guide to accompany you on your journey through the intricacies of Statistics.

Crafting this book was a labor of love, born from my desire to create an accessible and comprehensive guide that demystifies the world of statistics for beginners. My goal was to provide a resource that would enable you to utilize your time efficiently and effectively as you delve into the foundational concepts of statistics.

Drawing from my extensive experience in teaching and my passion for statistics, I have distilled my knowledge into this guide, aiming to pave the way for your success. It is my sincere hope that the insights and strategies within these pages will empower you to excel in your understanding of statistical principles.

If you have any questions, please contact me at reza@effortlessmath.com and I will be glad to assist. Your feedback will help me to greatly improve the quality of my books in the future and make this book even better. Furthermore, I expect that I have made a few minor errors somewhere in this study guide. If you think this to be the case, please let me know so I can fix the issue as soon as possible.

If this book has enriched your knowledge and you've found it to be a helpful resource, I would be delighted to hear about your experience. I encourage you to share your thoughts by leaving a review on the book's Amazon page. Your insights are not only appreciated but also instrumental in guiding others who are embarking on their statistical learning path.

I take the time to read every review personally, as they play a crucial role in ensuring that my work truly benefits and resonates with those who seek to understand statistics. Your review can make a significant difference in supporting fellow learners.

Best wishes for your continued success and discovery in the world of statistics!

Reza Nazari

Math teacher and author

Made in the USA
Las Vegas, NV
17 September 2024

95419956R00254